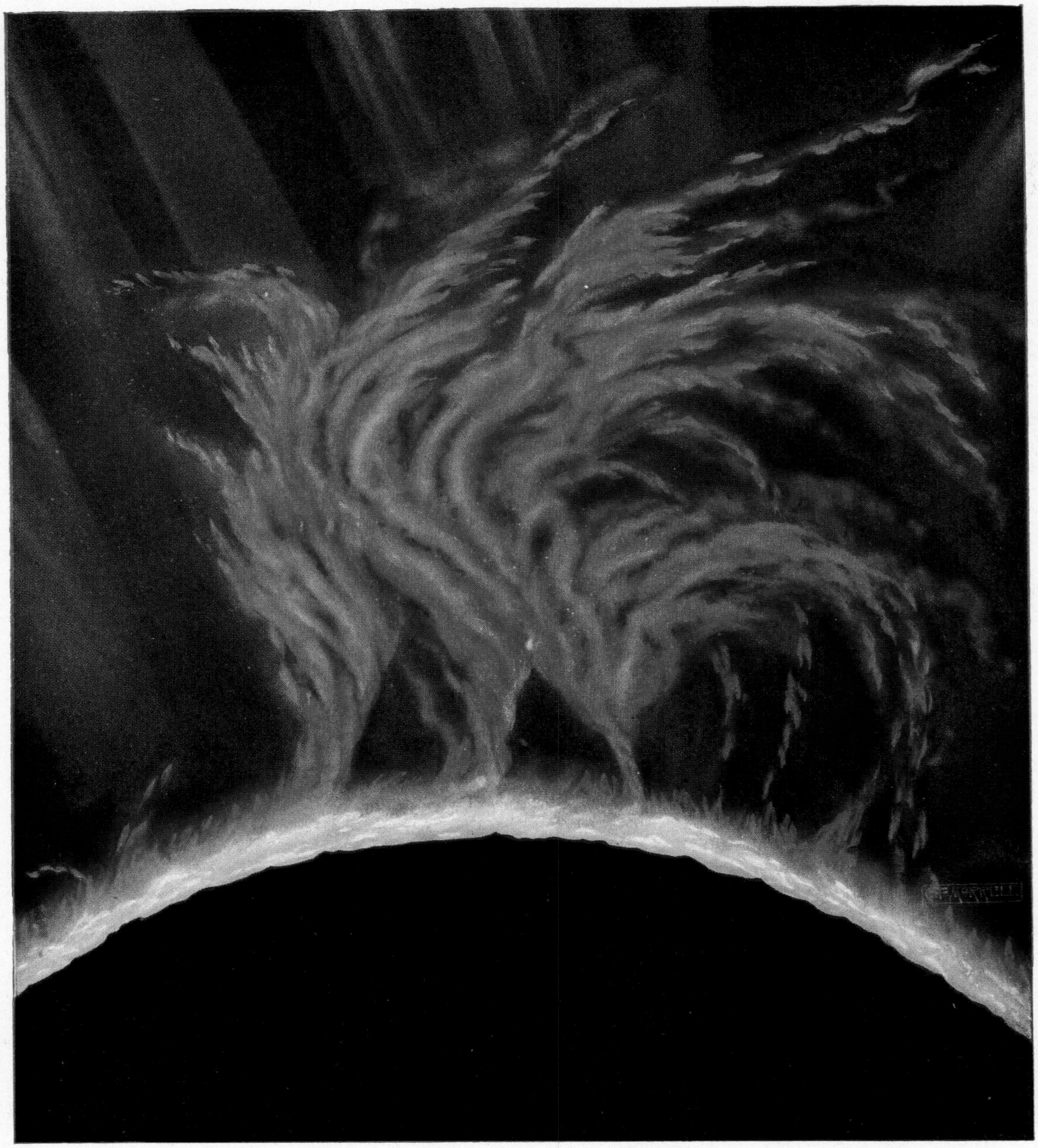

THE GREAT SCARLET SOLAR PROMINENCES, WHICH ARE SUCH A NOTABLE FEATURE OF THE SOLAR PHENOMENA, ARE IMMENSE OUTBURSTS OF FLAMING HYDROGEN RISING SOMETIMES TO A HEIGHT OF 500,000 MILES

THE OUTLINE OF SCIENCE

A PLAIN STORY SIMPLY TOLD

EDITED BY

J. ARTHUR THOMSON

REGIUS PROFESSOR OF NATURAL HISTORY IN THE UNIVERSITY OF ABERDEEN

WITH OVER 800 ILLUSTRATIONS

OF WHICH ABOUT 40 ARE IN COLOUR

IN FOUR VOLUMES

★

G. P. PUTNAM'S SONS
NEW YORK AND LONDON
The Knickerbocker Press

First Printing April, 1922
Second Printing April, 1922
Third Printing April, 1922
Fourth Printing April, 1922
Fifth Printing June, 1922
Sixth Printing June, 1922
Seventh Printing June, 1922
Eighth Printing June, 1922
Ninth Printing August, 1922
Tenth Printing September, 1922
Eleventh Printing Sept., 1922
Twelfth Printing, May, 1924
Thirteenth Printing, December, 1926

Made in the United States of America

INTRODUCTORY NOTE

By Professor J. Arthur Thomson

WAS it not the great philosopher and mathematician Leibnitz who said that the more knowledge advances the more it becomes possible to condense it into little books? Now this "Outline of Science" is certainly not a little book, and yet it illustrates part of the meaning of Leibnitz's wise saying. For here within reasonable compass there is a library of little books—an outline of many sciences.

It will be profitable to the student in proportion to the discrimination with which it is used. For it is not in the least meant to be of the nature of an Encyclopædia, giving condensed and comprehensive articles with a big full stop at the end of each. Nor is it a collection of "primers," beginning at the very beginning of each subject and working methodically onwards. That is not the idea.

What then is the aim of this book? It is to give the intelligent student-citizen, otherwise called "the man in the street," a bunch of intellectual keys by which to open doors which have been hitherto shut to him, partly because he got no glimpse of the treasures behind the doors, and partly because the portals were made forbidding by an unnecessary display of technicalities. Laying aside conventional modes of treatment and seeking rather to open up the subject as one might on a walk with a friend, the work offers the student what might be called informal introductions to the various departments of knowledge. To put it in another way, the articles are meant to be clues which the reader may follow till he has left his starting point very far behind. Perhaps when he has gone far on his own he will not be ungrateful to the simple book of "instructions to travellers" which this

"Outline of Science" is intended to be. The simple "bibliographies" appended to the various articles will be enough to indicate "first books." Each article is meant to be an invitation to an intellectual adventure, and the short lists of books are merely finger-posts for the beginning of the journey.

We confess to being greatly encouraged by the reception that has been given to the English serial issue of "The Outline of Science." It has been very hearty—we might almost say enthusiastic. For we agree with Professor John Dewey, that "the future of our civilisation depends upon the widening spread and deepening hold of the scientific habit of mind." And we hope that this is what "The Outline of Science" makes for. Information is all to the good; interesting information is better still; but best of all is the education of the scientific habit of mind. Another modern philosopher, Professor L. T. Hobhouse, has declared that the evolutionist's mundane goal is "the mastery by the human mind of the conditions, internal as well as external, of its life and growth." Under the influence of this conviction "The Outline of Science" has been written. For life is not for science, but science for life. And even more than science, to our way of thinking, is the individual development of the scientific way of looking at things. Science is our legacy; we must use it if it is to be our very own.

CONTENTS

ILLUSTRATIONS

The Outline of Science

INTRODUCTION

THERE is abundant evidence of a widened and deepened interest in modern science. How could it be otherwise when we think of the magnitude and the eventfulness of recent advances?

But the interest of the general public would be even greater than it is if the makers of new knowledge were more willing to expound their discoveries in ways that could be "understanded of the people." No one objects very much to technicalities in a game or on board a yacht, and they are clearly necessary for terse and precise scientific description. It is certain, however, that they can be reduced to a minimum without sacrificing accuracy, when the object in view is to explain "the gist of the matter." So this OUTLINE OF SCIENCE is meant for the general reader, who lacks both time and opportunity for special study, and yet would take an intelligent interest in the progress of science which is making the world always new.

The story of the triumphs of modern science is one of which Man may well be proud. Science reads the secret of the distant star and anatomises the atom; foretells the date of the comet's return and predicts the kinds of chickens that will hatch from a dozen eggs; discovers the laws of the wind that bloweth where it listeth and reduces to order the disorder of disease. Science is always setting forth on Columbus voyages, discovering new worlds and conquering them by understanding. For Knowledge means Foresight and Foresight means Power.

The idea of Evolution has influenced all the sciences, forcing us to think of *everything* as with a history behind it, for we have travelled far since Darwin's day. The solar system, the earth, the mountain ranges, and the great deeps, the rocks and crystals, the plants and animals, man himself and his social institutions—all must be seen as the outcome of a long process of Becoming. There are some eighty-odd chemical elements on the earth to-day, and it is now much more than a suggestion that these are the outcome of an inorganic evolution, element giving rise to element, going back and back to some primeval stuff, from which they were all originally derived, infinitely long ago. No idea has been so powerful a tool in the fashioning of New Knowledge as this simple but profound idea of Evolution, that the present is the child of the past and the parent of the future. And with the picture of a continuity of evolution from nebula to social systems comes a promise of an increasing control—a promise that Man will become not only a more accurate student, but a more complete master of his world.

It is characteristic of modern science that the whole world is seen to be more vital than before. Everywhere there has been a passage from the static to the dynamic. Thus the new revelations of the constitution of matter, which we owe to the discoveries of men like Professor Sir J. J. Thomson, Professor Sir Ernest Rutherford, and Professor Frederick Soddy, have shown the very dust to have a complexity and an activity heretofore unimagined. Such phrases as "dead" matter and "inert" matter have gone by the board.

The new theory of the atom amounts almost to a new conception of the universe. It bids fair to reveal to us many of nature's hidden secrets. The atom is no longer the indivisible particle of matter it was once understood to be. We know now that there is an atom within the atom—that what we thought was elementary can be dissociated and broken up. The present-day theories of the atom and the constitution of matter are the outcome of the comparatively recent discovery of such things as radium, the X-rays, and the wonderful revelations of such instruments as the spectroscope and other highly perfected scientific instruments.

The advent of the electron theory has thrown a flood of light on what before was hidden or only dimly guessed at. It has given us a new conception of the framework of the universe. We are beginning to know and realise of what matter is made and what electric phenomena mean. We can glimpse the vast stores of energy locked up in matter. The new knowledge has much to tell us about the origin and phenomena, not only of our own planet, but other planets, of the stars, and the sun. New light is thrown on the source of the sun's heat; we can make more than guesses as to its probable age. The great question to-day is: is there *one* primordial substance from which all the varying forms of matter have been evolved?

But the discovery of electrons is only one of the revolutionary changes which give modern science an entrancing interest.

As in chemistry and physics, so in the science of living creatures there have been recent advances that have changed the whole prospect. A good instance is afforded by the discovery of the "hormones," or chemical messengers, which are produced by ductless glands, such as the thyroid, the suprarenal, and the pituitary, and are distributed throughout the body by the blood. The work of physiologists like Professor Starling and Professor Bayliss has shown that these chemical messengers regulate what may be called the "pace" of the body, and bring about that regulated harmony and smoothness of working which we know as health. It is not too much to say that the discovery of hormones has changed the whole of physiology. Our knowledge of the human body far surpasses that of the past generation.

The persistent patience of microscopists and technical improvements like the "ultramicroscope" have greatly increased our knowledge of the invisible world of life. To the bacteria of a past generation have been added a multitude of microscopic *animal* microbes, such as that which causes Sleeping Sickness. The life-histories and the weird ways of many important parasites have been unravelled; and here again knowledge means mastery. To a degree which has almost surpassed expectations there has been a revelation of the intricacy of the stones and mortar of the house of life, and the microscopic study of germ-cells has wonderfully supplemented the epoch-making experimental study of heredity which began with Mendel. It goes without saying that no one can call himself educated who does not understand the central and simple ideas of Mendelism and other new departures in biology.

The procession of life through the ages and the factors in the sublime movement; the peopling of the earth by plants and animals and the linking of life to life in subtle interrelations, such as those between flowers and their insect-visitors; the life-histories of individual types and the extraordinary results of the new inquiry called "experimental embryology"—these also are among the subjects with which this OUTLINE will deal.

The behaviour of animals is another fascinating study, leading to a provisional picture of the dawn of mind. Indeed, no branch of science surpasses in interest that which deals with the ways and habits—the truly wonderful devices, adaptations, and instincts—of insects, birds, and mammals. We no longer deny a degree of intelligence to some members of the animal world—even the line between intelligence and reason is sometimes difficult to find.

Fresh contacts between physiology and the study of man's mental life; precise studies of the ways of children and wild peoples; and new methods like those of the psycho-analyst must also receive the attention they deserve, for they are giving us a "New Psychology" and the claims of psychical research must also be recognised by the open-minded.

The general aim of the OUTLINE is to give the reader a clear and concise view of the essentials of present-day science, so that he may follow with intelligence the modern advance and share appreciatively in man's continued conquest of his kingdom.

J. ARTHUR THOMSON.

I
THE ROMANCE OF THE HEAVENS

THE SCALE OF THE UNIVERSE—THE SOLAR SYSTEM

§ I

THE story of the triumphs of modern science naturally opens with Astronomy. The picture of the Universe which the astronomer offers to us is imperfect; the lines he traces are often faint and uncertain. There are many problems which have been solved, there are just as many about which there is doubt, and notwithstanding our great increase in knowledge, there remain just as many which are entirely unsolved.

> The problem of the structure and duration of the universe [said the great astronomer Simon Newcomb] is the most far-reaching with which the mind has to deal. Its solution may be regarded as the ultimate object of stellar astronomy, the possibility of reaching which has occupied the minds of thinkers since the beginning of civilisation. Before our time the problem could be considered only from the imaginative or the speculative point of view. Although we can to-day attack it to a limited extent by scientific methods, it must be admitted that we have scarcely taken more than the first step toward the actual solution. . . . What is the duration of the universe in time? Is it fitted to last for ever in its present form, or does it contain within itself the seeds of dissolution? Must it, in the course of time, in we know not how many millions of ages, be transformed into something very different from what it now is? This question is intimately associated with the question whether the stars form

a system. If they do, we may suppose that system to be permanent in its general features; if not, we must look further for our conclusions.

The Heavenly Bodies

The heavenly bodies fall into two very distinct classes so far as their relation to our Earth is concerned; the one class, a very small one, comprises a sort of colony of which the Earth is a member. These bodies are called *planets,* or wanderers. There are eight of them, including the Earth, and they all circle round the sun. Their names, in the order of their distance from the sun, are Mercury, Venus, Earth, Mars, Jupiter, Saturn, Uranus, Neptune, and of these Mercury, the nearest to the sun, is rarely seen by the naked eye. Uranus is practically invisible, and Neptune quite so. These eight planets, together with the sun, constitute, as we have said, a sort of little colony; this colony is called the Solar System.

The second class of heavenly bodies are those which lie *outside* the solar system. Every one of those glittering points we see on a starlit night is at an immensely greater distance from us than is any member of the Solar System. Yet the members of this little colony of ours, judged by terrestrial standards, are at enormous distances from one another. If a shell were shot in a straight line from one side of Neptune's orbit to the other it would take five hundred years to complete its journey. Yet this distance, the greatest in the Solar System as now known (excepting the far swing of some of the comets), is insignificant compared to the distances of the stars. One of the nearest stars to the earth that we know of is Alpha Centauri, estimated to be some twenty-five million millions of miles away. Sirius, the brightest star in the firmament, is double this distance from the earth.

We must imagine the colony of planets to which we belong as a compact little family swimming in an immense void. At distances which would take our shell, not hundreds, but millions

LAPLACE

One of the greatest mathematical astronomers of all time and the originator of the nebular theory.

Photo: Royal Astronomical Society.

PROFESSOR J. C. ADAMS

who, anticipating the great French mathematician, Le Verrier, discovered the planet Neptune by calculations based on the irregularities of the orbit of Uranus. One of the most dramatic discoveries in the history of Science.

Photo: Elliott & Fry, Ltd.

PROFESSOR EDDINGTON

Professor of Astronomy at Cambridge. The most famous of the English disciples of Einstein.

FIG. I.—DIAGRAMS OF THE SOLAR SYSTEM

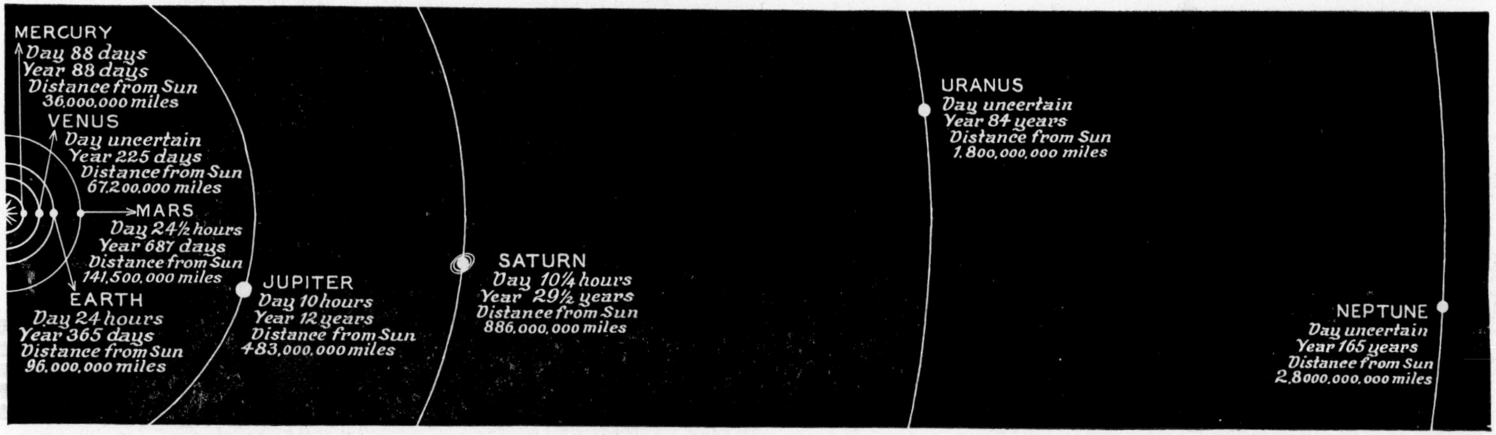

THE COMPARATIVE DISTANCES OF THE PLANETS

(Drawn approximately to scale)

The isolation of the Solar System is very great. On the above scale the *nearest* star (at a distance of 25 trillions of miles) would be over *one half mile* away. The hours, days, and years are the measures of time as we use them; that is: Jupiter's "Day" (one rotation of the planet) is made in ten of *our hours;* Mercury's "Year" (one revolution of the planet around the Sun) is eighty-eight of *our days.* Mercury's "Day" and "Year" are the same. This planet turns always the same side to the Sun.

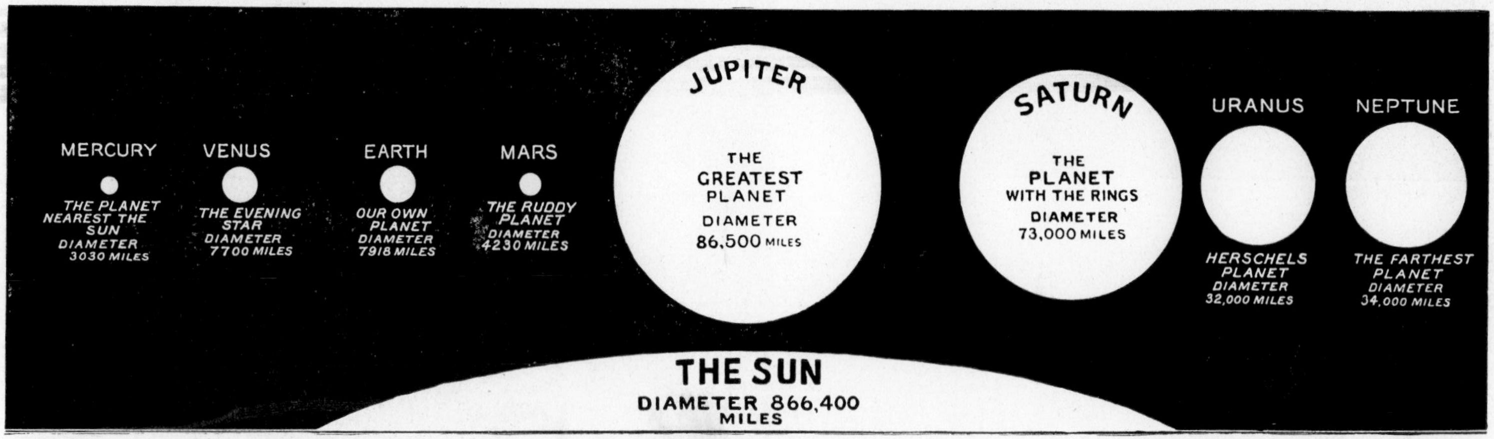

THE COMPARATIVE SIZES OF THE SUN AND THE PLANETS

(Drawn approximately to scale)

On this scale the Sun would be 17½ inches in diameter; it is far greater than all the planets put together. Jupiter, in turn, is greater than all the other planets put together.

of years to traverse, we reach the stars—or rather, a star, for the distances between stars are as great as the distance between the nearest of them and our Sun. The Earth, the planet on which we live, is a mighty globe bounded by a crust of rock many miles in thickness; the great volumes of water which we call our oceans lie in the deeper hollows of the crust. Above the surface an ocean of invisible gas, the atmosphere, rises to a height of about three hundred miles, getting thinner and thinner as it ascends.

Except when the winds rise to a high speed, we seem to live in a very tranquil world. At night, when the glare of the sun passes out of our atmosphere, the stars and planets seem to move across the heavens with a stately and solemn slowness. It was one of the first discoveries of modern astronomy that this movement is only apparent. The apparent creeping of the stars across the heavens at night is accounted for by the fact that the earth turns upon its axis once in every twenty-four hours. When we remember the size of the earth we see that this implies a prodigious speed.

In addition to this the earth revolves round the sun at a speed of more than a thousand miles a minute. Its path round the sun, year in year out, measures about 580,000,000 miles. The earth is held closely to this path by the gravitational pull of the sun, which has a mass 333,432 times that of the earth. If at any moment the sun ceased to exert this pull the earth would instantly fly off into space straight in the direction in which it was moving at the time, that is to say, at a tangent. This tendency to fly off at a tangent is continuous. It is the balance between it and the sun's pull which keeps the earth to her almost circular orbit. In the same way the seven other planets are held to their orbits.

Circling round the earth, in the same way as the earth circles round the sun, is our moon. Sometimes the moon passes directly between us and the sun, and cuts off the light from us.

We then have a total or partial eclipse of the sun. At other times the earth passes directly between the sun and the moon, and causes an eclipse of the moon. The great ball of the earth naturally trails a mighty shadow across space, and the moon is "eclipsed" when it passes into this.

The other seven planets, five of which have moons of their own, circle round the sun as the earth does. The sun's mass is immensely larger than that of all the planets put together, and all of them would be drawn into it and perish if they did not travel rapidly round it in gigantic orbits. So the eight planets, spinning round on their axes, follow their fixed paths round the sun. The planets are secondary bodies, but they are most important, because they are the only globes in which there can be life, as we know life.

If we could be transported in some magical way to an immense distance in space above the sun, we should see our Solar System as it is drawn in the accompanying diagram (Fig. 1), except that the planets would be mere specks, faintly visible in the light which they receive from the sun. (This diagram is drawn approximately to scale.) If we moved still farther away, trillions of miles away, the planets would fade entirely out of view, and the sun would shrink into a point of fire, a star. And here you begin to realize the nature of the universe. *The sun is a star. The stars are suns.* Our sun looks big simply because of its comparative nearness to us. The universe is a stupendous collection of millions of stars or suns, many of which may have planetary families like ours.

§ 2

The Scale of the Universe

How many stars are there? A glance at a photograph of star-clouds will tell at once that it is quite impossible to count them. The fine photograph reproduced in Figure 2 represents a very small patch of that pale-white belt, the Milky Way, which spans the sky at night. It is true that this is a particularly rich area of the Milky Way, but the entire belt of light has been resolved in this way into masses or clouds of stars. Astronomers have counted the stars in typical districts here and there, and from these partial counts we get some idea of the total number of stars. There are estimated to be between two and three thousand million stars.

Yet these stars are separated by inconceivable distances from each other, and it is one of the greatest triumphs of modern astronomy to have mastered, so far, the scale of the universe. For several centuries astronomers have known the relative distances from each other of the sun and the planets. If they could discover the actual distance of any one planet from any other, they could at once tell all the distances within the Solar System.

The sun is, on the latest measurements, at an average distance of 92,830,000 miles from the earth, for as the orbit of the earth is not a true circle, this distance varies. This means that in six months from now the earth will be right at the opposite side of its path round the sun, or 185,000,000 miles away from where it is now. Viewed or photographed from two positions so wide apart, the nearest stars show a tiny "shift" against the background of the most distant stars, and that is enough for the mathematician. He can calculate the distance of any star near enough to show this "shift." We have found that the nearest star to the earth, a recently discovered star, is twenty-five trillion miles away. Only thirty stars are known to be within a hundred trillion miles of us.

This way of measuring does not, however, take us very far away in the heavens. There are only a few hundred stars within five hundred trillion miles of the earth, and at that distance the "shift" of a star against the background (parallax, the astronomer calls it) is so minute that figures are very uncertain. At this point the astronomer takes up a new method. He learns the different types of stars, and then he is able to deduce more or less accurately the distance of a star of a known type from its faintness. He, of course, has instruments for gauging their light. As a result of twenty years work in this field, it is now known that the more distant stars of the Milky Way are at least a hundred thousand trillion (100,000,000,000,000,000) miles away from the sun.

Our sun is in a more or less central region of the universe, or a few hundred trillion miles from the actual centre. The remainder of the stars, which are all outside our Solar System, are spread out, apparently, in an enormous disc-like collection, so vast that even a ray of light, which travels at the rate of 186,000 miles a second, would take 50,000 years to travel from one end of it to the other. This, then is what we call our universe.

Are there other Universes?

Why do we say "our universe"? Why not *the* universe? It is now believed by many of our most distinguished astronomers that our colossal family of stars is only one of many universes. By a universe an astronomer means any collection of stars which are close enough to control each other's movements by gravitation; and it is clear that there might be many universes, in this sense, separated from each other by profound abysses of space. Probably there are.

For a long time we have been familiar with certain strange objects in the heavens which are called "spiral nebulæ" (Fig 4). We shall see at a later stage what a nebula is, and we shall see that some astronomers regard these spiral nebulæ as worlds "in the making." But some of the most eminent astronomers believe that they are separate universes—"island-universes" they call them—or great collections of millions of stars like our universe. There are certain peculiarities in the structure of the Milky Way which lead these astronomers to think that our universe may be

Photo: Harvard College Observatory.

FIG. 2.—THE MILKY WAY

Note the cloud-like effect.

FIG. 3—THE MOON ENTERING THE SHADOW CAST BY THE EARTH

The diagram shows the Moon partially eclipsed.

From a photograph taken at the Yerkes Observatory

FIG. 4.—THE GREAT NEBULA IN ANDROMEDA, MESSIER 31

a spiral nebula, and that the other spiral nebulæ are "other universes."

Vast as is the Solar System, then, it is excessively minute in comparison with the Stellar System, the universe of the Stars, which is on a scale far transcending anything the human mind can apprehend.

THE SOLAR SYSTEM

THE SUN

§ I

But now let us turn to the Solar System, and consider the members of our own little colony.

Within the Solar System there are a large number of problems that interest us. What is the size, mass, and distance of each of the planets? What satellites, like our Moon, do they possess? What are their temperatures? And those other, sporadic members of our system, comets and meteors, what are they? What are their movements? How do they originate? And the Sun itself, what is its composition, what is the source of its heat, how did it originate? Is it running down?

These last questions introduce us to a branch of astronomy which is concerned with the physical constitution of the stars, a study which, not so very many years ago, may well have appeared inconceivable. But the spectroscope enables us to answer even these questions, and the answer opens up questions of yet greater interest. We find that the stars can be arranged in an order of development—that there are stars at all stages of their life-history. The main lines of the evolution of the stellar universe can be worked out. In the sun and stars we have furnaces with temperatures enormously high; it is in such conditions that substances are resolved into their simplest forms, and it is thus we are enabled to obtain a knowledge of the most primitive forms of matter. It is in this direction that the spectroscope (which we shall refer to immediately) has helped us so much. It is to this wonderful instrument that we owe our knowledge of the composition of the sun and stars, as we shall see.

> "That the spectroscope will detect the millionth of a milligram of matter, and on that account has discovered new elements, commands our admiration; but when we find in addition that it will detect the nature of forms of matter trillions of miles away, and moreover, that it will measure the velocities with which these forms of matter are moving with an absurdly small per cent. of possible error, we can easily acquiesce in the statement that it is the greatest instrument ever devised by the brain and hand of man."

Such are some of the questions with which modern astronomy deals. To answer them requires the employment of instruments of almost incredible refinement and exactitude and also the full resources of mathematical genius. Whether astronomy be judged from the point of view of the phenomena studied, the vast masses, the immense distances, the æons of time, or whether it be judged as a monument of human ingenuity, patience, and the rarest type of genius, it is certainly one of the grandest, as it is also one of the oldest, of the sciences.

The Solar System

In the Solar System we include all those bodies dependent on the sun which circulate round it at various distances, deriving their light and heat from the sun—the planets and their moons, certain comets and a multitude of meteors: in other words, all bodies whose movements in space are determined by the gravitational pull of the sun.

The Sun

Thanks to our wonderful modern instruments and the ingenious methods used by astronomers, we have to-day a remarkable knowledge of the sun.

Look at the figure of the sun in the frontispiece. The picture represents an eclipse of the sun; the dark body of the moon has screened the sun's shining disc and taken the glare out of our eyes; we see a silvery halo surrounding the great orb on every side. It is the sun's atmosphere, or "crown" (corona), stretching for millions of miles into space in the form of a soft silvery-looking light; probably much of its light is sunlight reflected from particles of dust, although the spectroscope shows an element in the corona that has not so far been detected anywhere else in the universe and which in consequence has been named Coronium.

We next notice in the illustration that at the base of the halo there are red flames peeping out from the edges of the hidden disc. When one remembers that the sun is 866,000 miles in diameter, one hardly needs to be told that these flames are really gigantic. We shall see what they are presently.

Regions of the Sun

The astronomer has divided the sun into definite concentric regions or layers. These layers envelop the nucleus or central body of the sun somewhat as the atmosphere envelops our earth. It is through these vapour layers that the bright white body of the sun is seen. Of the innermost region, the heart or nucleus of the sun, we know almost nothing. The central body or nucleus is surrounded by a brilliantly luminous envelope or layer of vaporous matter which is what we see when we look at the sun and which the astronomer calls the photosphere.

Above—that is, overlying—the photosphere there is a second layer of glowing gases, which is known as the reversing layer. This layer is cooler than the underlying photosphere; it forms a veil of smoke-like haze and is of from 500 to 1,000 miles in thickness.

A third layer or envelope immediately lying over the last one is the region known as the chromosphere. The chromosphere extends from 5,000 to 10,000 miles in thickness—a "sea" of red tumultuous surging fire. Chief among the glowing gases is the vapour of hydrogen. The intense white heat of the photosphere beneath shines through this layer, overpowering its brilliant redness. From the uppermost portion of the chromosphere great fiery tongues of glowing hydrogen and calcium vapour shoot out for many thousands of miles, driven outward by some prodigious expulsive force. It is these red "prominences" which are such a notable feature in the picture of the eclipse of the sun already referred to.

During the solar eclipse of 1919 one of these red flames rose in less than seven hours from a height of 130,000 miles to more than 500,000 miles above the sun's surface. This immense column of red-hot gas, four or five times the thickness of the earth, was soaring upward at the rate of 60,000 miles an hour.

These flaming jets or prominences shooting out from the chromosphere are not to be seen every day by the naked eye; the dazzling light of the sun obscures them, gigantic as they are. They can be observed, however, by the spectroscope any day, and they are visible to us for a very short time during an eclipse of the sun. Some extraordinary outbursts have been witnessed. Thus the late Professor Young described one on September 7, 1871, when he had been examining a prominence by the spectroscope:

> It had remained unchanged since noon of the previous day—a long, low, quiet-looking cloud, not very dense, or brilliant, or in any way remarkable except for its size. At 12:30 p.m. the Professor left the spectroscope for a short time, and on returning half an hour later to his observations, he was astonished to find the gigantic Sun flame shattered to pieces. The solar atmosphere was filled with flying debris, and some of these portions reached a height of 100,000 miles above the solar surface. Moving with a velocity which, even at the distance of 93,000,000 miles, was almost perceptible to the eye, these fragments doubled their height in ten minutes. On January 30, 1885, another distinguished solar

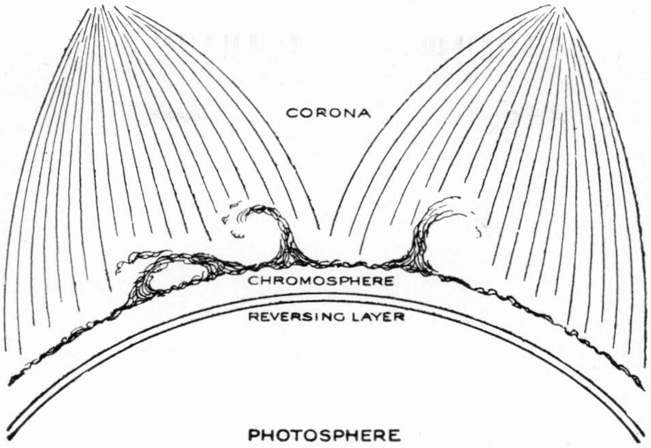

FIG. 5.—DIAGRAM SHOWING THE MAIN LAYERS OF THE SUN

Compare with frontispiece.

Photo: Royal Observatory, Greenwich.

FIG. 6.—SOLAR PROMINENCES SEEN AT TOTAL SOLAR ECLIPSE, May 29, 1919. TAKEN AT SOBRAL, BRAZIL.

The small Corona is also visible.

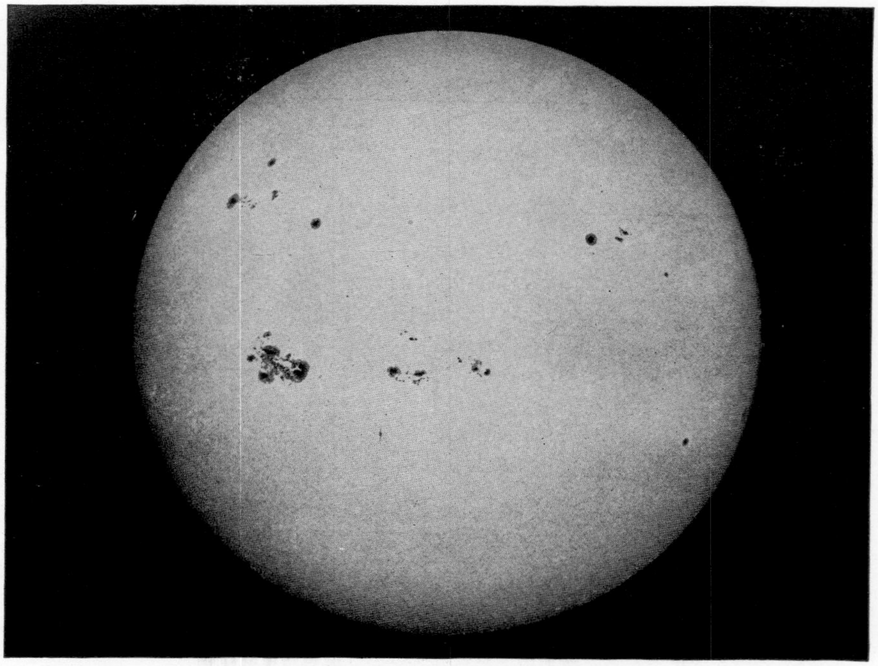

FIG. 7.—THE VISIBLE SURFACE OF THE SUN

A photograph taken at the Mount Wilson Observatory of the Carnegie Institution at Washington.

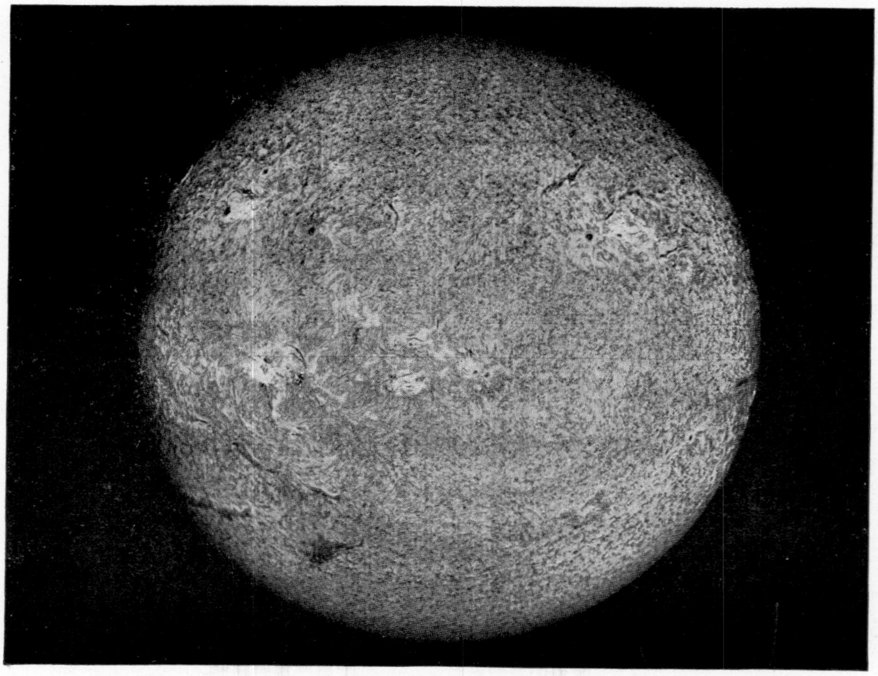

FIG. 8.—THE SUN

Photographed in the light of glowing hydrogen, at the Mount Wilson Observatory of the Carnegie Institution of Washington: vortex phenomena near the spots are especially prominent.

observer, the late Professor Tacchini of Rome, observed one of the greatest prominences ever seen by man. Its height was no less than 142,000 miles—eighteen times the diameter of the earth. Another mighty flame was so vast that supposing the eight large planets of the solar system ranged one on top of the other, the prominence would still tower above them.[1]

The fourth and uppermost layer or region is that of the corona, of immense extent and fading away into the surrounding sky—this we have already referred to. The diagram (Fig. 5) shows the dispositions of these various layers of the sun. It is through these several transparent layers that we see the white light body of the sun.

§ 2

The Surface of the Sun

Here let us return to and see what more we know about the photosphere—the sun's surface. It is from the photosphere that we have gained most of our knowledge of the composition of the sun, which is believed not to be a solid body. Examination of the photosphere shows that the outer surface is never at rest. Small bright cloudlets come and go in rapid succession, giving the surface, through contrasts in luminosity, a granular appearance. Of course, to be visible at all at 92,830,000 miles the cloudlets cannot be small. They imply enormous activity in the photosphere. If we might speak picturesquely the sun's surface resembles a boiling ocean of white-hot metal vapours. We have to-day a wonderful instrument, which will be described later, which dilutes, as it were, the general glare of the sun, and enables us to observe these fiery eruptions at any hour. The "oceans" of red-hot gas and white-hot metal vapour at the sun's surface are constantly driven by great storms. Some unimaginable energy streams out from the body or muscles of the sun and blows its outer layers into gigantic shreds, as it were.

[1] *The Romance of Astronomy,* by H. Macpherson.

The actual temperature at the sun's surface, or what appears to us to be the surface—the photosphere—is, of course, unknown, but careful calculation suggests that it is from 5,000° C. to 7,000° C. The interior is vastly hotter. We can form no conception of such temperatures as must exist there. Not even the most obdurate solid could resist such temperatures, but would be converted almost instantaneously into gas. But it would not be gas as we know gases on the earth. The enormous pressures that exist on the sun must convert even gases into thick treacly fluids. We can only infer this state of matter. It is beyond our power to reproduce it.

Sun-spots

It is in the brilliant photosphere that the dark areas known as sun-spots appear. Some of these dark spots—they are dark only by contrast with the photosphere surrounding them—are of enormous size, covering many thousands of square miles of surface. What they are we cannot positively say. They look like great cavities in the sun's surface. Some think they are giant whirlpools. Certainly they seem to be great whirling streams of glowing gases with vapours above them and immense upward and downward currents within them. Round the edges of the sun-spots rise great tongues of flame.

Perhaps the most popularly known fact about sun-spots is that they are somehow connected with what we call magnetic storms on earth. These magnetic storms manifest themselves in interruptions of our telegraphic and telephonic communications, in violent disturbances of the mariner's compass, and in exceptional auroral displays. The connection between the two sets of phenomena cannot be doubted, even although at times there may be a great spot on the sun without any corresponding "magnetic storm" effects on the earth.

A surprising fact about sun-spots is that they show definite periodic variations in number. The best-defined period is one of

Reproduced from "The Forces of Nature" (Messrs. Macmillan)

THE AURORA BOREALIS

The aurora borealis is one of the most beautiful spectacles in the sky. The colours and shape change every instant; sometimes a fan-like cluster of rays, at other times long golden draperies gliding one over the other. Blue, green, yellow, red, and white combine to give a glorious display of colour. The theory of its origin is still, in part, obscure, but there can be no doubt that the aurora is related to the magnetic phenomena of the earth and therefore is connected with the electrical influence of the sun.

about eleven years. During this period the spots increase to a maximum in number and then diminish to a minimum, the variation being more or less regular. Now this can only mean one thing. To be periodic the spots must have some deep-seated connection with the fundamental facts of the sun's structure and activities. Looked at from this point of view their importance becomes great.

It is from the study of sun-spots that we have learned that the sun's surface does not appear to rotate all at the same speed. The "equatorial" regions are rotating quicker than regions farther north or south. A point forty-five degrees from the equator seems to take about two and a half days longer to complete one rotation than a point on the equator. This, of course, confirms our belief that the sun cannot be a solid body.

What is its composition? We know that there are present, in a gaseous state, such well-known elements as sodium, iron, copper, zinc, and magnesium; indeed, we know that there is practically every element in the sun that we know to be in the earth. How do we know?

It is from the photosphere, as has been said, that we have won most of our knowledge of the sun. The instrument used for this purpose is the spectroscope; and before proceeding to deal further with the sun and the source of its energy it will be better to describe this instrument.

A WONDERFUL INSTRUMENT AND WHAT IT REVEALS

The spectroscope is an instrument for analysing light. So important is it in the revelations it has given us that it will be best to describe it fully. Every substance to be examined must first be made to glow, made luminous; and as nearly everything in the heavens *is* luminous the instrument has a great range in Astronomy. And when we speak of analysing light, we mean that the light may be broken up into waves of different lengths. What we call light is a series of minute waves in ether, and these waves are—measuring them from crest to crest, so to say—of various lengths. Each wave-length corresponds to a colour of the rainbow. The shortest waves give us a sensation of violet colour, and the largest waves cause a sensation of red. The rainbow, in fact, is a sort of natural spectrum. (The meaning of the rainbow is that the moisture-laden air has sorted out these waves, in the sun's light, according to their length.) Now the simplest form of spectroscope is a glass prism—a triangular-shaped piece of glass. If white light (sunlight, for example) passes through a glass prism, we see a series of rainbow-tinted colours. Anyone can notice this effect when sunlight is shining through any kind of cut glass—the stopper of a wine decanter, for instance. If, instead of catching with the eye the coloured lights as they emerge from the glass prism, we allow them to fall on a screen, we shall find that they pass, by continuous gradations, from red at the one end of the screen, through orange, yellow, green, blue, and indigo, to violet at the other end. *In other words, what we call white light is composed of rays of these several colours. They go to make up the effect which we call white.* And now just as water can be split up into its two elements, oxygen and hydrogen, so sunlight can be broken up into its primary colours, which are those we have just mentioned.

This range of colours, produced by the spectroscope, we call the solar spectrum, and these are, from the spectroscopic point of view, primary colours. Each shade of colour has its definite position in the spectrum. That is to say, the light of each shade of colour (corresponding to its wave-length) is reflected through a certain fixed angle on passing through the glass prism. Every possible kind of light has its definite position, and is denoted by a number which gives the wave-length of the vibrations constituting that particular kind of light.

Now, other kinds of light besides sunlight can be analysed.

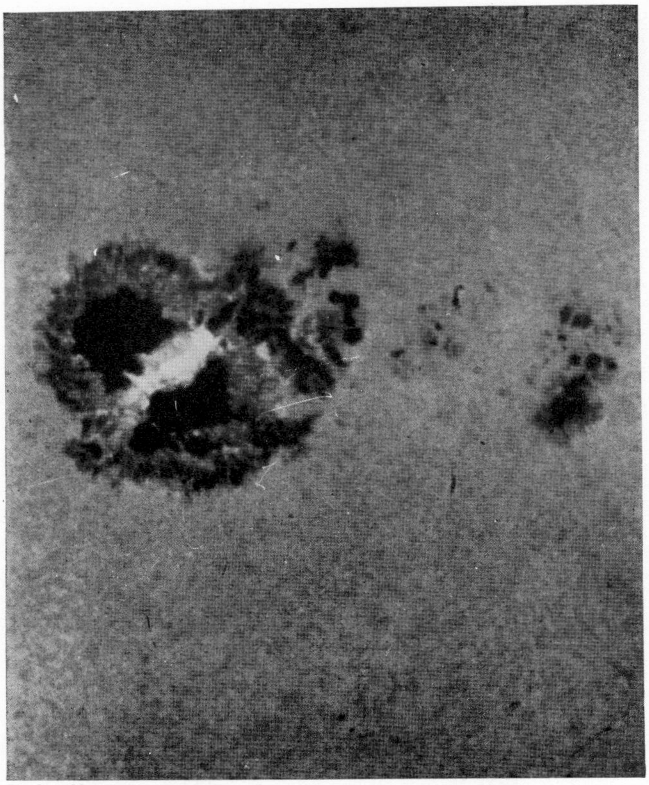

Yerkes Observatory

FIG. 9.—THE GREAT SUN-SPOT OF JULY 17, 1905

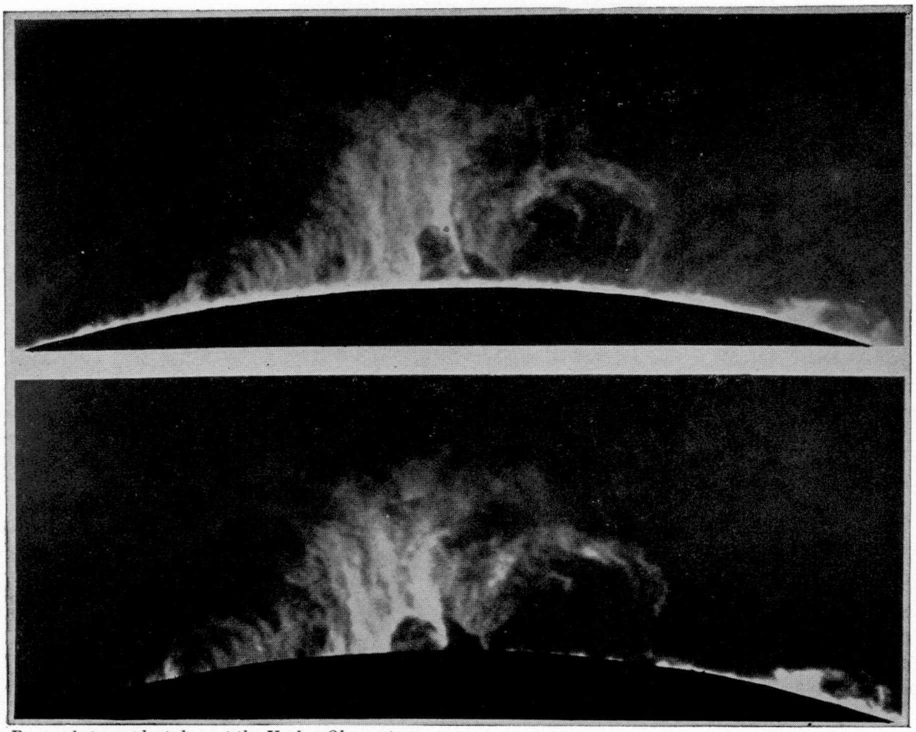

From photographs taken at the Yerkes Observatory.

FIG. 10.—SOLAR PROMINENCES

These are about 60,000 miles in height. The two photographs show the vast changes occurring in ten minutes. October 10, 1910.

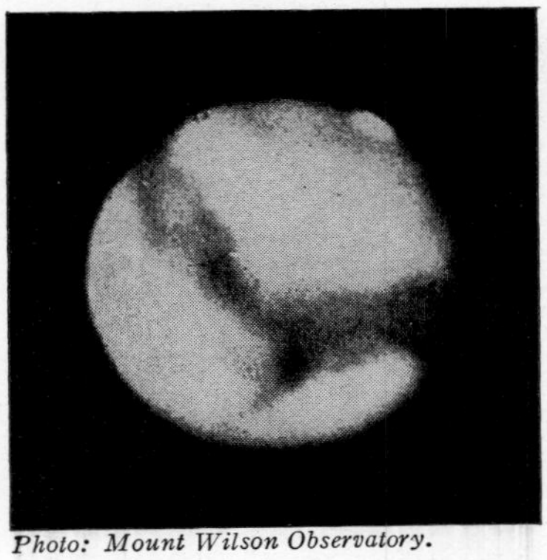

Photo: Mount Wilson Observatory.

FIG. 11.—MARS, October 5, 1909

Showing the dark markings and the Polar Cap.

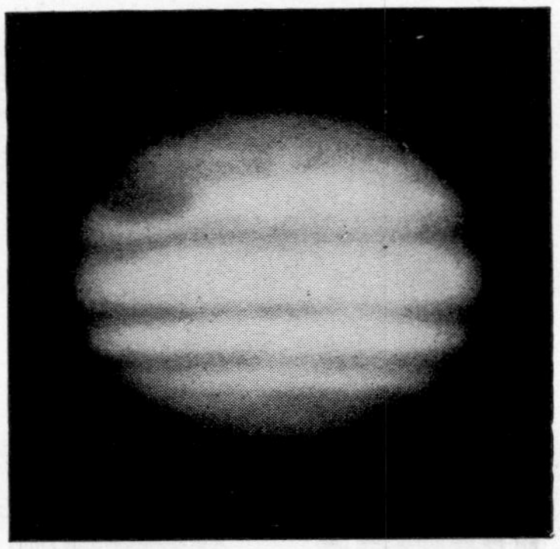

FIG. 12.—JUPITER

Showing the belts which are probably cloud formations.

Photo: Professor E. E. Barnard, Yerkes Observatory.

FIG. 13.—SATURN, November 19, 1911

Showing the rings, mighty swarms of meteorites.

Light from any substance which has been made incandescent may be observed with the spectroscope in the same way, and each element can be thus separated. It is found that each substance (in the same conditions of pressure, etc.) gives a constant spectrum of its own. *Each metal displays its own distinctive colour. It is obvious, therefore, that the spectrum provides the means for identifying a particular substance.* It was by this method that we discovered in the sun the presence of such well-known elements as sodium, iron, copper, zinc, and magnesium.

Every chemical element known, then, has a distinctive spectrum of its own when it is raised to incandescence, and this distinctive spectrum is as reliable a means of identification for the element as a human face is for its owner. Whether it is a substance glowing in the laboratory or in a remote star makes no difference to the spectroscope; if the light of any substance reaches it, that substance will be recognised and identified by the characteristic set of waves.

The spectrum of a glowing mass of gas will consist in a number of bright lines of various colours, and at various intervals; corresponding to each kind of gas, there will be a peculiar and distinctive arrangement of bright lines. But if the light from such a mass of glowing gas be made to pass through a cool mass of the *same* gas it will be found that dark lines replace the bright lines in the spectrum, the reason for this being that the cool gas absorbs the rays of light emitted by the hot gas. Experiments of this kind enable us to reach the important general statement that every gas, when cold, absorbs the same rays of light which it emits when hot.

Crossing the solar spectrum are hundreds and hundreds of dark lines. These could not at first be explained, because this fact of discriminative absorption was not known. We understand now. The sun's white light comes from the photosphere, but between us and the photosphere there is, as we have seen, another solar envelope of relatively cooler vapours—the reversing layer. Each constituent element in this outer envelope stops its own kind of light, that is, the kind of light made by incandescent atoms of the same element in the photosphere. The "stoppages" register themselves in the solar spectrum as dark lines placed exactly where the corresponding bright lines would have been. The explanation once attained, dark lines became as significant as bright lines. The secret of the sun's composition was out. We have found practically every element in the sun that we know to be in the earth. We have identified an element in the sun before we were able to isolate it on the earth. We have been able even to point to the coolest places on the sun, the centres of sun-spots, where alone the temperature seems to have fallen sufficiently low to allow chemical compounds to form.

It is thus we have been able to determine what the stars, comets, or nebulæ are made of.

A Unique Discovery

In 1868 Sir Norman Lockyer detected a light coming from the prominences of the sun which was not given by any substance known on earth, and attributed this to an unknown gas which he called helium, from the Greek *helios,* the sun. *In 1895 Sir William Ramsay discovered in certain minerals the same gas identified by the spectroscope.* We can say, therefore, that this gas was discovered in the sun nearly thirty years before it was found on earth; this discovery of the long-lost heir is as thrilling a chapter in the detective story of science as any in the sensational stories of the day, and makes us feel quite certain that our methods really tell us of what elements sun and stars are built up. The light from the corona of the sun, as we have mentioned indicates a gas still unknown on earth, which has been christened Coronium.

Measuring the Speed of Light

But this is not all; soon a new use was found for the spectrocope. We found that we could measure with it the most difficult

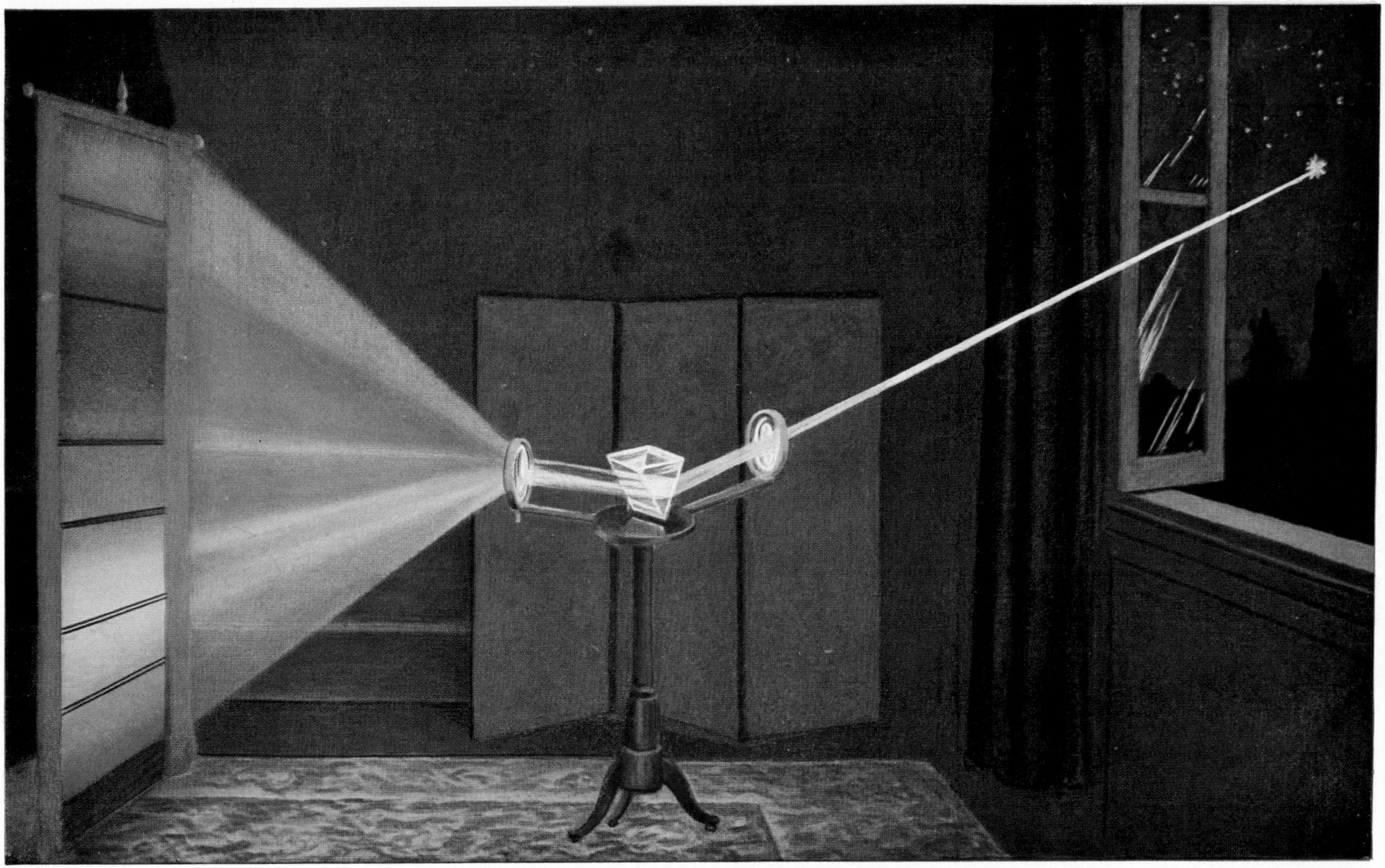

THE SPECTROSCOPE IS AN INSTRUMENT FOR ANALYSING LIGHT; IT PROVIDES THE MEANS FOR IDENTIFYING DIFFERENT SUBSTANCES

This pictorial diagram illustrates the principal of Spectrum Analysis, showing how sunlight is decomposed into its primary colours. What we call white light is composed of seven different colours. The diagram is relieved of all detail which would unduly obscure the simple process by which a ray of light is broken up by a prism into different wave-lengths. The spectrum rays have been greatly magnified.

of all speeds to measure, speed in the line of sight. Movement at right angles to the direction in which one is looking is, if there is sufficient of it, easy to detect, and, if the distance of the moving body is known, easy to measure. But movement in the line of vision is both difficult to detect and difficult to measure. Yet, even at the enormous distances with which astronomers have to deal, the spectroscope can detect such movement and furnish data for its measurement. If a luminous body containing, say, sodium is moving rapidly towards the spectroscope, it will be found that the sodium lines in the spectrum have moved slightly from their usual definite positions towards the violet end of the spectrum, the amount of the change of position increasing with the speed of the luminous body. If the body is moving away from the spectroscope the shifting of the spectral lines will be in the opposite direction, towards the red end of the spectrum. In this way we have discovered and measured movements that otherwise would probably not have revealed themselves unmistakably to us for thousands of years. In the same way we have watched, and measured the speed of, tremendous movements on the sun, and so gained proof that the vast disturbances we should expect there actually do occur.

IS THE SUN DYING?

§3

Now let us return to our consideration of the sun.

To us on the earth the most patent and most astonishing fact about the sun is its tremendous energy. Heat and light in amazing quantities pour from it without ceasing.

Where does this energy come from? Enormous jets of red glowing gases can be seen shooting outwards from the sun, like flames from a fire, for thousands of miles. Does this argue fire, as we know fire on the earth? On this point the scientist is sure. The sun is not burning, and combustion is not the source of its heat. Combustion is a chemical reaction between atoms. The conditions that make it possible are known and the results are predictable and measurable. But no chemical reaction of the nature of combustion as we know it will explain the sun's energy, nor indeed will any ordinary chemical reaction of any kind. If the sun were composed of combustible material throughout and the conditions of combustion as we understand them were always present, the sun would burn itself out in some thousands of years, with marked changes in its heat and light production as the process advanced. There is no evidence of such changes. There is, instead, strong evidence that the sun has been emitting light and heat in prodigious quantities, not for thousands, but for millions of years. Every addition to our knowledge that throws light on the sun's age seems to make for increase rather than decrease of its years. This makes the wonder of its energy greater.

And we cannot avoid the issue of the source of the energy by saying merely that the sun is gradually radiating away an energy that originated in some unknown manner, away back at the beginning of things. Reliable calculations show that the years required for the mere cooling of a globe like the sun could not possibly run to millions. In other words, the sun's energy must be subject to continuous and more or less steady renewal. However it may have acquired its enormous energy in the past, it must have some source of energy in the present.

The best explanation that we have to-day of this continuous accretion of energy is that it is due to shrinkage of the sun's bulk under the force of gravity. Gravity is one of the most mysterious forces of nature, but it is an obvious fact that bodies behave as if they attracted one another, and Newton worked out the law of this attraction. We may say, without trying to go too deeply into things, that every particle of matter attracts every other throughout the universe. If the diameter of the sun were to shrink by one mile all round, this would mean that all the millions of tons in the outer one-mile thickness would have a straight drop of one mile towards the centre. And that is not all, because obviously the layers below this outer mile would also drop inwards, each to a less degree than the one above it. What a tremendous movement of matter, however slowly it might take place! And what a tremendous energy would be involved! Astronomers calculate that the above shrinkage of one mile all round would require fifty years for its completion, assuming, reasonably, that there is close and continuous relationship between loss of heat by radiation and shrinkage. Even if this were true we need not feel over-anxious on this theory; before the sun became too cold to support life many millions of years would be required.

It was suggested at one time that falls of meteoric matter into the sun would account for the sun's heat. This position is hardly tenable now. The mere bulk of the meteoric matter required by the hypothesis, apart from other reasons, is against it. There is undoubtedly an enormous amount of meteoric matter moving about within the bounds of the solar system, but most of it seems to be following definite routes round the sun like the planets. The stray erratic quantities destined to meet their doom by collision with the sun can hardly be sufficient to account for the sun's heat.

Recent study of radio-active bodies has suggested another factor that may be working powerfully along with the force of gravitation to maintain the sun's store of heat. In radio-active bodies certain atoms seem to be undergoing disintegration. These atoms appear to be splitting up into very minute and primitive constituents. But since matter may be split up into such constituents, may it not be built up from them?

The question is whether these "radio-active" elements are undergoing disintegration, or formation, in the sun. If they are undergoing disintegration—and the sun itself is undoubtedly radio-active—then we have another source of heat for the sun that will last indefinitely.

THE PLANETS

LIFE IN OTHER WORLDS?

§ 1

It is quite clear that there cannot be life on the stars. Nothing solid or even liquid can exist in such furnaces as they are. Life exists only on planets, and even on these its possibilities are limited. Whether all the stars, or how many of them, have planetary families like our sun, we cannot positively say. If they have, such planets would be too faint and small to be visible tens of trillions of miles away. Some astronomers think that our sun may be exceptional in having planets, but their reasons are speculative and unconvincing. Probably a large proportion at least of the stars have planets, and we may therefore survey the globes of our own solar system and in a general way extend the results to the rest of the universe.

In considering the possibility of life as we know it we may at once rule out the most distant planets from the sun, Uranus and Neptune. They are probably intrinsically too hot. We may also pass over the nearest planet to the sun, Mercury. We have reason to believe that it turns on its axis in the same period as it revolves round the sun, and it must therefore always present the same side to the sun. This means that the heat on the sunlit side of Mercury is above boiling-point, while the cold on the other side must be between two and three hundred degrees below freezing-point.

The Planet Venus

The planet Venus, the bright globe which is known to all as the morning and evening "star," seems at first sight more promising as regards the possibility of life. It is of nearly the same size as the earth, and it has a good atmosphere, but there are many astronomers who believe that, like Mercury, it always presents the same face to the sun, and it would therefore have the same disadvantage—a broiling heat on the sunny side and the cold of

FIG. 14.—THE MOON

Showing a great plain and some typical craters. There are thousands of these craters, and some theories of their origin are explained on page 34.

FIG. 16.—THE MOON, AT NINE AND THREE-QUARTER DAYS

Note the mysterious "rays" diverging from the almost perfectly circular craters indicated by the arrows (Tycho, upper; Copernicus, lower), and also the mountains to the right with the lunar dawn breaking on them.

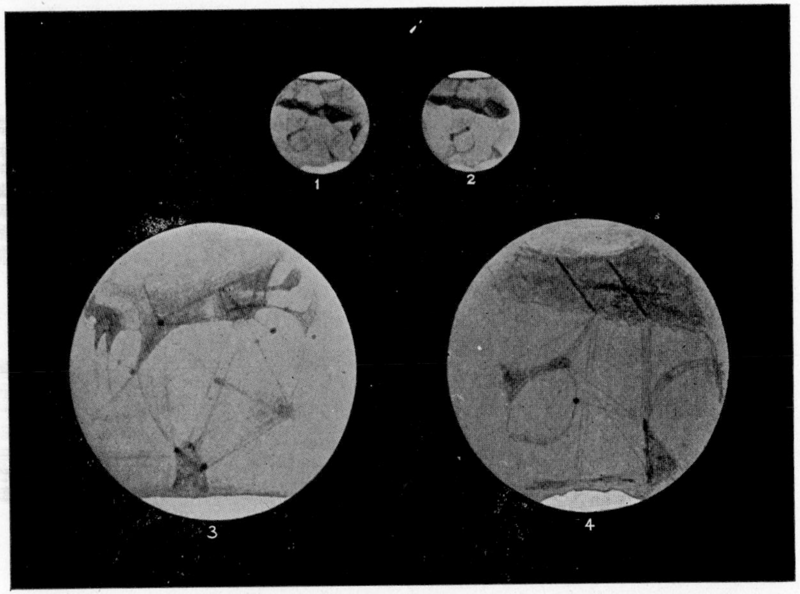

FIG. 15.—MARS

1, 2 Drawings by Prof. Lowell to accompany actual photographs of Mars showing many of the canals. Taken in 1907 by Mr. E. C. Slipher of the Lowell Observatory.
3 Drawing by Prof. Lowell made January 6, 1914.
4 Drawing by Prof. Lowell made January 21, 1914.
Nos. 1 and 2 show the effect of the planet's rotation. Nos. 3 and 4 depict quite different sections. Note the change in the polar snow-caps in the last two.

space on the opposite side. We are not sure. The surface of Venus is so bright—the light of the sun is reflected to us by such dense masses of cloud and dust—that it is difficult to trace any permanent markings on it, and thus ascertain how long it takes to rotate on its axis. Many astronomers believe that they have succeeded, and that the planet always turns the same face to the sun. If it does, we can hardly conceive of life on its surface, in spite of the cloud-screen.

We turn to Mars; and we must first make it clear why there is so much speculation about life on Mars, and why it is supposed that, if there *is* life on Mars, it must be more advanced than life on the earth.

Is there Life on Mars?

The basis of this belief is that if, as we saw, all the globes in our solar system are masses of metal that are cooling down, the smaller will have cooled down before the larger, and will be further ahead in their development. Now Mars is very much smaller than the earth, and must have cooled at its surface millions of years before the earth did. Hence, if a story of life began on Mars at all, it began long before the story of life on the earth. We cannot guess what sort of life-forms would be evolved in a different world, but we can confidently say that they would tend toward increasing intelligence; and thus we are disposed to look for highly intelligent beings on Mars.

But this argument supposes that the conditions of life, namely air and water, are found on Mars, and it is disputed whether they are found there in sufficient quantity. The late Professor Percival Lowell, who made a lifelong study of Mars, maintained that there are hundreds of straight lines drawn across the surface of the planet, and he claimed that they are beds of vegetation marking the sites of great channels or pipes by means of which the "Martians" draw water from their polar ocean. Professor W. H. Pickering, another high authority, thinks that the lines are long, narrow marshes fed by moist winds from the poles. There are certainly white polar caps on Mars. They seem to melt in the spring, and the dark fringe round them grows broader.

Other astronomers, however, say that they find no trace of water-vapour in the atmosphere of Mars, and they think that the polar caps may be simply thin sheets of hoar-frost or frozen gas. They point out that, as the atmosphere of Mars is certainly scanty, and the distance from the sun is so great, it may be too cold for the fluid water to exist on the planet.

If one asks why our wonderful instruments cannot settle these points, one must be reminded that Mars is never nearer than 34,000,000 miles from the earth, and only approaches to this distance once in fifteen or seventeen years. The image of Mars on the photographic negative taken in a big telescope is very small. Astronomers rely to a great extent on the eye, which is more sensitive than the photographic plate. But it is easy to have differences of opinion as to what the eye sees, and so there is a good deal of controversy.

In August, 1924, the planet will again be well placed for observation, and we may learn more about it. Already a few of the much-disputed lines, which people wrongly call "canals," have been traced on photographs. Astronomers who are sceptical about life on Mars are often not fully aware of the extraordinary adaptability of life. There was a time when the climate of the whole earth, from pole to pole, was semi-tropical for millions of years. No animal could then endure the least cold, yet now we have plenty of Arctic plants and animals. If the cold came slowly on Mars, as we have reason to suppose, the population could be gradually adapted to it. On the whole, it is possible that there is advanced life on Mars, and it is not impossible, in spite of the very great difficulties of a code of communication, that our "elder brothers" may yet flash across space the solution of many of our problems.

§2

Jupiter and Saturn

Next to Mars, going outward from the sun, is Jupiter. Between Mars and Jupiter, however, there are more than three hundred million miles of space, and the older astronomers wondered why this was not occupied by a planet. We now know that it contains about nine hundred "planetoids," or small globes of from five to five hundred miles in diameter. It was at one time thought that a planet might have burst into these fragments (a theory which is not mathematically satisfactory), or it may be that the material which is scattered in them was prevented by the nearness of the great bulk of Jupiter from uniting into one globe.

For Jupiter is a giant planet, and its gravitational influence must extend far over space. It is 1,300 times as large as the earth, and has nine moons, four of which are large, in attendance on it. It is interesting to note that the outermost moons of Jupiter and Saturn revolve round these planets in a direction contrary to the usual direction taken by moons round planets, and by planets round the sun. But there is no life on Jupiter.

The surface which we see in photographs (Fig. 12) is a mass of cloud or steam which always envelops the body of the planet. It is apparently red-hot. A red tinge is seen sometimes at the edges of its cloud-belts, and a large red region (the "red spot"), 23,000 miles in length, has been visible on it for half a century. There may be a liquid or solid core to the planet, but as a whole it is a mass of seething vapours whirling round on its axis once in every ten hours. As in the case of the sun, however, different latitudes appear to rotate at different rates. The interior of Jupiter is very hot, but the planet is not self-luminous. The planets Venus and Jupiter shine very brightly, but they have no light of their own; they reflect the sunlight.

Saturn is in the same interesting condition. The surface in the photograph (Fig. 13) is steam, and Saturn is so far away from the sun that the vaporisation of its oceans must necessarily be due to its own internal heat. It is too hot for water to settle on its surface. Like Jupiter, the great globe turns on its axis once in ten hours—a prodigious speed—and must be a swirling, seething mass of metallic vapours and gases. It is instructive to compare Jupiter and Saturn in this respect with the sun. They are smaller globes and have cooled down more than the central fire.

Saturn is a beautiful object in the telescope because it has ten moons (to include one which is disputed) and a wonderful system of "rings" round it. The so-called rings are a mighty swarm of meteorites—pieces of iron and stone of all sorts and sizes, which reflect the light of the sun to us. This ocean of matter is some miles deep, and stretches from a few thousand miles from the surface of the planet to 172,000 miles out in space. Some astronomers think that this is volcanic material which has been shot out of the planet. Others regard it as stuff which would have combined to form an eleventh moon but was prevented by the nearness of Saturn itself. There is no evidence of life on Saturn.

THE MOON

Mars and Venus are therefore the only planets, besides the earth, on which we may look for life; and in the case of Venus, the possibility is very faint. But what about the moons which attend the planets? They range in size from the little ten-miles-wide moons of Mars, to Titan, a moon of Saturn, and Ganymede, a satellite of Jupiter, which are about 3,000 miles in diameter. May there not be life on some of the larger of these moons? We will take our own moon as a type of the class.

A Dead World

The moon is so very much nearer to us than any other heavenly body that we have a remarkable knowledge of it. In Fig. 14 you have a photograph, taken in one of our largest telescopes,

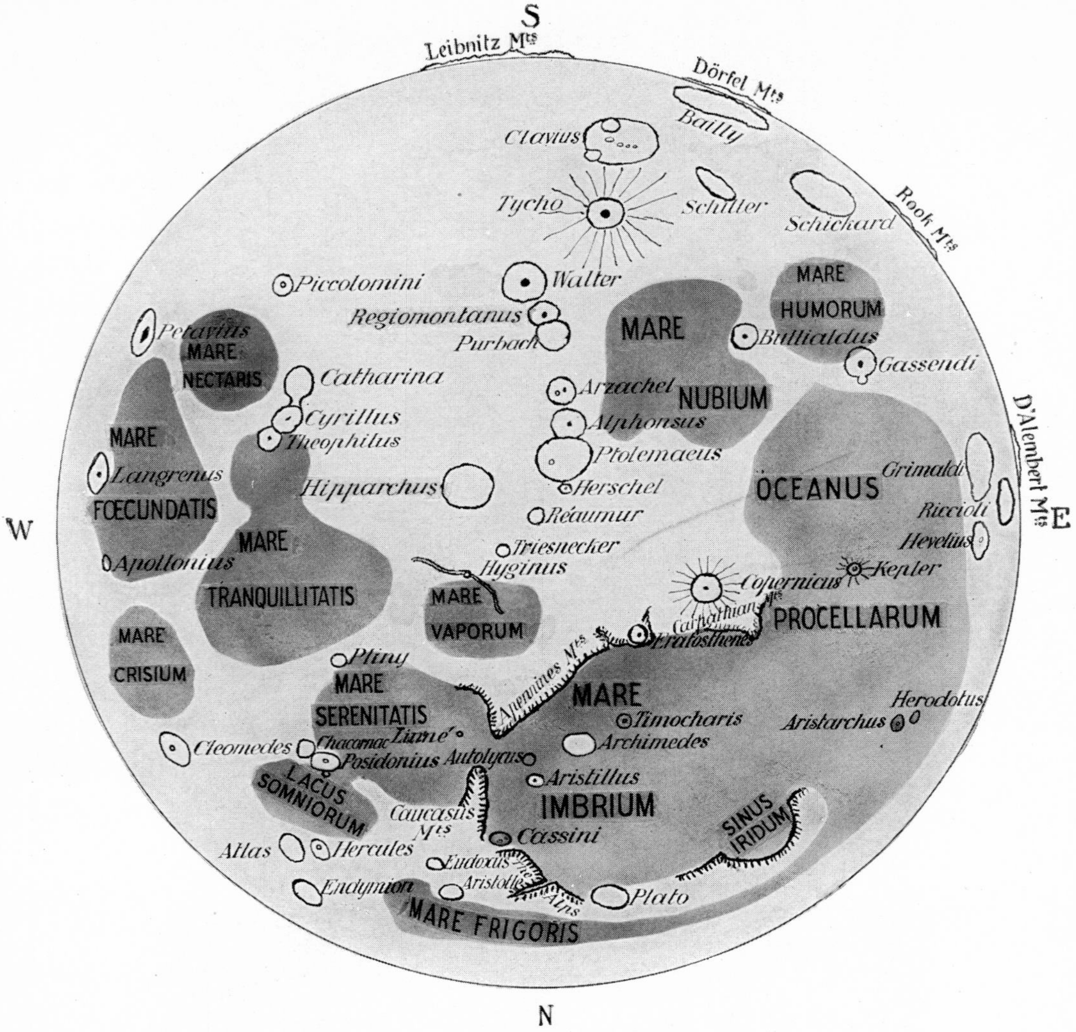

FIG. 17.—A MAP OF THE CHIEF PLAINS AND CRATERS OF THE MOON

The plains were originally supposed to be seas: hence the name "Mare."

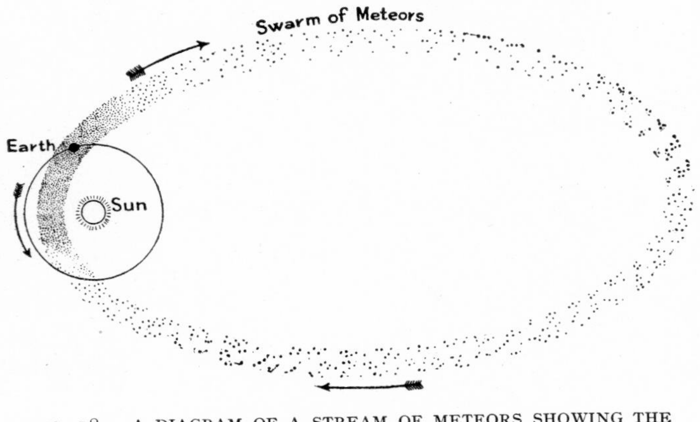

FIG. 18.—A DIAGRAM OF A STREAM OF METEORS SHOWING THE EARTH PASSING THROUGH THEM

Photo: Royal Observatory, Greenwich.

FIG. 19.—COMET, September 29, 1908

Notice the tendency to form a number of tails. (See photograph below.)

Photo: Royal Observatory, Greenwich.

FIG. 20.—COMET, October 3, 1908

The process has gone further and a number of distinct tails can now be counted.

of part of its surface. In a sense such a telescope brings the moon to within about fifty miles of us. We should see a city like London as a dark, sprawling blotch on the globe. We could just detect a Zeppelin or a Diplodocus as a moving speck against the surface. But we find none of these things. It is true that a few astronomers believe that they see signs of some sort of feeble life or movement on the moon. Professor Pickering thinks that he can trace some volcanic activity. He believes that there are areas of vegetation, probably of a low order, and that the soil of the moon may retain a certain amount of water in it. He speaks of a very thin atmosphere, and of occasional light falls of snow. He has succeeded in persuading some careful observers that there probably are slight changes of some kind taking place on the moon.

But there are many things that point to absence of air on the moon. Even the photographs we reproduce tell the same story. The edges of the shadows are all hard and black. If there had been an appreciable atmosphere it would have scattered the sun's light on to the edges and produced a gradual shading off such as we see on the earth. This relative absence of air must give rise to some surprising effects. There will be no sounds on the moon, because sounds are merely air waves. Even a meteor shattering itself to a violent end against the surface of the moon would make no noise. Nor would it herald its coming by glowing into a "shooting star," as it would on entering the earth's atmosphere. There will be no floating dust, no scent, no twilight, no blue sky, no twinkling of the stars. The sky will be always black and the stars will be clearly visible by day as by night. The sun's wonderful corona, which no man on earth, even by seizing every opportunity during eclipses, can hope to see for more than two hours in all in a long lifetime, will be visible all day. So will the great red flames of the sun. Of course, there will be no life, and no landscape effects and scenery effects due to vegetation.

The moon takes approximately twenty-seven of our days to

turn once on its axis. So for fourteen days there is continuous night, when the temperature must sink away down towards the absolute cold of space. This will be followed without an instant of twilight by full daylight. For another fourteen days the sun's rays will bear straight down, with no diffusion or absorption of their heat, or light, on the way. It does not follow, however, that the temperature of the moon's surface must rise enormously. It may not even rise to the temperature of melting ice. Seeing there is no air there can be no check on radiation. The heat that the moon gets will radiate away immediately. We know that amongst the coldest places on the earth are the tops of very high mountains, the points that have reared themselves nearest to the sun but farthest out of the sheltering blanket of the earth's atmosphere. The actual temperature of the moon's surface by day is a moot point. It may be below the freezing-point or above the boiling-point of water.

The Mountains of the Moon

The lack of air is considered by many astronomers to furnish the explanation of the enormous number of "craters" which pit the moon's surface. There are about a hundred thousand of these strange rings, and it is now believed by many that they are spots where very large meteorites, or even planetoids, splashed into the moon when its surface was still soft. Other astronomers think that they are the remains of gigantic bubbles which were raised in the moon's "skin," when the globe was still molten, by volcanic gases from below. A few astronomers think that they are, as is popularly supposed, the craters of extinct volcanoes. Our craters, on the earth, are generally deep cups, whereas these ring-formations on the moon are more like very shallow and broad saucers. Clavius, the largest of them, is 123 miles across the interior, yet its encircling rampart is not a mile high.

The mountains on the moon (Fig. 16) rise to a great height,

and are extraordinarily gaunt and rugged. They are like fountains of lava, rising in places to 26,000 and 27,000 feet. The lunar Apennines have three thousand steep and weird peaks. Our terrestrial mountains are continually worn down by frost acting on moisture and by ice and water, but there are none of these agencies operating on the moon. Its mountains are comparatively "everlasting hills."

The moon is interesting to us precisely because it is a dead world. It seems to show how the earth, or any cooling metal globe, will evolve in the remote future. We do not know if there was ever life on the moon, but in any case it cannot have proceeded far in development. At the most we can imagine some strange lowly forms of vegetation lingering here and there in pools of heavy gas, expanding during the blaze of the sun's long day, and frozen rigid during the long night.

METEORS AND COMETS

We may conclude our survey of the solar system with a word about "shooting stars," or meteors, and comets. There are few now who do not know that the streak of fire which suddenly lights the sky overhead at night means that a piece of stone or iron has entered our atmosphere from outer space, and has been burned up by friction. It was travelling at, perhaps, twenty or thirty miles a second. At seventy or eighty miles above our heads it began to glow, as at that height the air is thick enough to offer serious friction and raise it to a white heat. By the time the meteor reached about twenty miles or so from the earth's surface it was entirely dissipated, as a rule in fiery vapour.

Millions of Meteorites

It is estimated that between ten and a hundred million meteorites enter our atmosphere and are cremated, every day.

Most of them weigh only an ounce or two, and are invisible. Some of them weigh a ton or more, but even against these large masses the air acts as a kind of "torpedo-net." They generally burst into fragments and fall without doing damage.

It is clear that "empty space" is, at least within the limits of our solar system, full of these things. They swarm like fishes in the seas. Like the fishes, moreover, they may be either solitary or gregarious. The solitary bit of cosmic rubbish is the meteorite, which we have just examined. A "social" group of meteorites is the essential part of a comet. The nucleus, or bright central part, of the head of a comet (Fig. 19) consists of a swarm, sometimes thousands of miles wide, of these pieces of iron or stone. This swarm has come under the sun's gravitational influence, and is forced to travel round it. From some dark region of space it has moved slowly into our system. It is not then a comet, for it has no tail. But as the crowded meteors approach the sun, the speed increases. They give off fine vapour-like matter and the fierce flood of light from the sun sweeps this vapour out in an ever-lengthening tail. Whatever way the comet is travelling, the tail always points away from the sun.

A Great Comet

The vapoury tail often grows to an enormous length as the comet approaches the sun. The great comet of 1843 had a tail two hundred million miles long. It is, however, composed of the thinnest vapours imaginable. Twice during the nineteenth century the earth passed through the tail of a comet, and nothing was felt. The vapours of the tail are, in fact, so attenuated that we can hardly imagine them to be white-hot. They may be lit by some electrical force. However that may be, the comet dashes round the sun, often at three or four hundred miles a second, then may pass gradually out of our system once more. It may be a thousand years, or it may be fifty years, before

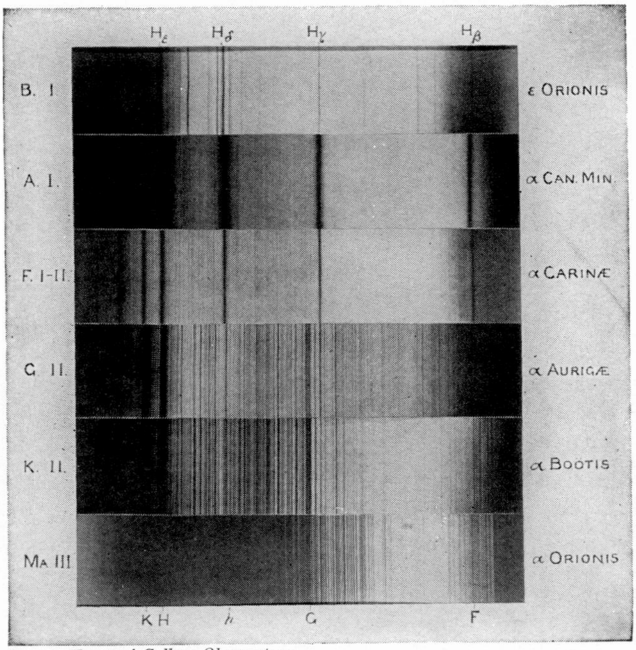

Photo: Harvard College Observatory.

FIG. 21.—TYPICAL SPECTRA

Six main types of stellar spectra. Notice the lines they have in common, showing what elements are met with in different types of stars. Each of these spectra corresponds to a different set of physical and chemical conditions.

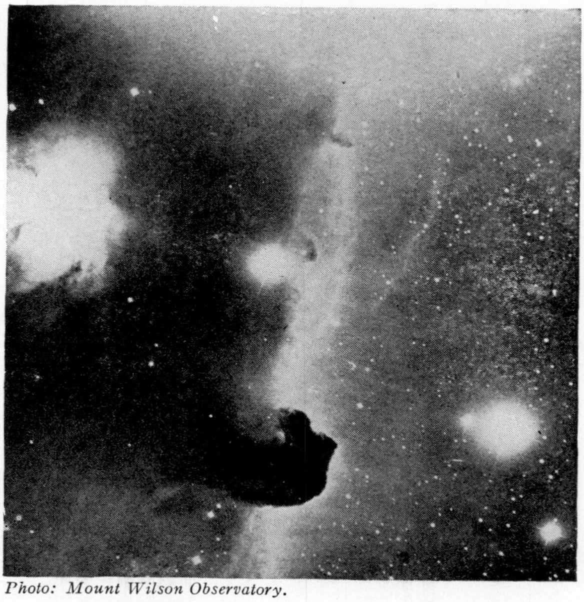

Photo: Mount Wilson Observatory.

FIG. 22.—A NEBULAR REGION SOUTH OF ZETA ORIONIS

Showing a great projection of "dark matter" cutting off the light from behind.

Photo: Astrophysical Observatory, Victoria, British Columbia.

FIG. 23.—STAR CLUSTER IN HERCULES

A wonderful cluster of stars. It has been estimated that the distance of this cluster is such that it would take light more than 100,000 years to reach us.

the monarch of the system will summon it again to make its fiery journey round his throne.

THE STELLAR UNIVERSE

§ 1

The immensity of the Stellar Universe, as we have seen, is beyond our apprehension. The sun is nothing more than a very ordinary star, perhaps an insignificant one. There are stars enormously greater than the sun. One such, Betelgeux, has recently been measured, and its diameter is more than 300 times that of the sun.

The Evolution of Stars

The proof of the similarity between our sun and the stars has come to us through the spectroscope. The elements that we find by its means in the sun are also found in the same way in the stars. Matter, says the spectroscope, is essentially the same everywhere, in the earth and the sun, in the comet that visits us once in a thousand years, in the star whose distance is incalculable, and in the great clouds of "fire-mist" that we call nebulæ.

In considering the evolution of the stars let us keep two points clearly in mind. The starting-point, the nebula, is no figment of the scientific imagination. Hundreds of thousands of nebulæ, besides even vaster irregular stretches of nebulous matter, exist in the heavens. But the stages of the evolution of this stuff into stars are very largely a matter of speculation. Possibly there is more than one line of evolution, and the various theories may be reconciled. And this applies also to the theories of the various stages through which the stars themselves pass on their way to extinction.

The light of about a quarter of a million stars has been analysed in the spectroscope, and it is found that they fall into about a dozen classes which generally correspond to stages in their evolution (Fig. 21).

The Age of Stars

In its main lines the spectrum of a star corresponds to its colour, and we may roughly group the stars into red, yellow, and white. This is also the order of increasing temperature, the red stars being the coolest and the white stars the hottest. We might therefore imagine that the white stars are the youngest, and that as they grow older and cooler they become yellowish, then red, and finally become invisible—just as a cooling white-hot iron would do. But a very interesting recent research shows that there are two kinds of red stars; some of them are amongst the oldest stars and some are amongst the youngest. The facts appear to be that when a star is first formed it is not very hot. It is an immense mass of diffuse gas glowing with a dull-red heat. It contracts under the mutual gravitation of its particles, and as it does so it grows hotter. It acquires a yellowish tinge. As it continues to contract it grows hotter and hotter until its temperature reaches a maximum as a white star. At this point the contraction process does not stop, but the heating process does. Further contraction is now accompanied by cooling, and the star goes through its colour changes again, but this time in the inverse order. It contracts and cools to yellow and finally to red. But when it again becomes a red star it is enormously denser and smaller than when it began as a red star. Consequently the red stars are divided into two classes called, appropriately, Giants and Dwarfs. This theory, which we owe to an American astronomer, H. N. Russell, has been successful in explaining a variety of phenomena, and there is consequently good reason to suppose it to be true. But the question as to how the red giant stars were formed has received less satisfactory and precise answers.

The most commonly accepted theory is the nebular theory.

THE NEBULAR THEORY

§ 2

Nebulæ are dim luminous cloud-like patches in the heavens, more like wisps of smoke in some cases than anything else. Both photography and the telescope show that they are very numerous, hundreds of thousands being already known and the number being continually added to. They are not small. Most of them are immensely large. Actual dimensions cannot be given, because to estimate these we must first know definitely the distance of the nebulæ from the earth. The distances of some nebulæ are known approximately, and we can therefore form some idea of size in these cases. The results are staggering. The mere visible surface of some nebulæ is so large that the whole stretch of the solar system would be too small to form a convenient unit for measuring it. A ray of light would require to travel for years to cross from side to side of such a nebula. Its immensity is inconceivable to the human mind.

There appear to be two types of nebulæ, and there is evidence suggesting that the one type is only an earlier form of the other; but this again we do not know.

The more primitive nebulæ would seem to be composed of gas in an extremely rarified form. It is difficult to convey an adequate idea of the rarity of nebular gases. The residual gases in a vacuum tube are dense by comparison. A cubic inch of air at ordinary pressure would contain more matter than is contained in millions of cubic inches of the gases of nebulæ. The light of even the faintest stars does not seem to be dimmed by passing through a gaseous nebula, although we cannot be sure on this point. The most remarkable physical fact about these gases is that they are luminous. Whence they derive their luminosity we do not know. It hardly seems possible to believe that extremely thin gases exposed to the terrific cold of space can be so hot as to be luminous and can retain their heat and their luminosity indefinitely. A cold luminosity due to electrification, like that of the aurora borealis, would seem to fit the case better.

Now the nebular theory is that out of great "fire-mists," such as we have described, stars are born. We do not know whether gravitation is the only or even the main force at work in a nebula, but it is supposed that under the action of gravity the far-flung "fire-mists" would begin to condense round centres of greatest density, heat being evolved in the process. Of course the condensation would be enormously slow, although the sudden irruption of a swarm of meteors or some solid body might hasten matters greatly by providing large, ready-made centres of condensation.

Spiral Nebulæ

It is then supposed that the contracting mass of gas would begin to rotate and to throw off gigantic streamers, which would in their turn form centres of condensation. The whole structure would thus form a spiral, having a dense region at its centre and knots or lumps of condensed matter along its spiral arms. Besides the formless gaseous nebulæ there are hundreds of thousands of "spiral" nebulæ such as we have just mentioned in the heavens. They are at all stages of development, and they are visible to us at all angles—that is to say, some of them face directly towards us, others are edge on, and some are in intermediate positions. It appears, therefore, that we have here a striking confirmation of the nebular hypothesis. But we must not go so fast. There is much controversy as to the nature of these spiral nebulæ. Some eminent astronomers think they are other stellar universes, comparable in size with our own. In any case they are vast structures, and if they represent stars in process of condensation, they must be giving birth to huge agglomerations of stars—to star clusters at least. These vast and enigmatic objects do not throw much light on the origin of our own solar system. The nebular hypothesis, which was invented by

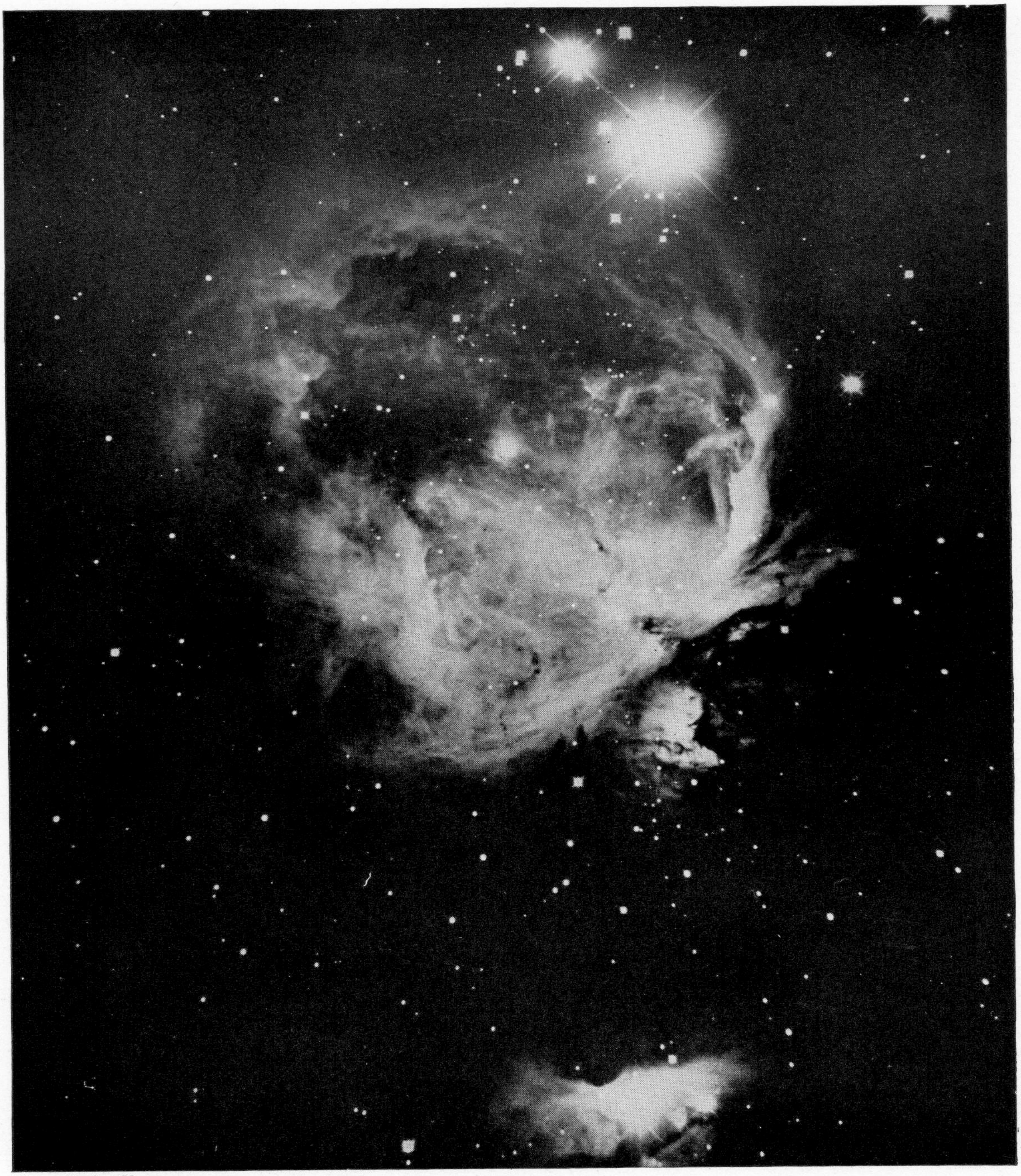

Photo: Yerkes Observatory.

FIG. 24.—THE GREAT NEBULA IN ORION

The most impressive nebula in the heavens. It is inconceivably greater in dimensions than the whole solar system.

Photo: Lick Observatory.

FIG. 25.—GIANT SPIRAL NEBULA, March 23, 1914

This spiral nebula is seen full on. Notice the central nucleus and the two spiral arms emerging from its opposite directions. Is matter flowing out of the nucleus into the arms or along the arms into the nucleus? In either case we should get two streams in opposite directions within the nucleus.

Laplace to explain the origin of our solar system, has not yet met with universal acceptance. The explanation offers grave difficulties, and it is best while the subject is still being closely investigated, to hold all opinions with reserve. It may be taken as probable, however, that the universe has developed from masses of incandescent gas.

THE BIRTH AND DEATH OF STARS

§ 3

Variable, New, and Dark Stars: Dying Suns

Many astronomers believe that in "variable stars" we have another star, following that of the dullest red star, in the dying of suns. The light of these stars varies periodically in so many days, weeks, or years. It is interesting to speculate that they are slowly dying suns, in which the molten interior periodically bursts through the shell of thick vapours that is gathering round them. What we saw about our sun seems to point to some such stage in the future. That is, however, not the received opinion about variable stars. It may be that they are stars which periodically pass through a great swarm of meteors or a region of space that is rich in cosmic dust of some sort, when, of course, a great illumination would take place.

One class of these variable stars, which takes its name from the star Algol, is of special interest. Every third night Algol has its light reduced for several hours. Modern astronomy has discovered that in this case there are really two stars, circulating round a common centre, and that every third night the fainter of the two comes directly between us and its companion and causes an "eclipse." This was until recently regarded as a most interesting case in which a dead star revealed itself to us by passing before the light of another star. But astronomers have in recent years invented something, the "selenium-cell," which is even more sensitive than the photographic plate, and on this the supposed dead star registers itself as very much alive. Algol is, however, interesting in another way. The pair of stars which we have discovered in it are hundreds of trillions of miles away from the earth, yet we know their masses and their distances from each other.

The Death and Birth of Stars

We have no positive knowledge of dead stars; which is not surprising when we reflect that a dead star means an invisible star! But when we see so many individual stars tending toward death, when we behold a vast population of all conceivable ages, we presume that there are many already dead. On the other hand, there is no reason to suppose that the universe as a whole is "running down." Some writers have maintained this, but their argument implies that we know a great deal more about the universe than we actually do. The scientific man does not know whether the universe is finite or infinite, temporal or eternal; and he declines to speculate where there are no facts to guide him. He knows only that the great gaseous nebulæ promise myriads of worlds in the future, and he concedes the possibility that new nebulæ may be forming in the ether of space.

The last, and not the least interesting, subject we have to notice is the birth of a "new star." This is an event which astronomers now announce every few years; and it is a far more portentous event than the reader imagines when it is reported in his daily paper. The story is much the same in all cases. We say that the star appeared in 1901, but you begin to realise the magnitude of the event when you learn that the distant "blaze" had really occurred about the time of the death of Luther! The light of the conflagration had been speeding toward us across space at 186,000 miles a second, yet it has taken nearly three centuries to reach us. To be visible at all to us at that distance the fiery outbreak must have been stupendous. If a mass of petroleum ten times the size of the earth were suddenly fired it would not be seen at such a distance. The new star had increased its light many hundredfold in a few days.

There is a considerable fascination about the speculation that in such cases we see the resurrection of a dead world, a means of renewing the population of the universe. What happens is that in some region of the sky where no star, or only a very faint star, had been registered on our charts, we almost suddenly perceive a bright star. In a few days it may rise to the highest brilliancy. By the spectroscope we learn that this distant blaze means a prodigious outpour of white-hot hydrogen at hundreds of miles a second. But the star sinks again after a few months, and we then find a nebula round it on every side. It is natural to suppose that a dead or dying sun has somehow been reconverted in whole or in part into a nebula. A few astronomers think that it may have partially collided with another star, or approached too closely to another, with the result we described on an earlier page. The general opinion now is that a faint or dead star had rushed into one of those regions of space in which there are immense stretches of nebulous matter, and been (at least in part) vaporised by the friction.

But the difficulties are considerable, and some astronomers prefer to think that the blazing star may merely have lit up a dark nebula which already existed. It is one of those problems on which speculation is most tempting but positive knowledge is still very incomplete. We may be content, even proud, that already we can take a conflagration that has occurred more than a thousand trillion miles away and analyse it positively into an outflame of glowing hydrogen gas at so many miles a second.

THE SHAPE OF OUR UNIVERSE

§ 4

Our Universe a Spiral Nebula

What is the shape of our universe, and what are its dimensions? This is a tremendous question to ask. It is like asking an intelligent insect, living on a single leaf in the midst of a great Brazilian forest, to say what is the shape and size of the forest. Yet man's ingenuity has proved equal to giving an answer even to this question, and by a method exactly similar to that which would be adopted by the insect. Suppose, for instance, that the forest was shaped as an elongated oval, and the insect lived on a tree near the centre of the oval. If the trees were approximately equally spaced from one another they would appear much denser along the length of the oval than across its width. This is the simple consideration that has guided astronomers in determining the shape of our stellar universe. There is one direction in the heavens along which the stars appear denser than in the directions at right angles to it. That direction is the direction in which we look towards the Milky Way. If we count the number of stars visible all over the heavens, we find they become more and more numerous as we approach the Milky Way. As we go farther and farther from the Milky Way the stars thin out until they reach a maximum sparseness in directions at right angles to the plane of the Milky Way. We may consider the Milky Way to form, as it were, the equator of our system, and the line at right angles to point to the north and south poles.

Our system, in fact, is shaped something like a lens, and our sun is situated near the centre of this lens. In the remoter part of this lens, near its edge, or possibly outside it altogether, lies the great series of star clouds which make up the Milky Way. All the stars are in motion within this system, but the very remarkable discovery has been made that these motions are not entirely random. The great majority of the stars whose motions can be measured fall into two groups drifting past one another in opposite directions. The velocity of one stream relative to the other is about twenty-five miles per second. The stars forming these two groups are thoroughly well mixed; it is not a case of an inner stream going one way and an outer stream the

Photo: Mount Wilson Observatory.

FIG. 26.—A SPIRAL NEBULA SEEN EDGE-ON

Notice the lens-shaped formation of the nucleus and the arm stretching as a band across it. See reference in the text to the resemblance between this and our stellar universe.

Photo: H. J. Shepstone.

100-INCH TELESCOPE, MOUNT WILSON

A reflecting telescope: the largest in the world. The mirror is situated at the base of the telescope.

other. But there are not quite as many stars going one way as the other. For every two stars in one stream there are three in the other. Now, as we have said, some eminent astronomers hold that the spiral nebulæ are universes like our own, and if we look at the two photographs (Figs. 25 and 26) we see that these spirals present features which, in the light of what we have just said about our system, are very remarkable. The nebula in Coma Berenices is a spiral edge-on to us, and we see that it has precisely the lens-shaped middle and the general flattened shape that we

THE SOLAR SYSTEM				
NAME	MEAN DISTANCE FROM SUN (IN MILLIONS OF MILES)	PERIOD OF REVOLUTION ROUND SUN (IN YEARS)	DIAMETER (IN MILES)	NUMBER OF SATELLITES
MERCURY	36 0	0 24	3030	0
VENUS	67 2	0·62	7700	0
EARTH	92 9	1 00	7918	1
MARS	141 5	1 88	4230	2
JUPITER	483 3	11 86	86500	9
SATURN	886 0	29·46	73000	10
URANUS	1781 9	84 02	31900	4
NEPTUNE	2971 6	164 78	34800	1
SUN	——	——	866400	——
MOON	——	——	2163	——

FIG. 27

have found in our own system. The nebula in Canes Venatici is a spiral facing towards us, and its shape irresistibly suggests motions along the spiral arms. This motion, whether it is towards or away from the central, lens-shaped portion, would cause a double streaming motion in that central portion of the kind we have found in our own system. Again, and altogether apart from these considerations, there are good reasons for supposing our Milky Way to possess a double-armed spiral structure. And the great patches of dark absorbing matter which are known to exist in the Milky Way (see Fig. 22) would give very much the mottled appearance we notice in the arms (which we see edge-on) of the nebula in Coma Berenices. The hypothesis, therefore, that our universe is a spiral nebula has much to be said for it. If it be accepted it greatly increases our estimate of the size of the material universe. For our central, lens-shaped system is calculated to extend towards the Milky Way for more than twenty thousand times a million million miles, and about a third of this distance towards what we have called the poles. If, as we suppose, each spiral nebula is an independent

STAR DISTANCES

STAR	DISTANCE IN LIGHT-YEARS
POLARIS	76
CAPELLA	49·4
RIGEL	466
SIRIUS	8·7
PROCYON	10·5
REGULUS	98·8
ARCTURUS	43·4
α CENTAURI	4·29
VEGA	34·7
SMALLER MAGELLANIC CLOUD	32,600 (ESTIMATED)
GREAT CLUSTER IN HERCULES	108,600 (ESTIMATED)

FIG. 28

The above distances are merely approximate and are subject to further revision. A "light-year" is the distance that light, travelling at the rate of 186,000 miles per second, would cover in one year.

stellar universe comparable in size with our own, then, since there are hundreds of thousands of spiral nebulæ, we see that the size of the whole material universe is indeed beyond our comprehension.

In this simple outline we have not touched on some of the more debatable questions that engage the attention of modern astronomers. Many of these questions have not yet passed the controversial stage; out of these will emerge the astronomy of the future. But we have seen enough to convince us that, whatever advances the future holds in store, the science of the heavens constitutes one of the most important stones in the wonderful fabric of human knowledge.

ASTRONOMICAL INSTRUMENTS

§ 1

The Telescope

The instruments used in modern astronomy are amongst the finest triumphs of mechanical skill in the world. In a great modern observatory the different instruments are to be counted by the score, but there are two which stand out pre-eminent as the fundamental instruments of modern astronomy. These instruments are the telescope and the spectroscope, and without them astronomy, as we know it, could not exist.

There is still some dispute as to where and when the first telescope was constructed; as an astronomical instrument, however, it dates from the time of the great Italian scientist Galileo, who, with a very small and imperfect telescope of his own invention, first observed the spots on the sun, the mountains of the moon, and the chief four satellites of Jupiter. A good pair of modern binoculars is superior to this early instrument of Galileo's, and the history of telescope construction, from that primitive instrument to the modern giant recently erected on Mount Wilson, California, is an exciting chapter in human progress. But the early instruments have only an historic interest: the era of modern telescopes begins in the nineteenth century.

During the last century telescope construction underwent an unprecedented development. An immense amount of interest was taken in the construction of large telescopes, and the different countries of the world entered on an exciting race to produce the most powerful possible instruments. Besides this rivalry of different countries there was a rivalry of methods. The telescope developed along two different lines, and each of these two types has its partisans at the present day. These types are known as *refractors* and *reflectors,* and it is necessary to mention, briefly, the principles employed in each. The *refractor* is the ordinary, familiar type of telescope. It consists, essentially, of a large lens at one end of a tube, and a small lens, called the eye-piece, at the other. The function of the large lens is to act as a sort of gigantic eye. It collects a large amount of light, an amount proportional to its size, and brings this light to a focus within the tube of the telescope. It thus produces a small but bright image, and the eye-piece magnifies this image. In the *reflector,* instead of a large lens at the top of the tube, a large mirror is placed at the bottom. This mirror is so shaped as to reflect the light that falls on it to a focus, whence the light is again led to an eye-piece. Thus the refractor and the reflector differ chiefly in their manner of gathering light. The powerfulness of the telescope depends on the size of the light-gatherer. A telescope with a lens four inches in diameter is four times as powerful as the one with a lens two inches in diameter, for the amount of light gathered obviously depends on the *area* of the lens, and the area varies as the *square* of the diameter.

The largest telescopes at present in existence are *reflectors.* It is much easier to construct a very large mirror than to construct a very large lens; it is also cheaper. A mirror is more likely to get out of order than is a lens, however, and any irregularity in the shape of a mirror produces a greater distorting effect than in a lens. A refractor is also more convenient to handle than is a reflector. For these reasons great refractors are still made, but the largest of them, the great Yerkes' refractor, is much smaller than the greatest reflector, the one on Mount Wilson, California. The lens of the Yerkes' refractor measures three feet four inches in diameter, whereas the Mount Wilson reflector has a diameter of no less than eight feet four inches.

THE YERKES 40-INCH REFRACTOR

(The largest *refracting* telescope in the world. Its big lens weighs 1,000 pounds, and its mammoth tube, which is 62 feet long, weighs about 12,000 pounds. The parts to be moved weigh approximately 22 tons.

The great *100-inch reflector* of the Mount Wilson reflecting telescope—the largest *reflecting* instrument in the world—weighs nearly 9,000 pounds and the moving parts of the telescope weigh about 100 tons.

The new *72-inch reflector* at the Dominion Astrophysical Observatory, near Victoria, B. C., weighs nearly 4,500 pounds, and the moving parts about 35 tons.)

Photo: H. J. Shepstone.

THE DOUBLE-SLIDE PLATE HOLDER ON YERKES 40-INCH REFRACTING TELESCOPE

The smaller telescope at the top of the picture acts as a "finder"; the field of view of the large telescope is so restricted that it is difficult to recognise, as it were, the part of the heavens being surveyed. The smaller telescope takes in a larger area and enables the precise object to be examined to be easily selected.

MODERN DIRECT-READING SPECTROSCOPE

(*By A. Hilger, Ltd.*)

The light is brought through one telescope, is split up by the prism and the resulting spectrum is observed through the other telescope.

But there is a device whereby the power of these giant instruments, great as it is, can be still further heightened. That device is the simple one of allowing the photographic plate to take the place of the human eye. Nowadays an astronomer seldom spends the night with his eye glued to the great telescope. He puts a photographic plate there. The photographic plate has this advantage over the eye, that it builds up impressions. However long we stare at an object too faint to be seen, we shall never see it. With the photographic plate, however, faint impressions go on accumulating. As hour after hour passes, the star which was too faint to make a perceptible impression on the plate goes on affecting it until finally it makes an impression which can be made visible. In this way the photographic plate reveals to us phenomena in the heavens which cannot be seen even through the most powerful telescopes.

Telescopes of the kind we have been discussing, telescopes for exploring the heavens, are mounted *equatorially;* that is to say, they are mounted on an inclined pillar parallel to the axis of the earth so that, by rotating round this pillar, the telescope is enabled to follow the apparent motion of a star due to the rotation of the earth. This motion is effected by clock-work, so that, once adjusted on a star, and the clock-work started, the telescope remains adjusted on that star for any length of time that is desired. But a great official observatory, such as Greenwich Observatory or the Observatory at Paris, also has *transit* instruments, or telescopes smaller than the equatorials and without the same facility of movement, but which, by a number of exquisite refinements, are more adapted to accurate measurements. It is these instruments which are chiefly used in the compilation of the *Nautical Almanac.* They do not follow the apparent motions of the stars. Stars are allowed to drift across the field of vision, and as each star crosses a small group of parallel wires in the eye-piece its precise time of passage is recorded. Owing to their relative fixity of position these instruments can be constructed to record the *positions* of stars with much greater accuracy than is possible to the more general and flexible mounting of equatorials. The recording of transit is comparatively dry work; the spectacular element is entirely absent; stars are treated merely as mathematical points. But these observations furnish the very basis of modern mathematical astronomy, and without them such publications as the *Nautical Almanac* and the *Connaissance du Temps* would be robbed of the greater part of their importance.

§ 2

The Spectroscope

We have already learnt something of the principles of the spectroscope, the instrument which, by making it possible to learn the actual constitution of the stars, has added a vast new domain to astronomy. In the simplest form of this instrument the analysing portion consists of a single prism. Unless the prism is very large, however, only a small degree of dispersion is obtained. It is obviously desirable, for accurate analytical work, that the dispersion—that is, the separation of the different parts of the spectrum—should be as great as possible. The dispersion can be increased by using a large number of prisms, the light emerging from the first prism, entering the second, and so on. In this way each prism produces its own dispersive effect and, when a number of prisms are employed, the final dispersion is considerable. A considerable amount of light is absorbed in this way, however, so that unless our primary source of light is very strong, the final spectrum will be very feeble and hard to decipher.

Another way of obtaining considerable dispersion is by using a *diffraction grating* instead of a prism. This consists essentially of a piece of glass on which lines are ruled by a diamond point. When the lines are sufficiently close together they split up light falling on them into its constituents and produce a spectrum.

The modern diffraction grating is a truly wonderful piece of work. It contains several thousands of lines to the inch, and these lines have to be spaced with the greatest accuracy. But in this instrument, again, there is a considerable loss of light.

We have said that every substance has its own distinctive spectrum, and it might be thought that, when a list of the spectra of different substances has been prepared, spectrum analysis would become perfectly straightforward. In practice, however, things are not quite so simple. The spectrum emitted by a substance is influenced by a variety of conditions. The pressure, the temperature, the state of motion of the object we are observing, all make a difference, and one of the most laborious tasks of the modern spectroscopist is to disentangle these effects from one another. Simple as it is in its broad outlines, spectroscopy is, in reality, one of the most intricate branches of modern science.

BIBLIOGRAPHY

(The following list of books may be useful to readers wishing to pursue further the study of Astronomy.)

Ball, *The Story of the Heavens.*
Ball, *The Story of the Sun.*
Forbes, *History of Astronomy.*
Hincks, *Astronomy.*
Kippax, *Call of the Stars.*
Lowell, *Mars and Its Canals.*
Lowell, *Evolution of Worlds.*
McKready, *A Beginner's Star-Book.*
Newcomb, *Popular Astronomy.*
Newcomb, *The Stars: A Study of the Universe.*
Olcott, *Field Book of the Stars.*
Price, *Essence of Astronomy.*
Serviss, *Curiosities of the Skies.*
Webb, *Celestial Objects for Common Telescopes.*
Young, *Text-Book of General Astronomy.*

II

THE STORY OF EVOLUTION

INTRODUCTORY

THE BEGINNING OF THE EARTH—MAKING A HOME FOR LIFE—THE FIRST LIVING CREATURES

§ 1

THE Evolution-idea is a master-key that opens many doors. It is a luminous interpretation of the world, throwing the light of the past upon the present. Everything is seen to be an antiquity, with a history behind it—a *natural history,* which enables us to understand in some measure how it has come to be as it is. We cannot say more than "understand in some measure," for while the *fact* of evolution is certain, we are only beginning to discern the *factors* that have been at work.

The evolution-idea is very old, going back to some of the Greek philosophers, but it is only in modern times that it has become an essential part of our mental equipment. It is now an everyday intellectual tool. It was applied to the origin of the solar system and to the making of the earth before it was applied to plants and animals; it was extended from these to man himself; it spread to language, to folk-ways, to institutions. Within recent years the evolution-idea has been applied to the chemical elements, for it appears that uranium may change into radium, that radium may produce helium, and that lead is the final stable result when the changes of uranium are complete. Perhaps all the elements may be the outcome of an inorganic evolution. Not less important is the extension of the evolution-idea to the world within as well as to the world without. For alongside of the evolution of bodies and brains is the evolution of feelings and emotions, ideas and imagination.

Organic evolution means that the present is the child of the past and the parent of the future. It is not a power or a principle; it is a process—a process of becoming. It means that the present-day animals and plants and all the subtle inter-relations between them have arisen in a natural knowable way from a preceding state of affairs on the whole somewhat simpler, and that again from forms and inter-relations simpler still, and so on backwards and backwards for millions of years till we lose all clues in the thick mist that hangs over life's beginnings.

Our solar system was once represented by a nebula of some sort, and we may speak of the evolution of the sun and the planets. But since it has been *the same material throughout* that has changed in its distribution and forms, it might be clearer to use some word like genesis. Similarly, our human institutions were once very different from what they are now, and we may speak of the evolution of government or of cities. But Man works with a purpose, with ideas and ideals in some measure controlling his actions and guiding his achievements, so that it is probably clearer to keep the good old word history for all processes of social becoming in which man has been a conscious agent. Now between the genesis of the solar system and the history of civilisation there comes the vast process of organic evolution. The word development should be kept for the becoming of the individual, the chick out of the egg, for instance.

Organic evolution is a continuous natural process of racial change, by successive steps in a definite direction, whereby distinctively new individualities arise, take root, and flourish, sometimes alongside of, and sometimes, sooner or later, in place of, the originative stock. Our domesticated breeds of pigeons and poultry are the results of evolutionary change whose origins are still with us in the Rock Dove and the Jungle Fowl; but in most cases in Wild Nature the ancestral stocks of present-day forms are long since extinct, and in many cases they are unknown. Evolution is a long process of coming and going, appearing and dis-

Photo: Rischgitz Collection.

CHARLES DARWIN

Greatest of naturalists, who made the idea of evolution current intellectual coin, and in his *Origin of Species* (1859) made the whole world new.

Photo: Rischgitz Collection.

LORD KELVIN

One of the greatest physicists of the nineteenth century. He estimated the age of the earth at 20,000,000 years. He had not at his disposal, however, the knowledge of recent discoveries, which have resulted in this estimate being very greatly increased.

Photo: Lick Observatory.

A GIANT SPIRAL NEBULA

Laplace's famous theory was that the planets and the earth were formed from great whirling nebulæ.

Photo: Natural History Museum.

METEORITE WHICH FELL NEAR SCARBOROUGH, AND IS NOW TO BE SEEN IN THE NATURAL HISTORY MUSEUM

It weighs about 56 lb., and is a "stony" meteorite, i.e., an aerolite.

appearing, a long-drawn-out sublime process like a great piece of music.

§ 2

The Beginning of the Earth

When we speak the language of science we cannot say "In the beginning," for we do not know of and cannot think of any condition of things that did not arise from something that went before. But we may qualify the phrase, and legitimately inquire into the beginning of the earth within the solar system. If the result of this inquiry is to trace the sun and the planets back to a nebula we reach only a relative beginning. The nebula has to be accounted for. And even before matter there may have been a pre-material world. If we say, as was said long ago, "In the beginning was Mind," we may be expressing or trying to express a great truth, but we have gone BEYOND SCIENCE.

The Nebular Hypothesis

One of the grandest pictures that the scientific mind has ever thrown upon the screen is that of the Nebular Hypothesis. According to Laplace's famous form of this theory (1796), the solar system was once a gigantic glowing mass, spinning slowly and uniformly around its centre. As the incandescent world-cloud of gas cooled and its speed of rotation increased the shrinking mass gave off a separate whirling ring, which broke up and gathered together again as the first and most distant planet. The main mass gave off another ring and another till all the planets, including the earth, were formed. The central mass persisted as the sun.

Laplace spoke of his theory, which Kant had anticipated forty-one years before, with scientific caution: "conjectures which I present with all the distrust which everything not the result of observation or of calculation ought to inspire." Subsequent research justified his distrust, for it has been shown that the original nebula need not have been hot and need not have been gaseous

Moreover, there are great difficulties in Laplace's theory of the separation of successive rings from the main mass, and of the condensation of a whirling gaseous ring into a planet.

So it has come about that the picture of a hot gaseous nebula revolving as a unit body has given place to other pictures. Thus Sir Norman Lockyer pointed out (1890) that the earth is gathering to itself millions of meteorites every day; this has been going on for millions of years; in distant ages the accretion may have been vastly more rapid and voluminous; and so the earth has grown! Now the meteoritic contributions are undoubted, but they require a centre to attract them, and the difficulty is to account for the beginning of a collecting centre or planetary nucleus. Moreover, meteorites are sporadic and erratic, scattered hither and thither rather than collecting into unit-bodies. As Professor Chamberlin says, "meteorites have rather the characteristics of the wreckage of some earlier organisation than of the parentage of our planetary system." Several other theories have been propounded to account for the origin of the earth, but the one that has found most favour in the eyes of authorities is that of Chamberlin and Moulton. According to this theory a great nebular mass condensed to form the sun, from which under the attraction of passing stars planet after planet, the earth included, was heaved off in the form of knotted spiral nebulæ, like many of those now observed in the heavens.

Of great importance were the "knots," for they served as collecting centres drawing flying matter into their clutches. Whatever part of the primitive bolt escaped and scattered was drawn out into independent orbits round the sun, forming the "planetesimals" which behave like minute planets. These planetesimals formed the food on which the knots subsequently fed.

The Growth of the Earth

It has been calculated that the newborn earth—the "earth-knot" of Chamberlin's theory—had a diameter of about 5,500 miles. But it grew by drawing planetesimals into itself until it had a diameter of over 8,100 miles at the end of its growing period. Since then it has shrunk, by periodic shrinkages which have meant the buckling up of successive series of mountains, and it has now a diameter of 7,918 miles. But during the shrinking the earth became more varied.

A sort of slow boiling of the internally hot earth often forced molten matter through the cold outer crust, and there came about a gradual assortment of lighter materials nearer the surface and heavier materials deeper down. The continents are built of the lighter materials, such as granites, while the beds of the great oceans are made of the heavier materials such as basalts. In limited areas land has often become sea, and sea has often given place to land, but the probability is that the distinction of the areas corresponding to the great continents and oceans goes back to a very early stage.

The lithosphere is the more or less stable crust of the earth, which may have been, to begin with, about fifty miles in thickness. It seems that the young earth had no atmosphere, and that ages passed before water began to accumulate on its surface—before, in other words, there was any hydrosphere. The water came from the earth itself, to begin with, and it was long before there was any rain dissolving out saline matter from the exposed rocks and making the sea salt. The weathering of the high grounds of the ancient crust by air and water furnished the material which formed the sandstones and mudstones and other sedimentary rocks, which are said to amount to a thickness of over fifty miles in all.

§ 3

Making a Home for Life

It is interesting to inquire how the callous, rough-and-tumble conditions of the outer world in early days were replaced by others that allowed of the germination and growth of that tender plant we call LIFE. There are very tough living creatures, but the average organism is ill suited for violence. Most living creatures are adapted to mild temperatures and gentle reactions. Hence the fundamental importance of the early atmosphere, heavy with planetesimal dust, in blanketing the earth against intensities of radiance from without, as Chamberlin says, and inequalities of radiance from within. This was the first preparation for life, but it was an atmosphere without free oxygen. Not less important was the appearance of pools and lakelets, of lakes and seas. Perhaps the early waters covered the earth. And water was the second preparation for life—water, that can dissolve a larger variety of substances in greater concentration than any other liquid; water, that in summer does not readily evaporate altogether from a pond, nor in winter freeze throughout its whole extent; water, that is such a mobile vehicle and such a subtle cleaver of substances; water, that forms over 80 per cent. of living matter itself.

Of great significance was the abundance of carbon, hydrogen, and oxygen (in the form of carbonic acid and water) in the atmosphere of the cooling earth, for these three wonderful elements have a unique *ensemble* of properties—ready to enter into reactions and relations, making great diversity and complexity possible, favouring the formation of the plastic and permeable materials that build up living creatures. We must not pursue the idea, but it is clear that the stones and mortar of the inanimate world are such that they built a friendly home for life.

Origin of Living Creatures upon the Earth

During the early chapters of the earth's history, no living creature that we can imagine could possibly have lived there. The temperature was too high; there was neither atmosphere nor surface water. Therefore it follows that at some uncertain, but inconceivably distant date, living creatures appeared upon

Reproduced from the Smithsonian Report, 1915.

A LIMESTONE CANYON

Many fossils of extinct animals have been found in such rock formations.

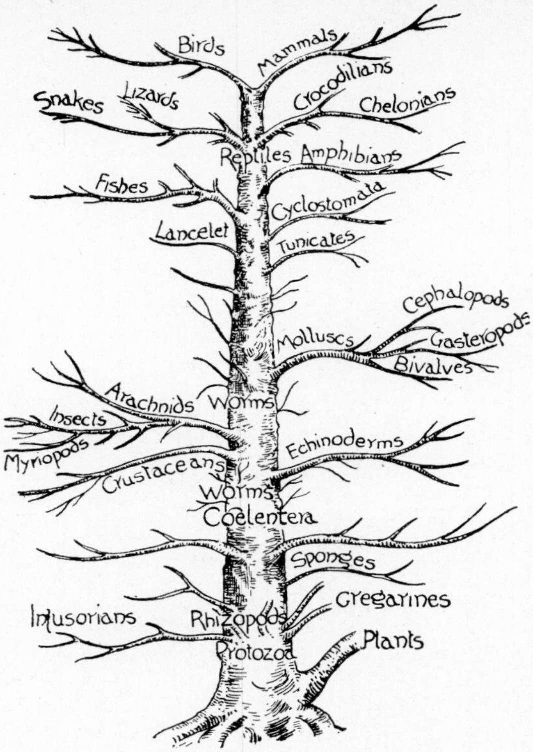

GENEALOGICAL TREE OF ANIMALS

Showing in order of evolution the general relations of the chief classes into which the world of living things is divided. This scheme represents the present stage of our knowledge, but is admittedly provisional.

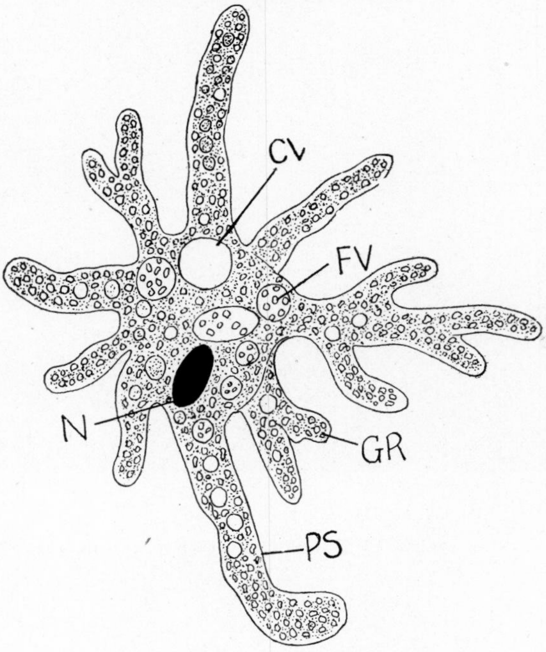

DIAGRAM OF AMŒBA
(Greatly magnified.)

The amœba is one of the simplest of all aminals, and gives us a hint of the original ancestors. It looks like a tiny irregular speck of greyish jelly, about 1/100th of an inch in diameter. It is commonly found gliding on the mud or weeds in ponds, where it engulfs its microscopic food by means of outflowing lobes (PS). The food vacuole (FV) contains ingested food. From the contractile vacuole (CV) the waste matter is discharged. N is the nucleus, GR, granules.

the earth. No one knows how, but it is interesting to consider possibilities.

From ancient times it has been a favourite answer that the dust of the earth may have become living in a way which is outside scientific description. This answer forecloses the question, and it is far too soon to do that. Science must often say "Ignoramus": Science should be slow to say "Ignorabimus."

A second position held by Helmholtz, Lord Kelvin, and others, suggests that minute living creatures may have come to the earth from elsewhere, in the cracks of a meteorite or among cosmic dust. It must be remembered that seeds can survive prolonged exposure to very low temperatures; that spores of bacteria can survive high temperature; that seeds of plants and germs of animals in a state of "latent life" can survive prolonged drought and absence of oxygen. It is possible, according to Berthelot, that as long as there is not molecular disintegration vital activities may be suspended for a time, and may afterwards recommence when appropriate conditions are restored. Therefore, one should be slow to say that a long journey through space is impossible. The obvious limitation of Lord Kelvin's theory is that it only shifts the problem of the origin of organisms (i.e. living creatures) from the earth to elsewhere.

The third answer is that living creatures of a very simple sort may have emerged on the earth's surface from not-living material, e.g. from some semi-fluid carbon compounds activated by ferments. The tenability of this view is suggested by the achievements of the synthetic chemists, who are able artificially to build up substances such as oxalic acid, indigo, salicylic acid, caffeine, and grape-sugar. We do not know, indeed, what in Nature's laboratory would take the place of the clever synthetic chemist, but there seems to be a tendency to complexity. Corpuscles form atoms, atoms form molecules, small molecules large ones.

Various concrete suggestions have been made in regard to the possible origin of living matter, which will be dealt with in a later chapter. So far as we know of what goes on to-day, there is no evidence of spontaneous generation; organisms seem always to arise from pre-existing organisms of the same kind; where any suggestion of the contrary has been fancied, there have been flaws in the experimenting. But it is one thing to accept the verdict "omne vivum e vivo" as a fact to which experiment has not yet discovered an exception and another thing to maintain that this must always have been true or must always remain true.

If the synthetic chemists should go on surpassing themselves, if substances like white of egg should be made artificially, and if we should get more light on possible steps by which simple living creatures may have arisen from not-living materials, this would not greatly affect our general outlook on life, though it would increase our appreciation of what is often libelled as "inert" matter. If the dust of the earth did naturally give rise very long ago to living creatures, if they are in a real sense born of her and of the sunshine, then the whole world becomes more continuous and more vital, and all the inorganic groaning and travailing becomes more intelligible.

§ 4

The First Organisms upon the Earth

We cannot have more than a speculative picture of the first living creatures upon the earth or, rather, in the waters that covered the earth. A basis for speculation is to be found, however, in the simplest creatures living to-day, such as some of the bacteria and one-celled animalcules, especially those called Protists, which have not taken any very definite step towards becoming either plants or animals. No one can be sure, but there is much to be said for the theory that the first creatures were microscopic globules of living matter, not unlike the simplest bacteria of to-day, but able to live on air, water, and dissolved salts. From such a source may have originated a race of one-celled marine organisms which were able to manufacture chlorophyll, or something like chlorophyll, that is to say, the green pigment which makes it possible for plants to utilise the energy of the sunlight in breaking up carbon dioxide and in building up (photosynthesis) carbon compounds like sugars and starch. These little units were probably encased in a cell-wall of cellulose, but their boxed-in energy expressed itself in the undulatory movement of a lash or flagellum, by means of which they propelled themselves energetically through the water. There are many similar organisms to-day, mostly in water, but some of them—simple one-celled plants—paint the tree-stems and even the paving-stones green in wet weather. According to Prof. A. H. Church there was a long chapter in the history of the earth when the sea that covered everything teemed with these green flagellates—the originators of the Vegetable Kingdom.

On another tack, however, there probably evolved a series of simple predatory creatures, not able to build up organic matter from air, water, and salts, but devouring their neighbours. These units were not closed in with cellulose, but remained naked, with their living matter or protoplasm flowing out in changeful processes, such as we see in the Amœbæ in the ditch or in our own white blood corpuscles and other amœboid cells. These were the originators of the animal kingdom. Thus from very simple Protists the first animals and the first plants may have arisen. All were still very minute, and it is worth remembering that had there been any scientific spectator after our kind upon the earth during these long ages, he would have lamented the entire absence of life, although the seas were teeming. The simplest forms of life and the protoplasm which Huxley called the physical basis of life will be dealt with in the chapter on Biology in a later section of this work.

FIRST GREAT STEPS IN EVOLUTION

THE FIRST PLANTS—THE FIRST ANIMALS—BEGINNINGS OF BODIES—EVOLUTION OF SEX—BEGINNING OF NATURAL DEATH

§ 1

The Contrast between Plants and Animals

However it may have come about, there is no doubt at all that one of the first great steps in Organic Evolution was the forking of the genealogical tree into Plants and Animals—the most important parting of the ways in the whole history of Nature.

Typical plants have chlorophyll; they are able to feed at a low chemical level on air, water, and salts, using the energy of the sunlight in their photosynthesis. They have their cells boxed in by cellulose walls, so that their opportunities for motility are greatly restricted. They manufacture much more nutritive material than they need, and live far below their income. They have no ready way of getting rid of any nitrogenous waste matter that they may form, and this probably helps to keep them sluggish.

Animals, on the other hand, feed at a high chemical level, on the carbohydrates (e.g. starch and sugar), fats, and proteins (e.g. gluten, albumin, casein) which are manufactured by other animals, or to begin with, by plants. Their cells have not cellulose walls, nor in most cases much wall of any kind, and motility in the majority is unrestricted. Animals live much more nearly up to their income. If we could make for an animal and a plant of equal weight two fractions showing the ratio of the upbuilding, constructive, chemical processes to the down-breaking, disruptive, chemical processes that go on in their respective bodies, the ratio for the plant would be much greater than the corresponding ratio for the animal. In other words, animals take the munitions which plants laboriously manufacture and explode them in locomotion

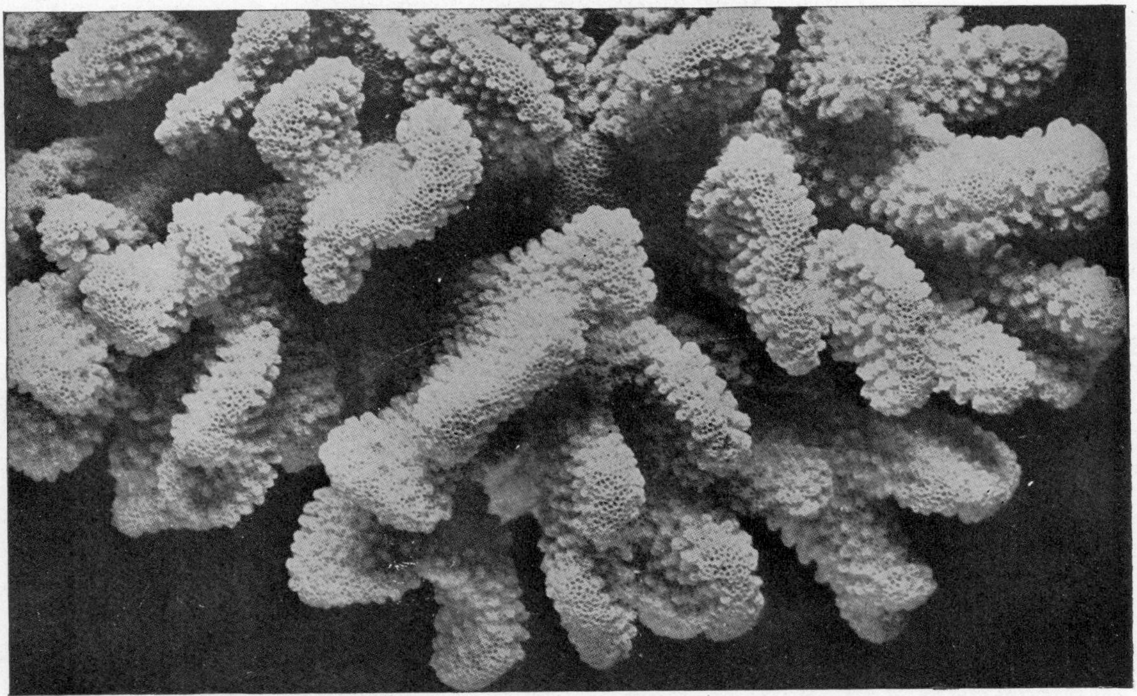

From the Smithsonian Report, 1917

A PIECE OF A REEF-BUILDING CORAL, BUILT UP BY A LARGE COLONY OF SMALL SEA-ANEMONE-LIKE POLYPS, EACH OF WHICH FORMS FROM THE SALTS OF THE SEA A SKELETON OR SHELL OF LIME

The wonderful mass of corals, which are very beautiful, are the skeleton remains of hundreds of these little creatures.

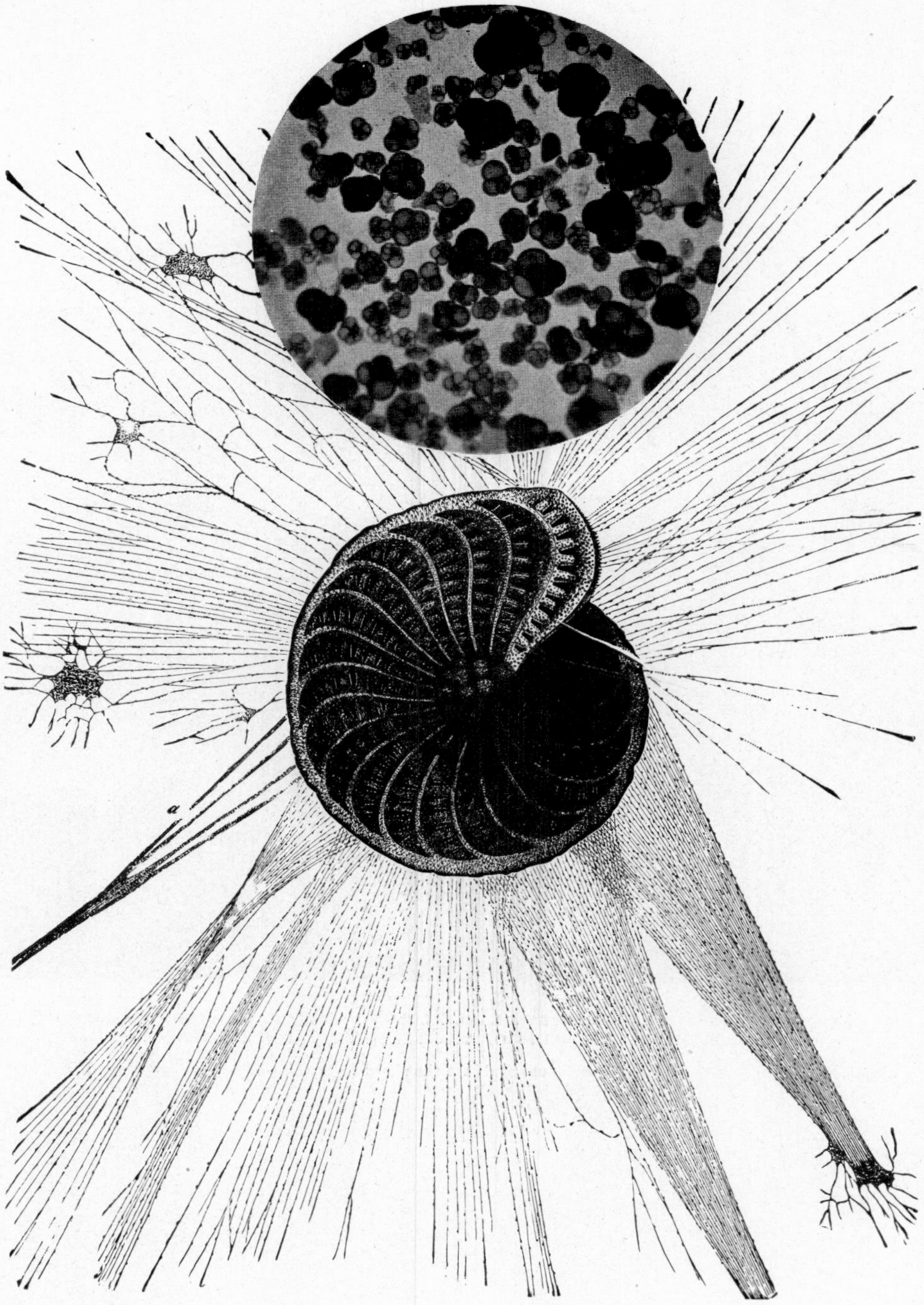

Photo: J. J. Ward, F.E.S.

THE INSET CIRCLE SHOWS A GROUP OF CHALK-FORMING ANIMALS, OR FORAMINIFERA, EACH ABOUT THE SIZE OF A VERY SMALL PIN'S HEAD

They form a great part of the chalk cliffs of Dover and similar deposits which have been raised from the floor of an ancient sea.

THE ENORMOUSLY ENLARGED ILLUSTRATION IS THAT OF A COMMON FORAMINIFER (POLYSTOMELLA) SHOWING THE SHELL IN THE CENTRE AND THE OUTFLOWING NETWORK OF LIVING MATTER, ALONG WHICH GRANULES ARE CONTINUALLY TRAVELLING, AND BY WHICH FOOD PARTICLES ARE ENTANGLED AND DRAWN IN

Reproduced by permission of the Natural History Museum (after Max Schultze).

and work; and the entire system of animate nature depends upon the photosynthesis that goes on in green plants.

As the result of much more explosive life, animals have to deal with much in the way of nitrogenous waste products, the ashes of the living fire, but these are usually got rid of very effectively, e.g. in the kidney filters, and do not clog the system by being deposited as crystals and the like, as happens in plants. Sluggish animals like sea-squirts which have no kidneys are exceptions that prove the rule, and it need hardly be said that the statements that have been made in regard to the contrasts between plants and animals are general statements. There is often a good deal of the plant about the animal, as in sedentary sponges, zoophytes, corals, and sea-squirts, and there is often a little of the animal about the plant, as we see in the movements of all shoots and roots and leaves, and occasionally in the parts of the flower. But the important fact is that on the early forking of the genealogical tree, i.e. the divergence of plants and animals, there depended and depends all the higher life of the animal kingdom, not to speak of mankind. The continuance of civilisation, the upkeep of the human and animal population of the globe, and even the supply of oxygen to the air we breathe, depend on the silent laboratories of the green leaves, which are able with the help of the sunlight to use carbonic acid, water, and salts to build up the bread of life.

§ 2

The Beginnings of Land Plants

It is highly probable that for long ages the waters covered the earth, and that all the primeval vegetation consisted of simple Flagellates in the universal Open Sea. But contraction of the earth's crust brought about elevations and depressions of the sea-floor, and in places the solid substratum was brought near enough the surface to allow the floating plants to begin to settle down without getting out of the light. This is how Professor

Church pictures the beginning of a fixed vegetation—a very momentous step in evolution. It was perhaps among this early vegetation that animals had their first successes. As the floor of the sea in these shallow areas was raised higher and higher there was a beginning of dry land. The sedentary plants already spoken of were the ancestors of the shore seaweeds, and there is no doubt that when we go down at the lowest tide and wade cautiously out among the jungle of vegetation only exposed on such occasions we are getting a glimpse of very ancient days. *This* is the forest primeval.

The Protozoa

Animals below the level of zoophytes and sponges are called Protozoa. The word obviously means "First Animals," but all that we can say is that the very simplest of them may give us some hint of the simplicity of the original first animals. For it is quite certain that the vast majority of the Protozoa to-day are far too complicated to be thought of as primitive. Though most of them are microscopic, each is an animal complete in itself, with the same fundamental bodily attributes as are manifested in ourselves. They differ from animals of higher degree in not being built up of the unit areas or corpuscles called cells. They have no cells, no tissues, no organs, in the ordinary acceptation of these words, but many of them show a great complexity of internal structure, far exceeding that of the ordinary cells that build up the tissues of higher animals. They are complete living creatures which have not gone in for body-making.

In the dim and distant past there was a time when the only animals were of the nature of Protozoa, and it is safe to say that one of the great steps in evolution was the establishment of three great types of Protozoa: (*a*) Some were very active, the Infusorians, like the slipper animalcule, the night-light (Noctiluca), which makes the seas phosphorescent at night, and the deadly Trypanosome, which causes Sleeping Sickness.

(*b*) Others were very sluggish, the parasitic Sporozoa, like the malaria organism which the mosquito introduces into man's body. (*c*) Others were neither very active nor very passive, the Rhizopods, with out-flowing processes of living matter. This amœboid line of evolution has been very successful; it is represented by the Rhizopods, such as Amœbæ and the chalk-forming Forminifera and the exquisitely beautiful flint-shelled Radiolarians of the open sea. They have their counterparts in the amœboid cells of most multicellular animals, such as the phagocytes which migrate about in the body, engulfing and digesting intruding bacteria, serving as sappers and miners when something has to be broken down and built up again, and performing other useful offices.

§ 3

The Making of a Body

The great naturalist Louis Agassiz once said that the biggest gulf in Organic Nature was that between the unicellular and the multicellular animals (Protozoa and Metazoa). But the gulf was bridged very long ago when sponges, stinging animals, and simple worms were evolved, and showed, for the first time, a "body." What would one not give to be able to account for the making of a body, one of the great steps in evolution! No one knows, but the problem is not altogether obscure.

When an ordinary Protozoon or one-celled animal divides into two or more, which is its way of multiplying, the daughter-units thus formed float apart and live independent lives. But there are a few Protozoa in which the daughter-units are not quite separated off from one another, but remain coherent. Thus Volvox, a beautiful green ball, found in some canals and the like, is a colony of a thousand or even ten thousand cells. It has almost formed a body! But in this "colony-making" Protozoon, and in others like it, the component cells are all of one kind, whereas in true multicellular animals there are different kinds of cells, showing division of labour. There are some other Protozoa in which the nucleus or kernel divides into many nuclei within the cell. This is seen in the Giant Amœba (Pelomyxa), sometimes found in duck-ponds, or the beautiful Opalina, which always lives in the hind part of the frog's food-canal. If a portion of the living matter of these Protozoa should gather round each of the nuclei, then *that would be the beginning of a body.* It would be still nearer the beginning of a body if division of labour set in, and if there was a setting apart of egg-cells and sperm-cells distinct from body-cells.

It was possibly in some such way that animals and plants with a body were first evolved. Two points should be noticed, that body-making is not essentially a matter of size, though it made large size possible. For the body of a many-celled Wheel Animalcule or Rotifer is no bigger than many a Protozoon. Yet the Rotifer—we are thinking of Hydatina—has nine hundred odd cells, whereas the Protozoon has only one, except in forms like Volvox. Secondly, it is a luminous fact that *every many-celled animal from sponge to man that multiplies in the ordinary way begins at the beginning again as a "single cell,"* the fertilised egg-cell. It is, of course, not an ordinary single cell that develops into an earthworm or a butterfly, an eagle, or a man; it is a cell in which a rich inheritance, the fruition of ages, is somehow condensed; but it is interesting to bear in mind the elementary fact that every many-celled creature, reproduced in the ordinary way and not by budding or the like, starts as a fertilised egg-cell. The coherence of the daughter-cells into which the fertilised egg-cell divides is a reminiscence, as it were, of the primeval coherence of daughter-units that made the first body possible.

The Beginning of Sexual Reproduction

A freshwater Hydra, growing on the duckweed usually multiplies by budding. It forms daughter-buds, living images of itself; a check comes to nutrition and these daughter-buds go

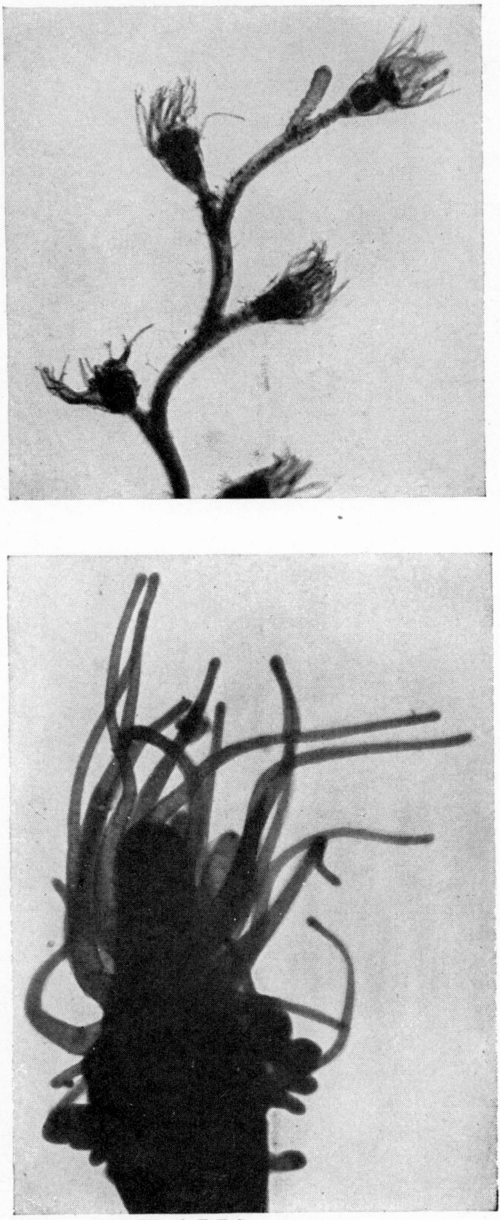

Photos: J. J. Ward, F.E.S.

A PLANT-LIKE ANIMAL, OR ZOOPHYTE, CALLED OBELIA

Consisting of a colony of small polyps, whose stinging tentacles are well shown greatly enlarged in the lower photograph.

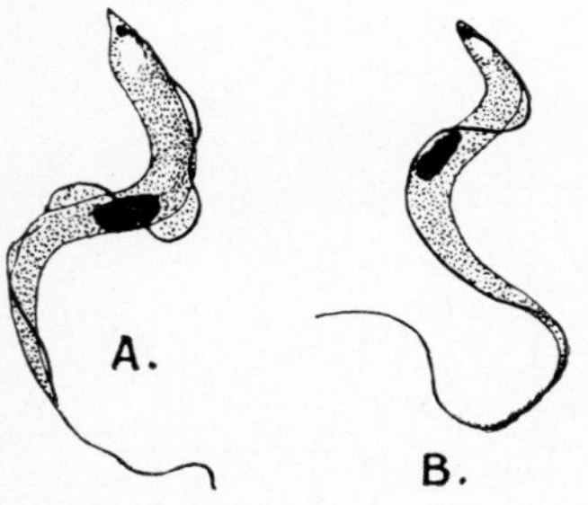

Reproduced by permission of "The Quart. Journ. Mic. Sci."

TRYPANOSOMA GAMBIENSE
(Very highly magnified.)

The microscopic animal Trypanosome, which causes Sleeping Sickness. The study of these organisms has of late years acquired an immense importance on account of the widespread and dangerous maladies to which some of them give rise. It lives in the blood of man, who is infected by the bite of a Tse-tse fly which carries the parasite from some other host.

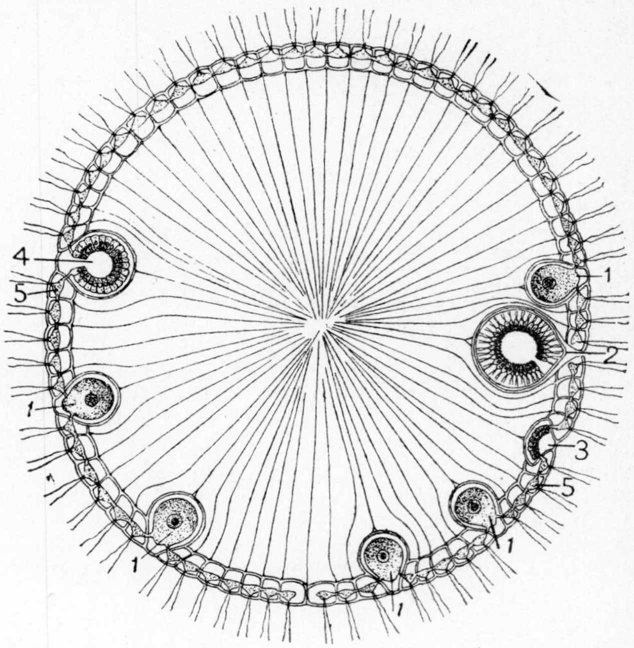

VOLVOX

The Volvox is found in some canals and the like. It is one of the first animals to suggest the beginning of a body. It is a colony of a thousand or even ten thousand cells, but they are all cells of one kind. In *multicellular* animals the cells are of *different* kinds with different functions. Each of the ordinary cells (marked 5) has two lashes or flagella. Daughter colonies inside the Parent colony are being formed at 3, 4, and 2. The development of germ-cells is shown at 1.

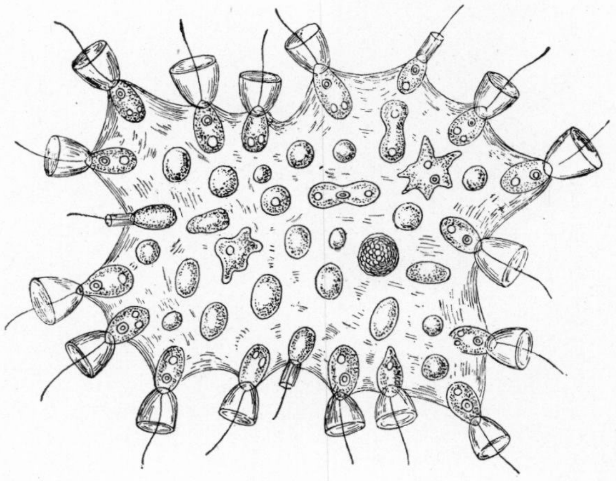

PROTEROSPONGIA

One of the simplest multicellular animals, illustrating the beginning of a body. There is a setting apart of egg-cells and sperm-cells, distinct from body-cells; the collared lashed cells on the margin are different in kind from those farther in. Thus, as in indubitable multicellular animals, division of labour has begun.

free. A big sea-anemone may divide in two or more parts, which become separate animals. This is asexual reproduction, which means that the multiplication takes place by dividing into two or many portions, and not by liberating egg-cells and sperm-cells. Among animals as among plants, asexual reproduction is very common. But it has great disadvantages, for it is apt to be physiologically expensive, and it is beset with difficulties when the body shows great division of labour, and is very intimately bound into unity. Thus, no one can think of a bee or a bird multiplying by division or by budding. Moreover, if the body of the parent has suffered from injury or deterioration, the result of this is bound to be handed on to the next generation if asexual reproduction is the only method.

Splitting into two or many parts was the old-fashioned way of multiplying, but one of the great steps in evolution was the discovery of a better method, namely, sexual reproduction. The gist of this is simply that during the process of body-building (by the development of the fertilised egg-cell) certain units, *the germ-cells,* do not share in forming ordinary tissues or organs, but remain apart, continuing the full inheritance which was condensed in the fertilised egg-cell. *These cells kept by themselves are the originators of the future reproductive cells of the mature animal;* they give rise to the egg-cells and the sperm-cells.

The advantages of this method are great. (1) The new generation is started less expensively, for it is easier to shed germ-cells into the cradle of the water than to separate off half of the body. (2) It is possible to start a great many new lives at once, and this may be of vital importance when the struggle for existence is very keen, and when parental care is impossible. (3) The germ-cells are little likely to be prejudicially affected by disadvantageous dints impressed on the body of the parent—little likely unless the dints have peculiarly penetrating consequences, as in the case of poisons. (4) A further advantage is implied in the formation of two kinds of germ-cells—the ovum or egg-cell, with a considerable amount of building material and often with a legacy of nutritive yolk; the spermatozoon or sperm-cell, adapted to move in fluids and to find the ovum from a distance, thus securing change-provoking cross-fertilisation.

§ 4

The Evolution of Sex

Another of the great steps in organic evolution was the differentiation of two different physiological types, the male or sperm-producer and the female or egg-producer. It seems to be a deep-seated difference in constitution, which leads one egg to develop into a male, and another, lying beside it in the nest, into a female. In the case of pigeons it seems almost certain, from the work of Professor Oscar Riddle, that there are two kinds of egg, a male-producing egg and a female-producing egg, which differ in their yolk-forming and other physiological characters.

In sea-urchins we often find two creatures superficially indistinguishable, but the one is a female with large ovaries and the other is a male with equally large testes. Here the physiological difference does not affect the body as a whole, but the reproductive organs or gonads only, though more intimate physiology would doubtless discover differences in the blood or in the chemical routine (metabolism). In a large number of cases, however, there are marked superficial differences between the sexes, and everyone is familiar with such contrasts as peacock and peahen, stag and hind. In such cases the physiological difference between the sperm-producer and the ovum-producer, for this is the essential difference, saturates through the body and expresses itself in masculine and feminine structures and modes of behaviour. The expression of the masculine and feminine characters is in some cases under the control of hormones or chemical messengers which are carried by the blood from the reproductive organs throughout the body, and pull the trigger which brings about the development of an antler or a wattle or a decorative plume or a capacity for vocal and saltatory display. In some cases it is certain that the female carries in a latent state the masculine features, but these are kept from expressing themselves by other chemical messengers from the ovary. Of these chemical messengers more must be said later on.

Recent research has shown that while the difference between male and female is very deep-rooted, corresponding to a difference in gearing, it is not always clear-cut. Thus a hen-pigeon may be very masculine, and a cock-pigeon very feminine. The difference is in degree, not in kind.

§ 5

What is the meaning of the universal or almost universal inevitableness of death? A Sequoia or "Big Tree" of California has been known to live for over two thousand years, but eventually it died. A centenarian tortoise has been known, and a sea-anemone sixty years of age; but eventually they die. What is the meaning of this apparently inevitable stoppage of bodily life?

The Beginning of Natural Death

There are three chief kinds of death. (*a*) The great majority of animals come to a violent end, being devoured by others or killed by sudden and extreme changes in their surroundings. (*b*) When an animal enters a new habitat, or comes into new associations with other organisms, it may be invaded by a microbe or by some larger parasite to which it is unaccustomed and to which it can offer no resistance. With many parasites a "live-and-let-live" compromise is arrived at, but new parasites are apt to be fatal, as man knows to his cost when he is bitten by a tse-tse fly which infects him with the microscopic animal (a Trypanosome) that causes Sleeping Sickness. In many animals the parasites are not troublesome as long as the host is vigorous, but if the host is out of condition the parasites may get the upper hand, as in the so-called "grouse disease," and become fatal. (*c*) But besides violent death and microbic (or parasitic) death, there is natural death. This is in great part to be regarded as the price paid for a body. A body worth having implies complexity or division of labour, and this implies certain internal furnishings of a more or less stable kind in which the effects of wear and tear are apt to accumulate. It is not the living matter itself that grows old so much as the framework in which it works—the furnishings of the vital laboratory. There are various processes of rejuvenescence, e.g. rest, repair, change, reorganisation, which work against the inevitable processes of senescence, but sooner or later the victory is with ageing. Another deep reason for natural death is to be found in the physiological expensiveness of reproduction, for many animals, from worms to eels, illustrate natural death as the nemesis of starting new lives. Now it is a very striking fact that to a large degree the simplest animals or Protozoa are exempt from natural death. They are so relatively simple that they can continually recuperate by rest and repair; they do not accumulate any bad debts. Moreover, their modes of multiplying, by dividing into two or many units, are very inexpensive physiologically. It seems that in some measure this bodily immortality of the Protozoa is shared by some simple many-celled animals like the freshwater Hydra and Planarian worms. Here is an interesting chapter in evolution, the evolution of means of evading or staving off natural death. Thus there is the well-known case of the Paloloworm of the coral-reefs where the body breaks up in liberating the germ-cells, but the head-end remains fixed in a crevice of the coral, and buds out a new body at leisure.

Along with the evolution of the ways of avoiding death should be considered also the gradual establishment of the length of life best suited to the welfare of the species, and the punctuation of the life-history to suit various conditions.

Photo: J. J. Ward, F.E.S.

GREEN HYDRA

A little freshwater polyp, about half an inch long, with a crown of tentacles round the mouth. It is seen giving off a bud, a clear illustration of asexual reproduction. When a tentacle touches some small organism the latter is paralysed and drawn into the mouth.

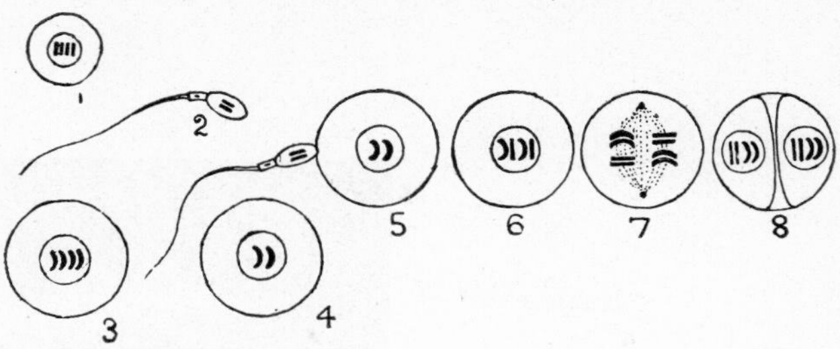

DIAGRAM ILLUSTRATING THE BEGINNING OF INDIVIDUAL LIFE

1. An immature *sperm*-cell, with 4 chromosomes (nuclear bodies) represented as rods.
2. A mature sperm-cell, with 2 chromosomes.
3. An immature *egg*-cell, with 4 chromosomes represented as curved bodies
4. A mature egg-cell, with 2 chromosomes.
5. The spermatozoon fertilises the ovum, introducing 2 chromosomes.
6. The fertilised ovum, with 4 chromosomes, 2 of paternal origin and 2 of maternal origin.
7. The chromosomes lie at the equator, and each is split longitudinally. The centrosome introduced by the spermatozoon has divided into two centrosomes, one at each pole of the nucleus. These play an important part in the division or segmentation of the egg.
8. The fertilised egg has divided into two cells. Each cell has 2 paternal and 2 maternal chromosomes.

Photo: J. J. Ward, F.E.S.

EARTHWORM

Earthworms began the profitable habit of moving with one end of the body always in front, and from worms to man the great majority of animals have bilateral symmetry.

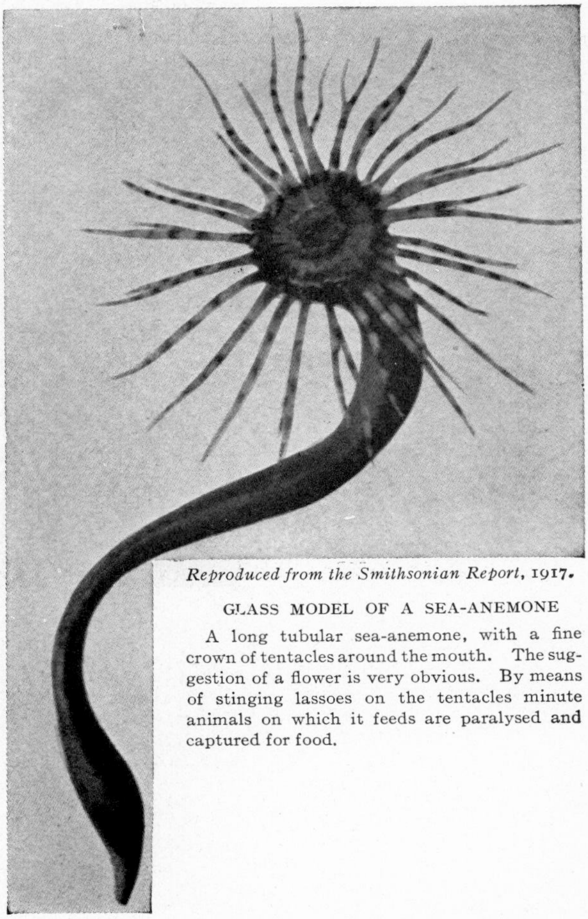

Reproduced from the Smithsonian Report, 1917.

GLASS MODEL OF A SEA-ANEMONE

A long tubular sea-anemone, with a fine crown of tentacles around the mouth. The suggestion of a flower is very obvious. By means of stinging lassoes on the tentacles minute animals on which it feeds are paralysed and captured for food.

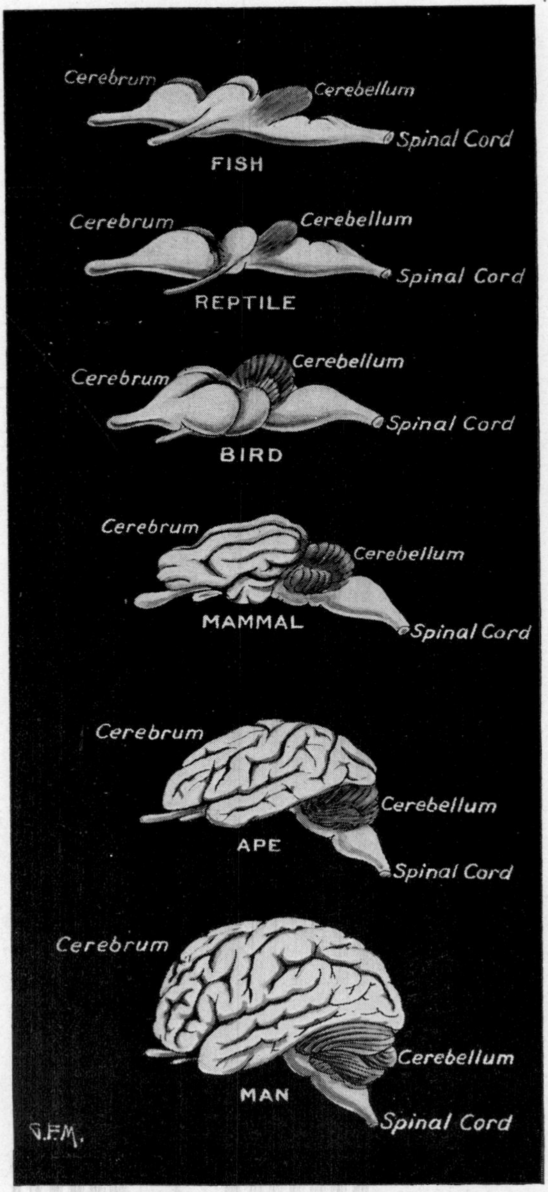

THIS DRAWING SHOWS THE EVOLUTION OF THE BRAIN FROM FISH TO MAN

The Cerebrum, the seat of intelligence, increases in proportion to the other parts. In mammals it becomes more and more convoluted. The brain, which lies in one plane in fishes, becomes gradually curved on itself. In birds it is more curved than the drawing shows.

§ 6

Great Acquisitions

In animals like sea-anemones and jellyfishes the general symmetry of the body is radial; that is to say, there is no right or left, and the body might be halved along many planes. It is a kind of symmetry well suited for sedentary or for drifting life. But worms began the profitable habit of moving with one end of the body always in front, and from worms to man the great majority of animals have bilateral symmetry. They have a right and a left side, and there is only one cut that halves the body. This kind of symmetry is suited for a more strenuous life than radial animals show; it is suited for pursuing food, for avoiding enemies, for chasing mates. And *with the establishment of bilateral symmetry must be associated the establishment of head-brains,* the beginning of which is to be found in some simple worm-types.

Among the other great acquisitions gradually evolved we may notice: a well-developed head with sense-organs, the establishment of large internal surfaces such as the digestive and absorptive wall of the food-canal, the origin of quickly contracting striped muscle and of muscular appendages, the formation of blood as a distributing medium throughout the body, from which all the parts take what they need and to which they also contribute.

Another very important acquisition, almost confined (so far as is known) to backboned animals, was the evolution of what are called glands of internal secretion, such as the thyroid and the supra-renal. These manufacture subtle chemical substances which are distributed by the blood throughout the body, and have a manifold influence in regulating and harmonising the vital processes. Some of these chemical messengers are called hormones, which stimulate organs and tissues to greater activity; others are called chalones, which put on a brake. Some regulate growth and others rapidly alter the pressure and composition of the blood. Some of them call into active development certain parts of the body which have been as it were, waiting for an appropriate trigger-pulling. Thus, at the proper time, the milk-glands of a mammalian mother are awakened from their dormancy. This very interesting outcome of evolution will be dealt with in another portion of this work.

THE INCLINED PLANE OF ANIMAL BEHAVIOUR

§ 1

Before passing to a connected story of the gradual emergence of higher and higher forms of life in the course of the successive ages—the procession of life, as it may be called—it will be useful to consider the evolution of animal behaviour.

Evolution of Mind

A human being begins as a microscopic fertilised egg-cell, within which there is condensed the long result of time—Man's inheritance. The long period of nine months before birth, with its intimate partnership between mother and offspring, is passed as it were in sleep, and no one can make any statement in regard to the mind of the unborn child. Even after birth the dawn of mind is as slow as it is wonderful. To begin with, there is in the ovum and early embryo no nervous system at all, and it develops very gradually from simple beginnings. Yet as mentality cannot come in from outside, we seem bound to conclude that the potentiality of it—whatever that means—resides in the individual from the very first. The particular kind of activity known to us as thinking, feeling, and willing is the most intimate part of our experience, known to us directly apart from our senses, and the possibility of that must be implicit in the germ-cell just as the genius of Newton was implicit in a very miserable specimen of an infant. Now what is true of the individual is true also of the race—there is a gradual evolution of that aspect of the living

OKAPI AND GIRAFFE

The Okapi is one of the great zoölogical discoveries. It gives a good idea of what the Giraffe's ancestors were like. The Okapi was unknown until discovered in 1900 by Sir Harry Johnston in Central Africa, where these strange animals have probably lived in dense forests from time immemorial.

creature's activity which we call mind. We cannot put our finger on any point and say: Before this stage there was no mind. Indeed, many facts suggest the conclusion that wherever there is life there is some degree of mind—even in the plants. Or it might be more accurate to put the conclusion in another way, that the activity we call life has always in some degree an inner or mental aspect.

In another part of this book there is an account of the dawn of mind in backboned animals; what we aim at here is an outline of what may be called the inclined plane of animal behaviour.

A very simple animal accumulates a little store of potential energy, and it proceeds to expend this, like an explosive, by acting on its environment. It does so in a very characteristic self-preservative fashion, so that it burns without being consumed and explodes without being blown to bits. It is characteristic of the organism that it remains a going concern for a longer or shorter period—its length of life. Living creatures that expended their energy ineffectively or self-destructively would be eliminated in the struggle for existence. When a simple one-celled organism explores a corner of the field seen under a microscope, behaving to all appearance very like a dog scouring a field seen through a telescope, it seems permissible to think of something corresponding to mental endeavour associated with its activity. This impression is strengthened when an amœba pursues another amœba, overtakes it, engulfs it, loses it, pursues it again, recaptures it, and so on. What is quite certain is that the behaviour of the animalcule is not like that of a potassium pill fizzing about in a basin of water, nor like the lurching movements of a gun that has got loose and "taken charge" on board ship. Another feature is that the locomotor activity of an animalcule often shows a distinct individuality: it may swim, for instance, in a loose spiral.

But there is another side to vital activity besides acting upon the surrounding world; the living creature is acted on by influences from without. The organism acts on its environment; that is the one side of the shield: the environment acts upon the organism; that is the other side. If we are to see life whole we must recognise these two sides of what we call living, and it is missing an important part of the history of animal life if we fail to see that evolution implies becoming more advantageously sensitive to the environment, making more of its influences, shutting out profitless stimuli, and opening more gateways to knowledge. The bird's world is a larger and finer world than an earthworm's; the world means more to the bird than to the worm.

The Trial and Error Method

Simple creatures act with a certain degree of spontaneity on their environment, and they likewise react effectively to surrounding stimuli. Animals come to have definite "answers back," sometimes several, sometimes only one, as in the case of the Slipper Animalcule, which reverses its cilia when it comes within the sphere of some disturbing influence, retreats, and, turning upon itself tentatively, sets off again in the same general direction as before, but at an angle to the previous line. If it misses the disturbing influence, well and good; if it strikes it again, the tactics are repeated until a satisfactory way out is discovered or the stimulation proves fatal.

It may be said that the Slipper Animalcule has but one answer to every question, but there are many Protozoa which have several enregistered reactions. When there are alternative reactions which are tried one after another, the animal is pursuing what is called the trial-and-error method, and a higher note is struck.

There is an endeavour after satisfaction, and a trial of answers. When the creature profits by experience to the extent of giving the right answer first, there is the beginning of learning.

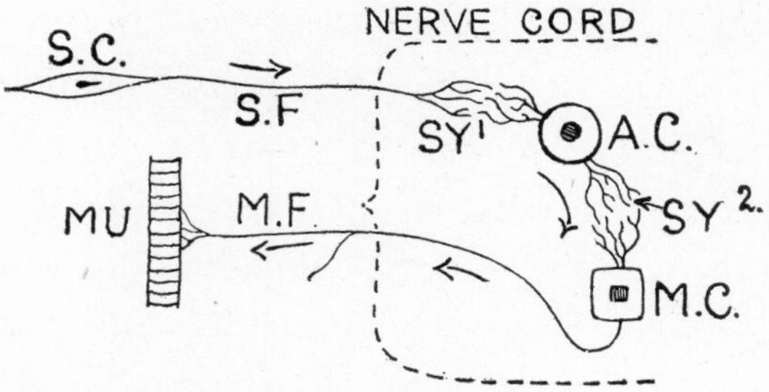

DIAGRAM OF A SIMPLE REFLEX ARC IN A BACKBONELESS ANIMAL LIKE AN EARTHWORM

1. A sensory nerve-cell (S.C.) on the surface receives a stimulus.

2. The stimulus travels along the sensatory nerve-fibre (S.F.)

3. The sensory nerve-fibre branches in the nerve-cord.

4. Its branches come into close contact (SY^1) with those of an associative or communicating nerve-cell (A.C.).

5. Other branches of the associative cell come into close contact (SY^2) with the branches or dendrites of a motor nerve-cell (M.C.).

6. An impulse or command travels along the motor nerve-fibre or axis cylinder of the motor nerve-cell.

7. The motor nerve-fibre ends on a muscle-fibre (M.F.) near the surface. This moves and the reflex action is complete.

Photo: British Museum (Natural History).

THE YUCCA MOTH

The Yucca Moth, emerging from her cocoon, flies at night to a Yucca flower and collects pollen from the stamens, holding a little ball of it in her mouth-parts. She then visits another flower and lays an egg in the seed-box. After this she applies the pollen to the tip of the pistil, thus securing the fertilisation of the flower and the growth of the ovules in the pod. Yucca flowers in Britain do not produce seeds because there are no Yucca Moths.

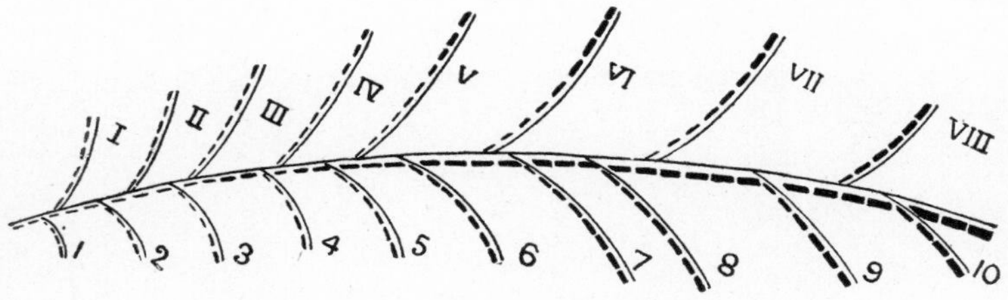

INCLINED PLANE OF ANIMAL BEHAVIOUR

Diagram illustrating animal behaviour. The main line represents the general life of the creature. On the upper side are activities implying initiative; on the lower side actions which are almost automatic.

Upper Side.—I. Energetic actions. II. Simple tentatives. III. Trial-and-error methods. IV. Non-intelligent experiments. V. Experiential "learning." VI. Associative "learning." VII. Intelligent behaviour. VIII. Rational conduct (man).

Lower Side.—1. Reactions to environment. 2. Enregistered reactions. 3. Simple reflex actions. 4. Compound reflex actions. 5. Tropisms. 6. Enregistered rhythms. 7. Simple instincts. 8. Chain instincts. 9. Instinctive activities influenced by intelligence. 10. Subconscious cerebration at a high level (man).

Photo: J. J. Ward, F.E.S.

VENUS' FLY-TRAP

One of the most remarkable plants in the world, which captures its prey by means of a trap formed from part of its leaf. It has been induced to snap at and hold a bristle. If an insect lighting on the leaf touches one of six very sensitive hairs, which pull the trigger of the movement, the two halves of the leaf close rapidly and the fringing teeth on the margin interlock, preventing the insect's escape. Then follows an exudation of digestive juice.

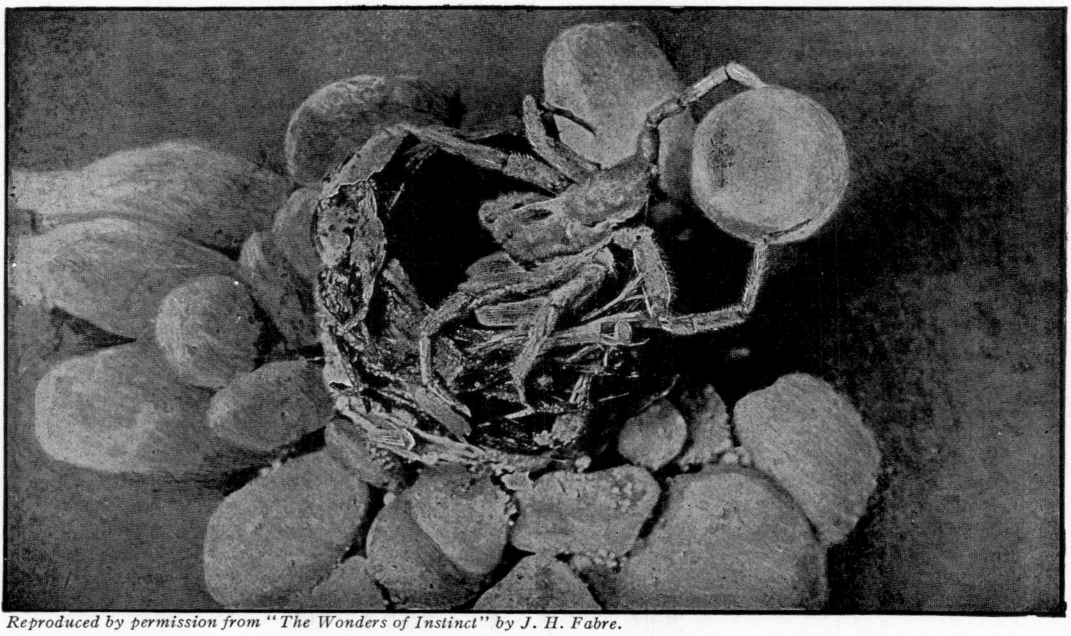

Reproduced by permission from "The Wonders of Instinct" by J. H. Fabre.

A SPIDER SUNNING HER EGGS

A kind of spider, called Lycosa, lying head downwards at the edge of her nest, and holding her silken cocoon—the bag containing the eggs—up towards the sun in her hindmost pair of legs. This extraordinary proceeding is believed to assist in the hatching.

Reflex Actions

Among simple multicellular animals, such as sea-anemones, we find the beginnings of reflex actions, and a considerable part of the behaviour of the lower animals is reflex. That is to say, there are laid down in the animal in the course of its development certain prearrangements of nerve-cells and muscle-cells which secure that a fit and proper answer is given to a frequently recurrent stimulus. An earthworm half out of its burrow becomes aware of the light tread of a thrush's foot, and jerks itself back into its hole before anyone can say "reflex action." What is it that happens?

Certain sensory nerve-cells in the earthworm's skin are stimulated by vibrations in the earth; the message travels down a sensory nerve-fibre from each of the stimulated cells and enters the nerve-cord. The sensory fibres come into vital connection with branches of intermediary, associative, or communicating cells, which are likewise connected with motor nerve-cells. To these the message is thus shunted. From the motor nerve-cells an impulse or command travels by motor nerve-fibres, one from each cell, to the muscles, which contract. If this took as long to happen as it takes to describe, even in outline, it would not be of much use to the earthworm. But the motor answer follows the sensory stimulus almost instantaneously. The great advantage of establishing or enregistering these reflex chains is that the answers are practically ready-made or inborn, not requiring to be learned. It is not necessary that the brain should be stimulated if there is a brain; nor does the animal will to act, though in certain cases it may by means of higher controlling nerve-centres keep the natural reflex response from being given, as happens, for instance, when we control a cough or a sneeze on some solemn occasion. The evolutionary method, if we may use the expression, has been to enregister ready-made responses; and as we ascend the animal kingdom, we find reflex actions becoming complicated and often linked together, so that the occurrence of one pulls the trigger of another, and so on in a chain. The behaviour of the insectivorous plant called Venus's fly-trap when it shuts on an insect is like a reflex action in an animal, but plants have no definite nervous system.

What are Called Tropisms

A somewhat higher level on the inclined plane is illustrated by what are called "tropisms," obligatory movements which the animal makes, adjusting its whole body so that physiological equilibrium results in relation to gravity, pressure, currents, moisture, heat, light, electricity, and surfaces of contact. A moth is flying past a candle; the eye next the light is more illumined than the other; a physiological inequilibrium results, affecting nerve-cells and muscle-cells; the outcome is that the moth automatically adjusts its flight so that both eyes become equally illumined; in doing this it often flies into the candle.

It may seem bad business that the moth should fly into the candle, but the flame is an utterly artificial item in its environment to which no one can expect it to be adapted. These tropisms play an important rôle in animal behaviour.

§ 2

Instinctive Behaviour

On a higher level is instinctive behaviour, which reaches such remarkable perfection in ants, bees, and wasps. In its typical expression instinctive behaviour depends on inborn capacities; it does not require to be learned; it is independent of practice or experience, though it may be improved by both; it is shared equally by all members of the species of the same sex (for the female's instincts are often different from the male's); it refers to particular conditions of life that are of vital importance, though they may occur only once in a lifetime. The female Yucca Moth emerges from the cocoon when the Yucca flower puts forth its bell-like blossoms. She flies to a flower, collects some pollen from the stamens, kneads it into a pill-like ball, and stows this away under her chin. She flies to an older Yucca flower and lays her eggs in some of the ovules within the seed-box, but before she does so she has to deposit on the stigma the ball of pollen. From this the pollen-tubes grow down and the pollen-nucleus of a tube fertilises the egg-cell in an ovule, so that the possible seeds become real seeds, for it is only a fraction of them that the Yucca Moth has destroyed by using them as cradles for her eggs. Now it is plain that the Yucca Moth has no individual experience of Yucca flowers, yet she secures the continuance of her race by a concatenation of actions which form part of her instinctive repertory.

From a physiological point of view instinctive behaviour is like a chain of compound reflex actions, but in some cases, at least, there is reason to believe that the behaviour is suffused with awareness and backed by endeavour. This is suggested in exceptional cases where the stereotyped routine is departed from to meet exceptional conditions. It should also be noted that just as ants, hive bees, and wasps exhibit in most cases purely instinctive behaviour, but move on occasion on the main line of trial and error or of experimental initiative, so among birds and mammals the intelligent behaviour is sometimes replaced by instinctive routine. Perhaps there is no instinctive behaviour without a spice of intelligence, and no intelligent behaviour without an instinctive element. The old view that instinctive behaviour was originally intelligent, and that instinct is "lapsed intelligence," is a tempting one, and is suggested by the way in which habitual intelligent actions cease in the individual to require intelligent control, but it rests on the unproved hypothesis that the acquisitions of the individual can be entailed on the race. It is almost certain that instinct is on a line of evolution quite different from intelligence, and that it is nearer to the inborn inspirations of the calculating boy or the musical genius than to the plodding methods of intelligent learning.

Animal Intelligence

The higher reaches of the inclined plane of behaviour show intelligence in the strict sense. They include those kinds of behaviour which cannot be described without the suggestion that the animal makes some sort of perceptual inference, not only profiting by experience but learning by ideas. Such intelligent actions show great individual variability; they are plastic and adjustable in a manner rarely hinted at in connection with instincts where routine cannot be departed from without the creature being nonplussed; they are not bound up with particular circumstances as instinctive actions are, but imply an appreciative awareness of relations.

When there is an experimenting with general ideas, when there is *conceptual* as contrasted with *perceptual* inference, we speak of Reason, but there is no evidence of this below the level of man. It is not, indeed, always that we can credit man with rational conduct, but he has the possibility of it ever within his reach.

Animal instinct and intelligence will be illustrated in another part of this work. We are here concerned simply with the general question of the evolution of behaviour. There is a main line of tentative experimental behaviour both below and above the level of intelligence, and it has been part of the tactics of evolution to bring about the hereditary enregistration of capacities of effective response, the advantages being that the answers come more rapidly and that the creature is left free, if it chooses, for higher adventures.

There is no doubt as to the big fact that in the course of evolution animals have shown an increasing complexity and masterfulness of behaviour, that they have become at once more controlled and more definitely free agents, and that the inner aspect of the behaviour—experimenting, learning, thinking, feeling, and willing—has come to count for more and more.

§ 3

Evolution of Parental Care

Mammals furnish a crowning instance of a trend of evolution which expresses itself at many levels—the tendency to bring forth the young at a well-advanced stage and to an increase of parental care associated with a decrease in the number of offspring. There is a British starfish called *Luidia* which has two hundred millions of eggs in a year, and there are said to be several millions of eggs in conger-eels and some other fishes. These illustrate the spawning method of solving the problem of survival. Some animals are naturally prolific, and the number of eggs which they sow broadcast in the waters allows for enormous infantile mortality and obviates any necessity for parental care.

But some other creatures, by nature less prolific, have found an entirely different solution of the problem. They practise parental care and they secure survival with greatly economised reproduction. This is a trend of evolution particularly characteristic of the higher animals. So much so that Herbert Spencer formulated the generalisation that the size and frequency of the animal family is inverse ratio to the degree of evolution to which the animal has attained.

Now there are many different methods of parental care which secure the safety of the young, and one of these is called viviparity. The young ones are not liberated from the parent until they are relatively well advanced and more or less able to look after themselves. This gives the young a good send-off in life, and their chances of death are greatly reduced. In other words, the animals that have varied in the direction of economised reproduction may keep their foothold in the struggle for existence if they have varied at the same time in the direction of parental care. In other cases it may have worked the other way round.

In the interesting archaic animal called *Peripatus,* which has to face a modern world too severe for it, one of the methods of meeting the environing difficulties is the retention of the offspring for many months within the mother, so that it is born a fully-formed creature. There are only a few offspring at a time, and, although there are exceptional cases like the summer green-flies, which are very prolific though viviparous, the general rule is that viviparity is associated with a very small family. The case of flowering plants stands by itself, for although they illustrate a kind of viviparity, the seed being embryos, an individual plant may have a large number of flowers and therefore a huge family.

Viviparity naturally finds its best illustrations among terrestrial animals, where the risks to the young life are many, and it finds its climax among mammals.

Now it is an interesting fact that the three lowest mammals, the Duckmole and two Spiny Ant-eaters, lay eggs, i.e. are oviparous; that the Marsupials, on the next grade, bring forth their young, as it were, prematurely, and in most cases stow them away in an external pouch; while all the others—the Placentals—show a more prolonged antenatal life and an intimate partnership between the mother and the unborn young.

§ 4

There is another way of looking at the sublime process of evolution. It has implied a mastery of all the possible haunts of life; it has been a progressive conquest of the environment.

1. It is highly probable that living organisms found their foothold in the stimulating conditions of the shore of the sea—the shallow water, brightly illumined, seaweed-growing shelf fringing the Continents. This littoral zone was a propitious, environment where sea and fresh water, earth and air all meet, where there is stimulating change, abundant oxygenation and a copious supply of nutritive material in what the streams bring down and in the rich seaweed vegetation.

THE HOATZIN INHABITS BRITISH GUIANA

The newly hatched bird has claws on its thumb and first finger and so is enabled to climb on the branches of trees with great dexterity until such time as the wings are strong enough to sustain it in flight.

Photograph, from the British Museum (Natural History), of a drawing by Mr. E. Wilson.

PERIPATUS

A widely distributed old-fashioned type of animal, somewhat like a permanent caterpillar. It has affinities both with worms and with insects. It has a velvety skin, minute diamond-like eyes, and short stump-like legs. A defenceless, weaponless animal, it comes out at night, and is said to capture small insects by squirting jets of slime from its mouth.

Photo: W. S. Berridge, F.Z.S.

ROCK KANGAROO CARRYING ITS YOUNG IN A POUCH

The young are born so helpless that they cannot even suck. The mother places them in the external pouch, and fitting their mouths on the teats injects the milk. After a time the young ones go out and in as they please.

It is not an easy haunt of life, but none the worse for that, and it is tenanted to-day by representatives of practically every class of animals from infusorians to sea-shore birds and mammals.

The Cradle of the Open Sea

2. The open-sea or pelagic haunt includes all the brightly illumined surface waters beyond the shallow water of the shore area.

It is perhaps the easiest of all the haunts of life, for there is no crowding, there is considerable uniformity, and an abundance of food for animals is afforded by the inexhaustible floating "sea-meadows" of microscopic Algæ. These are reincarnated in minute animals like the open-sea crustaceans, which again are utilised by fishes, these in turn making life possible for higher forms like carnivorous turtles and toothed whales. It is quite possible that the open sea was the original cradle of life and perhaps Professor Church is right in picturing a long period of pelagic life before there was any sufficiently shallow water to allow the floating plants to anchor. It is rather in favour of this view that many shore animals such as crabs and starfishes, spend their youthful stages in the relatively safe cradle of the open sea, and only return to the more strenuous conditions of their birthplace after they have gained considerable strength of body. It is probably safe to say that the honour of being the original cradle of life lies between the shore of the sea and the open sea.

The Great Deeps

3. A third haunt of life is the floor of the Deep Sea, the abyssal area, which occupies more than a half of the surface of the globe. It is a region of extreme cold—an eternal winter; of utter darkness—an eternal night—relieved only by the fitful gleams of "phosphorescent" animals; of enormous pressure —2½ tons on

the square inch at a depth of 2,500 fathoms; of profound calm, unbroken silence, immense monotony. And as there are no plants in the great abysses, the animals must live on one another, and, in the long run, on the rain of moribund animalcules which sink from the surface through the miles of water. It seems a very unpromising haunt of life, but it is abundantly tenanted, and it gives us a glimpse of the insurgent nature of the living creature that the difficulties of the Deep Sea should have been so effectively conquered. It is probable that the colonising of the great abysses took place in relatively recent times, for the fauna does not include many very antique types. It is practically certain that the colonisation was due to littoral animals which followed the food-débris, millennium after millennium, further and further down the long slope from the shore.

The Freshwaters

4. A fourth haunt of life is that of the fresh-waters, including river and lake, pond and pool, swamp and marsh. It may have been colonised by gradual migration up estuaries and rivers, or by more direct passage from the seashore into the brackish swamp. Or it may have been in some cases that partially land-locked corners of ancient seas became gradually turned into fresh-water basins. The animal population of the freshwaters is very representative, and is diversely adapted to meet the characteristic contingencies—the risk of being dried up, the risk of being frozen hard in winter, and the risk of being left high and dry after floods or of being swept down to the sea.

Conquest of the Dry Land

5. The terrestrial haunt has been invaded age after age by contingents from the sea or from the freshwaters. We must recognise the worm invasion, which led eventually to the making of the fertile soil, the invasion due to air-breathing Arthropods

which led eventually to the important linkage between flowers and their insect visitors, and the invasion due to air-breathing Amphibians, which led eventually to the higher terrestrial animals and to the development of intelligence and family affection. Besides these three great invasions, there were minor ones such as that leading to land-snails, for there has been a widespread and persistent tendency among aquatic animals to try to possess the dry land.

Getting on to dry land had a manifold significance.

It implied getting into a medium with a much larger supply of oxygen than there is dissolved in the water. But the oxygen of the air is more difficult to capture, especially when the skin becomes hard or well protected, as it is almost bound to become in animals living on dry ground. Thus this leads to the development of *internal surfaces,* such as those of lungs, where the oxygen taken into the body may be absorbed by the blood. In most animals the blood goes to the surface of oxygen-capture; but in insects and their relatives there is a different idea—of taking the air to the blood or in greater part to the area of oxygen-combustion, the living tissues. A system of branching air-tubes takes air into every hole and corner of the insect's body, and this thorough aeration is doubtless in part the secret of the insect's intense activity. The blood never becomes impure.

The conquest of the dry land also implied a predominance of that kind of locomotion which may be compared to punting, when the body is pushed along by pressing a lever against a hard substratum. And it also followed that with few exceptions the body of the terrestrial animal tended to be compact, readily lifted off the ground by the limbs or adjusted in some other way so that there may not be too large a surface trailing on the ground. An animal like a jellyfish, easily supported in the water, would be impossible on land. Such apparent exceptions as earthworms, centipedes, and snakes are not difficult to explain, for the earthworm is a burrower which eats its way through the soil, the centipede's long body is supported by numerous hard legs, and the snake pushes itself along by means of the large ventral scales to which the lower ends of very numerous ribs are attached.

Methods of Mastering the Difficulties of Terrestrial Life

A great restriction attendant on the invasion of the dry land is that locomotion becomes limited to one plane, namely, the surface of the earth. This is in great contrast to what is true in the water, where the animal can move up or down, to right or to left, at any angle and in three dimensions. It surely follows from this that the movements of land animals must be rapid and precise, unless, indeed, safety is secured in some other way. Hence it is easy to understand why most land animals have very finely developed striped muscles, and why a beetle running on the ground has far more numerous muscles than a lobster swimming in the sea.

Land animals were also handicapped by the risks of drought and of frost, but these were met by defences of the most diverse description, from the hairs of woolly caterpillars to the fur of mammals, from the carapace of tortoises to the armour of armadillos. In other cases, it is hardly necessary to say, the difficulties may be met in other ways, as frogs meet the winter by falling into a lethargic state in some secluded retreat.

Another consequence of getting on to dry land is that the eggs or young can no longer be set free anyhow, as is possible when the animal is surrounded by water, which is in itself more or less of a cradle. If the eggs were laid or the young liberated on dry ground, the chances are many that they would be dried up or devoured. So there are numerous ways in which land animals secure the safety of their young, e.g. by burying them in the ground, or by hiding them in nests, or by carrying them about for a prolonged period either before or after birth. This may mean great safety for the young, this may make it possible to have

Photo: Rischgitz.

PROFESSOR THOMAS HENRY HUXLEY (1825–95)

One of the most distinguished of zoologists, with unsurpassed gifts as a teacher and expositor. He did great service in gaining a place for science in ordinary education and in popular estimation. No one championed Evolutionism with more courage and skill.

BARON CUVIER, 1769–1832

One of the founders of modern Comparative Anatomy. A man of gigantic intellect, who came to Paris as a youth from the provinces, and became the director of the higher education of France and a peer of the Empire. He was opposed to Evolutionist ideas, but he had anatomical genius.

AN ILLUSTRATION SHOWING VARIOUS METHODS OF FLYING AND SWOOPING

Gull, with a feather-wing, a true flier. Fox-bat, with a skin-wing, a true flier. Flying Squirrel, with a parachute of skin, able to swoop from tree to tree, but not to fly. Flying Fish, with pectoral fins used as volplanes in a great leap due to the tail. To some extent able to sail in albatros fashion.

only a small family, and this may tend to the evolution of parental care and the kindly emotions. Thus it may be understood that from the conquest of the land many far-reaching consequences have followed.

Finally, it is worth dwelling on the risks of terrestrial life, because they enable us better to understand why so many land animals have become burrowers and others climbers of trees, why some have returned to the water and others have taken to the air. It may be asked, perhaps, why the land should have been colonised at all when the risks and difficulties are so great. The answer must be that necessity and curiosity are the mother and father of invention. Animals left the water because the pools dried up, or because they were overcrowded, or because of inveterate enemies, but also because of that curiosity and spirit of adventure which, from first to last, has been one of the spurs of progress.

Conquering the Air

6. The last great haunt of life is the air, a mastery of which must be placed to the credit of insects, Pterodactyls, birds, and bats. These have been the successes, but it should be noted that there have been many brilliant failures, which have not attained to much more than parachuting. These include the Flying Fishes, which take leaps from the water and are carried for many yards and to considerable heights, holding their enlarged pectoral fins taut or with little more than a slight fluttering. There is a so-called Flying Frog (*Rhacophorus*) that skims from branch to branch, and the much more effective Flying Dragon (*Draco volans*) of the Far East, which has been mentioned already. Among mammals there are Flying Phalangers, Flying Lemurs, and more besides, all attaining to great skill as parachutists, and illustrating the endeavour to master the air which man has realised in a way of his own.

The power of flight brings obvious advantages. A bird feeding on the ground is able to evade the stalking carnivore by suddenly rising into the air; food and water can be followed rapidly and to great distances; the eggs or the young can be placed in safe situations; and birds in their migrations have made a brilliant conquest both of time and space. Many of them know no winter in their year, and the migratory flight of the Pacific Golden Plover from Hawaii to Alaska and back again does not stand alone.

THE PROCESSION OF LIFE THROUGH THE AGES

§ 1

The Rock Record

How do we know when the various classes of animals and plants were established on the earth? How do we know the order of their appearance and the succession of their advances? The answer is: by reading the Rock Record. In the course of time the crust of the earth has been elevated into continents and depressed into ocean-troughs, and the surface of the land has been buckled up into mountain ranges and folded in gentler hills and valleys. The high places of the land have been weathered by air and water in many forms, and the results of the weathering have been borne away by rivers and seas, to be laid down again elsewhere as deposits which eventually formed sandstones, mudstones, and similar sedimentary rocks. Much of the material of the original crust has thus been broken down and worked up again many times over, and if the total thickness of the sedimentary rocks is added up it amounts, according to some geologists, to a total of 67 miles. In most cases, however, only a small part of this thickness is to be seen in one place, for the deposits were usually formed in limited areas at any one time.

The Use of Fossils

When the sediments were accumulating age after age, it naturally came about that remains of the plants and animals living at the time were buried, and these formed the fossils by the aid of which it is possible to read the story of the past. By careful piecing together of evidence the geologist is able to determine the order in which the different sedimentary rocks were laid down, and thus to say, for instance, that the Devonian period was the time of the origin of Amphibians. In other cases the geologist utilises the fossils in his attempt to work out the order of the strata when these have been much disarranged. For the simpler fossil forms of any type must be older than those that are more complex. There is no vicious circle here, for the general succession of strata is clear, and it is quite certain that there were fishes before there were amphibians, and amphibians before there were reptiles, and reptiles before there were birds and mammals. In certain cases, e.g. of fossil horses and elephants, the actual historical succession has been clearly worked out.

If the successive strata contained good samples of all the plants and animals living at the time when the beds were formed, then it would be easy to read the record of the rocks, but many animals were too soft to become satisfactory fossils, many were eaten or dissolved away, many were destroyed by heat and pressure, so that the rock record is like a library very much damaged by fire and looting and decay.

§ 2

The Geological Time-table

The long history of the earth and its inhabitants is conveniently divided into eras. Thus, just as we speak of the ancient, mediæval, and modern history of mankind, so we may speak of Palæozoic, Mesozoic and Cenozoic eras in the history of the earth as a whole.

Geologists cannot tell us except in an approximate way how long the process of evolution has taken. One of the methods is to estimate how long has been required for the accumulation of the salts of the sea, for all these have been dissolved out of the rocks since rain began to fall on the earth. Dividing the total amount of saline matter by what is contributed every year in modern times, we get about a hundred million years as the age of the sea. But as the present rate of salt-accumulation is probably much greater than it was during many of the geological periods, the prodigious age just mentioned is in all likelihood far below the mark. Another method is to calculate how long it would take to form the sedimentary rocks, like sandstones and mudstones, which have a *total* thickness of over fifty miles, though the *local* thickness is rarely over a mile. As most of the materials have come from the weathering of the earth's crust, and as the annual amount of weathering now going on can be estimated, the time required for the formation of the sedimentary rocks of the world can be approximately calculated. There are some other ways of trying to tell the earth's age and the length of the successive periods, but no certainty has been reached.

The eras marked on the table (page 92) as *before the Cambrian* correspond to about thirty-two miles of thickness of strata; and all the subsequent eras with fossil-bearing rocks to a thickness of about twenty-one miles—in itself an astounding fact. Perhaps thirty million years must be allotted to the Pre-Cambrian eras, eighteen to the Palæozoic, nine to the Mesozoic, three to the Cenozoic, making a grand total of sixty millions.

The Establishment of Invertebrate Stocks

It is an astounding fact that at least half of geological time (the Archæozoic and Proterozoic eras) passed before there were living creatures with parts sufficiently hard to form fossils. In the latter part of the Proterozoic era there are traces of one-celled marine animals (Radiolarians) with shells of flint, and of worms that wallowed in the primal mud. It is plain that as regards the most primitive creatures the rock record tells us little.

From Knipe's "Nebula to Man."

ANIMALS OF THE CAMBRIAN PERIOD

e.g. Sponges, Jellyfish, Starfish, Sea-lilies, Water-fleas, and Trilobites

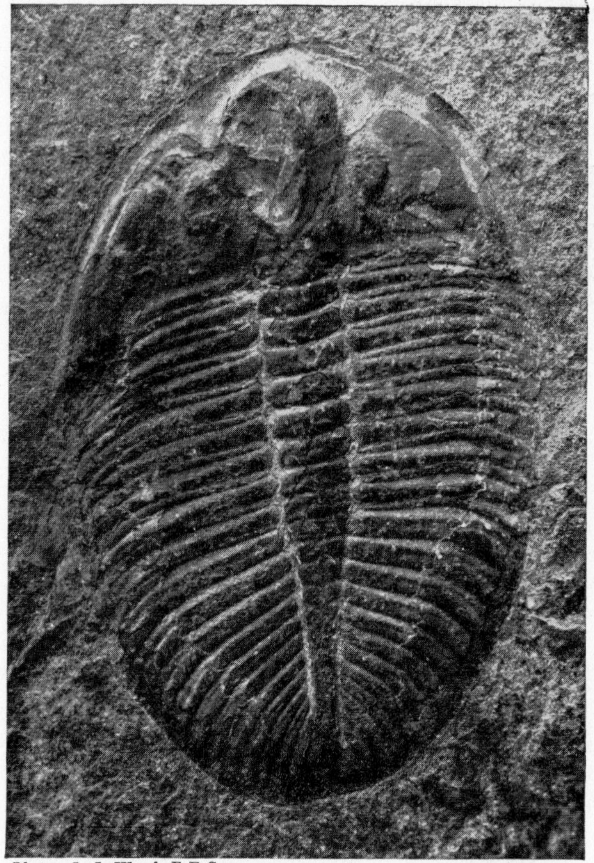

Photo: J. J. Ward, F.E.S.

A TRILOBITE

Trilobites were ancient seashore animals, abundant from the Upper Cambrian to the Carboniferous eras. They have no direct descendants to-day. They were jointed-footed animals, allied to Crustaceans and perhaps also to King-crabs. They were able to roll themselves up in their ring-armour.

Photo: British Museum (Natural History).

THE GAMBIAN MUD-FISH, PROTOPTERUS

It can breathe oxygen dissolved in water by its gills; it can also breathe dry air by means of its swim-bladder, which has become a lung. It is a *double-breather*, showing evolution in process. For seven months of the year, the dry season, it can remain inert in the mud, getting air through an open pipe to the surface. When water fills the pools it can use its gills again. Mud-nests or mud encasements with the lung-fish inside have often been brought to Britain and the fish when liberated were quite lively.

THE ARCHÆOPTERYX

(*After William Leche of Stockholm.*)

A good restoration of the oldest known bird, Archæopteryx (Jurassic Era). It was about the size of a crow; it had teeth on both jaws; it had claws on the thumb and two fingers; and it had a long lizard-like tail. But it had feathers, proving itself a true bird.

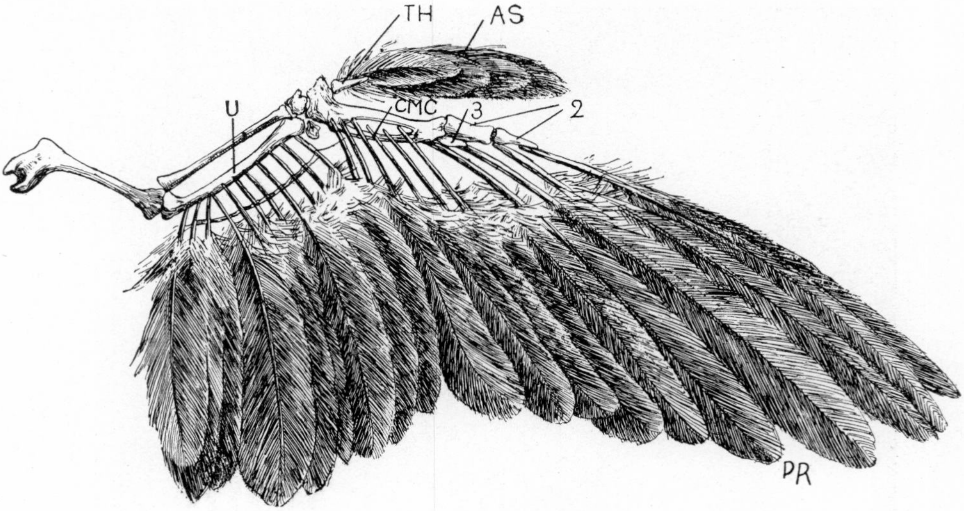

WING OF A BIRD, SHOWING THE ARRANGEMENT OF THE FEATHERS

The longest feathers or primaries (PR) are borne by the two fingers (2 and 3), and their palm-bones (CMC); the second longest or secondaries are borne by the ulna bone (U) of the fore-arm; there is a separate tuft (AS) on the thumb (TH).

The rarity of direct traces of life in the oldest rocks is partly due to the fact that the primitive animals would be of delicate build, but it must also be remembered that the ancient rocks have been profoundly and repeatedly changed by pressure and heat, so that the traces which did exist would be very liable to obliteration. And if it be asked what right we have to suppose the presence of living creatures in the absence or extreme rarity of fossils, we must point to great accumulations of limestone which indicate the existence of calcareous algæ, and to deposits of iron which probably indicate the activity of iron-forming Bacteria. Ancient beds of graphite similarly suggest that green plants flourished in these ancient days.

§ 3

The Era of Ancient Life (Palæozoic)

The *Cambrian* period was the time of the establishment of the chief stocks of backboneless animals such as sponges, jellyfishes, worms, sea-cucumbers, lamp-shells, trilobites, crustaceans, and molluscs. There is something very eloquent in the broad fact that the peopling of the seas had definitely begun some thirty million years ago, for Professor H. F. Osborn points out that in the Cambrian period there was already a colonisation of the shore of the sea, the open sea, and the deep waters.

The *Ordovician* period was marked by abundant representation of the once very successful class of Trilobites—jointed-footed, antenna-bearing, segmented marine animals, with numerous appendages and a covering of chitin. They died away entirely with the end of the Palæozoic era. Also very notable was the abundance of predatory cuttlefishes, the bullies of the ancient seas. But it was in this period that the first backboned animals made their appearance—an epoch-making step in evolution. In other words, true fishes were evolved—destined in the course of ages to replace the cuttlefishes (which are mere molluscs) in dominating the seas.

RECENT TIMES		Human civilisation.
CENOZOIC ERA	PLEISTOCENE OR GLACIAL TIME	Last great Ice Age.
	MIOCENE AND PLIOCENE TIMES	Emergence of Man.
	EOCENE AND OLIGOCENE TIMES	Rise of higher mammals.
MESOZOIC ERA	CRETACEOUS PERIOD	Rise of primitive mammals, flowering plants, and higher insects.
	JURASSIC PERIOD	Rise of birds and flying reptiles.
	TRIASSIC PERIOD	Rise of dinosaur reptiles.
PALÆOZOIC ERA	PERMIAN PERIOD	Rise of reptiles.
	CARBONIFEROUS PERIOD	Rise of insects.
	DEVONIAN PERIOD	First amphibians.
	SILURIAN PERIOD	Land animals began.
	ORDOVICIAN PERIOD	First fishes.
	CAMBRIAN PERIOD	Peopling of the sea.
PROTEROZOIC AGES	Many of the Backboneless stocks began.	
ARCHÆOZOIC AGES	Living creatures began to be upon the earth.	
FORMATIVE TIMES	Making of continents and ocean-basins.	
	Beginnings of atmosphere and hydrosphere.	
	Cooling of the earth.	
	Establishment of the solar system.	

In the *Silurian* period in which the peopling of the seas went on apace, there was the first known attempt at colonising the dry land. For in Silurian rocks there are fossil scorpions, and that implies ability to breathe dry air—by means of internal surfaces, in this case known as lungbooks. It was also towards the end of the Silurian, when a period of great aridity set in, that fishes appeared related to our mud-fishes or double-breathers (Dipnoi), which have lungs as well as gills. This, again, meant utilising dry air, just as the present-day mud-fishes do when the water disappears from the pools in hot weather. The lung-fishes or mud-fishes of to-day are but three in number, one in Queensland, one in South America, and one in Africa, but they are extremely

PICTORIAL REPRESENTATION OF THE SUCCESSIVE STRATA OF THE EARTH'S CRUST, WITH SUGGESTIONS OF CHARACTERISTIC FOSSILS

E.g. Fish and Trilobite in the Devonian (red), a large Amphibian in the Carboniferous (blue), Reptiles in Permian (light red), the first Mammal in the Triassic (blue), the first Bird in the Jurassic (yellow), Giant Reptiles in the Cretaceous (white), then follow the Tertiary strata with progressive mammals, and Quaternary at the top with man and mammoth.

interesting "living fossils," binding the class of fishes to that of amphibians. It is highly probable that the first invasion of the dry land should be put to the credit of some adventurous worms, but the second great invasion was certainly due to air-breathing Arthropods, like the pioneer scorpion we mentioned.

The *Devonian* period, including that of the Old Red Sandstone, was one of the most significant periods in the earth's history. For it was the time of the establishment of flowering plants upon the earth and of terrestrial backboned animals. One would like to have been the discoverer of the Devonian footprint of *Thinopus,* the first known Amphibian foot-print—an eloquent vestige of the third great invasion of the dry land. It was probably from a stock of Devonian lung-fishes that the first Amphibians sprang, but it was not till the next period that they came to their own. While they were still feeling their way, there was a remarkable exuberance of shark-like and heavily armoured fishes in the Devonian seas.

EVOLUTION OF LAND ANIMALS

§ 1

Giant Amphibians and Coal-measures

The *Carboniferous* period was marked by a mild moist climate and a luxuriant vegetation in the swampy low grounds. It was a much less strenuous time than the Devonian period; it was like a very long summer. There were no trees of the type we see now, but there were forests of club-mosses and horsetails which grew to a gigantic size compared with their pigmy representatives of to-day. In these forests the jointed-footed invaders of the dry land ran riot in the form of centipedes, spiders, scorpions, and insects, and on these the primeval Amphibians fed. The appearance of insects made possible a new linkage of far-reaching importance, namely, the cross-fertilisation of flowering plants by their insect visitors, and from this time onwards it may be said that flowers and their visitors have evolved hand in hand.

Cross-fertilisation is much surer by insects than by the wind, and cross-fertilisation is more advantageous than self-fertilisation because it promotes both fertility and plasticity. It was probably in this period that *coloured* flowers—attractive to insect-visitors—began to justify themselves as beauty became useful, and began to relieve the monotonous green of the horsetail and club-moss forests, which covered great tracts of the earth for millions of years. In the Carboniferous forests there were also land-snails, representing one of the minor invasions of the dry land, tending on the whole to check vegetation. They, too, were probably preyed upon by the Amphibians, some of which attained a large size. Each age has had its giants, and those of the Carboniferous were Amphibians called Labyrinthodonts, some of which were almost as big as donkeys. It need hardly be said that it was in this period that most of the Coal-measures were laid down by the immense accumulation of the spores and debris of the club-moss forests. Ages afterwards, it was given to man to tap this great source of energy—traceable back to the sunshine of millions of years ago. Even then it was true that no plant or animal lives or dies to itself!

The Acquisitions of Amphibians.

As Amphibians had their Golden Age in the Carboniferous period we may fitly use this opportunity of indicating the advances in evolution which the emergence of Amphibians implied. (1) In the first place the passage from water to dry land was the beginning of a higher and more promiseful life, taxed no doubt by increased difficulties. The natural question rises why animals should have migrated from water to dry land at all when great difficulties were involved in the transition. The answers must be: (*a*) that local drying up of water-basins or elevations of the land surface often made the old haunts untenable; (b) that there may have been great congestion and competition in the old quarters; and (*c*) that there has been an undeniable endeavour

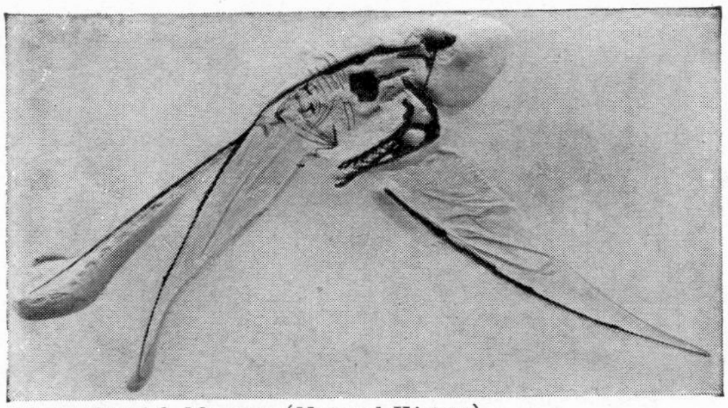

Photo: British Museum (Natural History).

FOSSIL OF A PTERODACTYL OR EXTINCT FLYING DRAGON

The wing is made of a web of skin extended on the enormously elongated outermost finger. The long tail served for balancing and steering. The Pterodactyls varied from the size of sparrows to a wing-span of fifteen feet—the largest flying creatures.

From Knipe's "Nebula to Man.

PARIASAURUS: AN EXTINCT VEGETARIAN TRIASSIC REPTILE

Total length about 9 feet. (Remains found in Cape Colony, South Africa.)

From Knipe's "Nebula to Man."

TRICERATOPS: A HUGE EXTINCT REPTILE

(From remains found in Cretaceous strata of Wyoming, U.S.A.)

This Dinosaur, about the size of a large rhinoceros, had a huge three-horned skull with a remarkable bony collar over the neck. But, as in many other cases, its brain was so small that it could have passed down the spinal canal in which the spinal cord lies. Perhaps this partly accounts for the extinction of giant reptiles.

Photo: "Daily Mail."

THE DUCKMOLE OR DUCK-BILLED PLATYPUS OF AUSTRALIA

The Duckmole or Duck-billed Platypus of Australia is a survivor of the most primitive mammals. It harks back to reptiles, e.g. in being an egg-layer, in having comparatively large eggs, and in being imperfectly warm-blooded. It swims well and feeds on small water-animals. It can also burrow.

after well-being throughout the history of animal life. In the same way with mankind, migrations were prompted by the setting in of prolonged drought, by over-population, and by the spirit of adventure. (2) In Amphibians for the first time the non-digitate paired fins of fishes were replaced by limbs with fingers and toes. This implied an advantageous power of grasping, of holding firm, of putting food into the mouth, of feeling things in three dimensions. (3) We cannot be positive in regard to the soft parts of the ancient Amphibians known only as fossils, but if they were in a general way like the frogs and toads, newts and salamanders of the present day, we may say that they made among other acquisitions the following: true ventral lungs, a three-chambered heart, a movable tongue, a drum to the ear, and lids to the eyes. It is very interesting to find that though the tongue of the tadpole has some muscle-fibres in it, they are not strong enough to effect movement, recalling the tongue of fishes, which has not any muscles at all. Gradually, as the tadpole becomes a frog, the muscle-fibres grow in strength, and make it possible for the full-grown creature to shoot out its tongue upon insects. This is probably a recapitulation of what was accomplished in the course of millennia in the history of the Amphibian race. (4) Another acquisition made by Amphibians was a voice, due, as in ourselves, to the rapid passage of air over taut membranes (vocal cords) stretched in the larynx. It is an interesting fact that for millions of years there was upon the earth no sound of life at all, only the noise of wind and wave, thunder and avalanche. Apart from the instrumental music of some insects, perhaps beginning in the Carboniferous, the first vital sounds were due to Amphibians, and theirs certainly was the first voice—surely one of the great steps in organic evolution.

Evolution of the Voice

The first use of the voice was probably that indicated by our frogs and toads—it serves as a sex-call. That is the meaning of the trumpeting with which frogs herald the spring, and it is often only in the males that the voice is well developed. But if we look forward, past Amphibians altogether, we find the voice becoming a maternal call helping to secure the safety of the young—a use very obvious when young birds squat motionless at the sound of the parent's danger-note. Later on, probably, the voice became an infantile call, as when the unhatched crocodile pipes from within the deeply buried egg, signalling to the mother that it is time to be unearthed. Higher still the voice expresses emotion, as in the song of birds, often outside the limits of the breeding time. Later still, particular sounds become words, signifying particular things or feelings, such as "food," "danger," "home," "anger," and "joy." Finally words become a medium of social intercourse and as symbols help to make it possible for man to reason.

§ 2

The Early Reptiles

In the *Permian* period reptiles appeared, or perhaps one should say, began to assert themselves. That is to say, there was an emergence of backboned animals which were free from water and relinquished the method of breathing by gills, which Amphibians retained in their young stages at least. The unhatched or unborn reptile breathes by means of a vascular hood spread underneath the eggshell and absorbing dry air from without. It is an interesting point that this vascular hood, called the allantois, is represented in the Amphibians by an unimportant bladder growing out from the hind end of the food-canal. A great step in evolution was implied in the origin of this antenatal hood or fœtal membrane and another one—of protective significance—called the amnion, which forms a water-bag over the delicate embryo. The step meant total emancipation from the water and from gill-breathing, and the two fœtal membranes, the amnion and the allantois, persist not only in all reptiles but in birds and mammals as well. These higher Vertebrates are therefore called Amniota in contrast to the Lower Vertebrates or Anamnia (the Amphibians, Fishes, and primitive types).

It is a suggestive fact that the embryos of all reptiles, birds, and mammals show gill-clefts—*a tell-tale evidence of their distant aquatic ancestry.* But these embryonic gill-clefts are not used for respiration and show no trace of gills except in a few embryonic reptiles and birds where their dwindled vestiges have been recently discovered. As to the gill-clefts, they are of no use in higher Vertebrates except that the first becomes the Eustachian tube leading from the ear-passage to the back of the mouth. The reason why they persist when only one is of any use, and that in a transformed guise, would be difficult to interpret except in terms of the Evolution theory. They illustrate the lingering influence of a long pedigree, the living hand of the past, the tendency that individual development has to recapitulate racial evolution. In a condensed and telescoped manner, of course, for what took the race a million years may be recapitulated by the individual in a week!

In the Permian period the warm moist climate of most of the Carboniferous period was replaced by severe conditions, culminating in an Ice Age which spread from the Southern Hemisphere throughout the world. With this was associated a waning of the Carboniferous flora, and the appearance of a new one, consisting of ferns, conifers, ginkgos, and cycads, which persisted until near the end of the Mesozoic era. The Permian Ice Age lasted for millions of years, and was most severe in the Far South. Of course, it was a very different world then, for North Europe was joined to North America, Africa to South America, and Australia to Asia. It was probably during the Permian Ice Age that many of the insects divided their life-history into two main chapters—the feeding, growing, moulting, immature, larval stages, e.g. caterpillars, and the more ascetic, non-growing, non-moulting, winged phase, adapted for reproduction. Between these there intervened the quiescent, well-protected pupa stage or chrysalis, probably adapted to begin with as a means of surviving the severe winter. For it is easier for an animal to survive when the vital processes are more or less in abeyance.

Disappearance of many Ancient Types

We cannot leave the last period of the Palæozoic era and its prolonged ice age without noticing that it meant the entire cessation of a large number of ancient types, especially among plants and backboneless animals, which now disappear for ever. It is necessary to understand that the animals of ancient days stand in three different relations to those of to-day. (*a*) There are ancient types that have living representatives, sometimes few and sometimes many, sometimes much changed and sometimes but slightly changed. The lamp-shell, *Lingulella,* of the Cambrian and Ordovician period has a very near relative in the *Lingula* of to-day. There are a few extremely conservative animals. (*b*) There are ancient types which have no living representatives, except in the guise of transformed descendants, as the King-crab (*Limulus*) may be said to be a transformed descendant of the otherwise quite extinct race to which Eurypterids or Sea-scorpions belonged. (*c*) There are altogether extinct types—*lost races*—which have left not a wrack behind. For there is not any representation to-day of such races as Graptolites and Trilobites.

Looking backwards over the many millions of years comprised in the Palæozoic era, what may we emphasise as the most salient features? There was in the *Cambrian* the establishment of the chief classes of backboneless animals; in the *Ordovician* the first fishes and perhaps the first terrestrial plants; in the *Silurian* the emergence of air-breathing Invertebrates and mud-fishes; in the *Devonian* the appearance of the first Amphibians, from which all higher land animals are descended, and the establishment of a land flora; in the *Carboniferous* the great Club-moss forests and an exuberance of air-breathing insects and their allies; in the *Permian* the first reptiles and a new flora.

THE GEOLOGICAL MIDDLE AGES

§ 1

The Mesozoic Era

In a broad way the Mesozoic era corresponds with the Golden Age of reptiles, and with the climax of the Conifer and Cycad flora, which was established in the Permian. But among the Conifers and Cycads our modern flowering plants were beginning to show face tentatively, just like birds and mammals among the great reptiles.

In the *Triassic* period the exuberance of reptilian life which marked the Permian was continued. Besides Turtles which still persist, there were Ichthyosaurs, Plesiosaurs, Dinosaurs, and Pterosaurs, none of which lasted beyond the Mesozoic era. Of great importance was the rise of the Dinosaurs in the Triassic, for it is highly probable that within the limits of this vigorous and plastic stock—some of them bipeds—we must look for the ancestors of both birds and mammals. Both land and water were dominated by reptiles, some of which attained to gigantic size. Had there been any zoologist in those days, he would have been very sagacious indeed if he had suspected that reptiles did not represent the climax of creation.

The Flying Dragons

The *Jurassic* period showed a continuance of the reptilian splendour. They radiated in many directions, becoming adapted to many haunts. Thus there were many Fish Lizards paddling in the seas, many types of terrestrial dragons stalking about on land, many swiftly gliding alligator-like forms, and the Flying Dragons which began in the Triassic attained to remarkable success and variety. Their wing was formed by the extension of a great fold of skin on the enormously elongated outermost finger, and they varied from the size of a sparrow to a spread of over five feet. A soldering of the dorsal vertebræ as in our Flying Birds was an adaptation to striking the air with some force, but as there is not more than a slight keel, if any, on the breast-bone, it is unlikely that they could fly far. For we know from our modern birds that the power of flight may be to some extent gauged from the degree of development of the keel, which is simply a great ridge for the better insertion of the muscles of flight. It is absent, of course, in the Running Birds, like the ostrich, and it has degenerated in an interesting way in the burrowing parrot (*Stringops*) and a few other birds that have "gone back."

The First Known Bird

But the Jurassic is particularly memorable because its strata have yielded two fine specimens of the first known bird, *Archæopteryx.* These were entombed in the deposits which formed the fine-grained lithographic stones of Bavaria, and practically every bone in the body is preserved except the breast-bone. Even the feathers have left their marks with distinctness. This oldest known bird—too far advanced to be the first bird—was about the size of a crow and was probably of arboreal habits. Of great interest are its reptilian features, so pronounced that one cannot evade the evolutionist suggestion. It had teeth in both jaws, which no modern bird has; it had a long lizard-like tail, which no modern bird has; it had claws on three fingers, and a sort of half-made wing. That is to say, it does not show, what all modern birds show, a fusion of half the wrist-bones with the whole of the palm-bones, the well-known carpo-metacarpus bone which forms a basis for the longest pinions. In many reptiles, such as Crocodiles, there are peculiar bones running across the abdomen beneath the skin, the so-called "abdominal ribs," and it seems an eloquent detail to find these represented in *Archæopteryx,* the earliest known bird. No modern bird shows any trace of them.

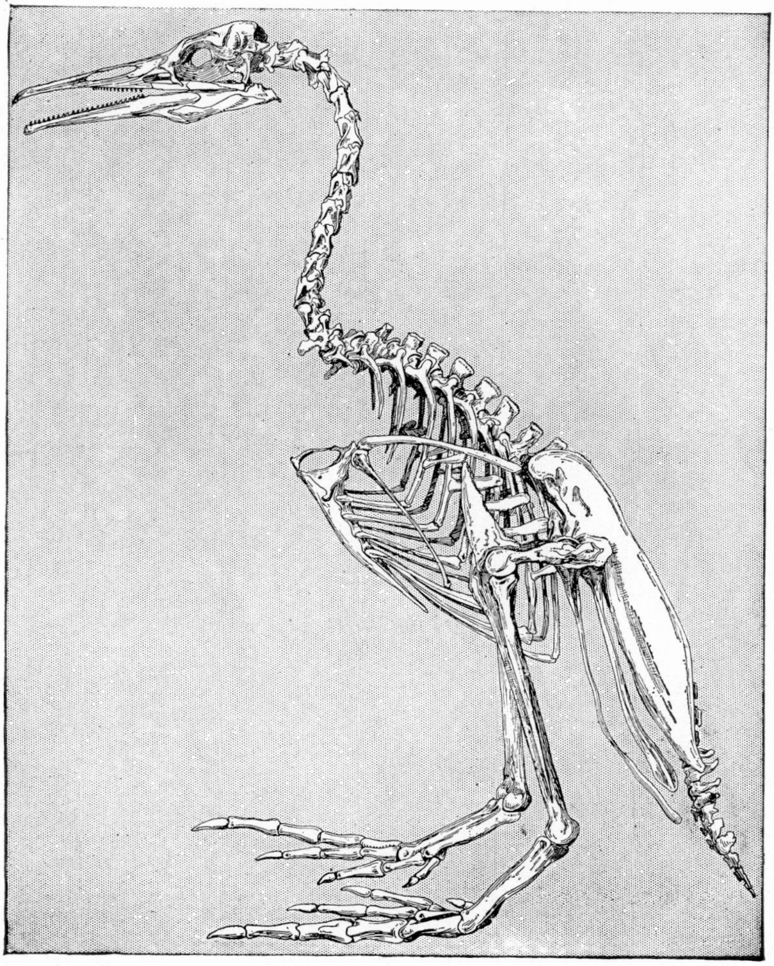

SKELETON OF AN EXTINCT FLIGHTLESS TOOTHED BIRD, HESPERORNIS

(*After Marsh.*)

The bird was five or six feet high, something like a swimming ostrich, with a very powerful leg but only a vestige of a wing. There were sharp teeth in a groove. The modern divers come nearest to this ancient type.

SIX STAGES IN THE EVOLUTION OF THE HORSE, SHOWING GRADUAL INCREASE IN SIZE

(*After Lull and Matthew.*)

1. Four-toed horse, Eohippus, about one foot high. Lower Eocene, N. America.
2. Another four-toed horse, Orohippus, a little over a foot high. Middle Eocene, N. America.
3. Three-toed horse, Mesohippus, about the size of a sheep. Middle Oligocene, N. America.
4. Three-toed horse, Merychippus, Miocene, N. America. Only one toe reaches the ground on each foot, but the remains of two others are prominent.
5. The first one-toed horse, Pliohippus, about forty inches high at the shoulder. Pliocene, N. America.
6. The modern horse, running on the third digit of each foot.

There is no warrant for supposing that the flying reptiles or Pterodactyls gave rise to birds, for the two groups are on different lines, and the structure of the wings is entirely different. Thus the long-fingered Pterodactyl wing was a parachute wing, while the secret of the bird's wing has its centre in the feathers. It is highly probable that birds evolved from certain Dinosaurs which had become bipeds, and it is possible that they were for a time swift runners that took "flying jumps" along the ground. Thereafter, perhaps, came a period of arboreal apprenticeship during which there was much gliding from tree to tree before true flight was achieved. It is an interesting fact that the problem of flight has been solved four times among animals—by insects, by Pterodactyls, by birds, and by bats; and that the four solutions are on entirely different lines.

In the *Cretaceous* period the outstanding events included the waning of giant reptiles, the modernising of the flowering plants, and the multiplication of small mammals. Some of the Permian reptiles, such as the dog-toothed Cynodonts, were extraordinarily mammal-like, and it was probably from among them that definite mammals emerged in the Triassic. Comparatively little is known of the early Triassic mammals save that their back-teeth were marked by numerous tubercles on the crown, but they were gaining strength in the late Triassic when small arboreal insectivores, not very distant from the modern tree-shrews (*Tupaia*), began to branch out in many directions indicative of the great divisions of modern mammals, such as the clawed mammals, hoofed mammals, and the race of monkeys or Primates. In the Upper Cretaceous there was an exuberant "radiation" of mammals, adaptive to the conquest of all sorts of haunts, and this was vigorously continued in Tertiary times.

There is no difficulty in the fact that the earliest remains of definite mammals in the Triassic precede the first-known bird in the Jurassic. For although we usually rank mammals as higher than birds (being mammals ourselves, how could we do otherwise?), there are many ways in which birds are pre-eminent, e.g. in skeleton, musculature, integumentary structures, and respiratory system. The fact is that birds and mammals are on two quite different tacks of evolution, not related to one another, save in having a common ancestry in extinct reptiles. Moreover, there is no reason to believe that the Jurassic *Archæopteryx* was the first bird in any sense except that it is the first of which we have any record. In any case it is safe to say that birds came to their own before mammals did.

Looking backwards, we may perhaps sum up what is most essential in the Mesozoic era in Professor Schuchert's sentence: "The Mesozoic is the Age of Reptiles, and yet the little mammals and the toothed birds are storing up intelligence and strength to replace the reptiles when the cycads and conifers shall give way to the higher flowering plants."

§ 2

The Cenozoic or Tertiary Era

In the *Eocene* period there was a replacement of the small-brained archaic mammals by big-brained modernised types, and with this must be associated the covering of the earth with a garment of grass and dry pasture. Marshes were replaced by meadows and browsing by grazing mammals. In the spreading meadows an opportunity was also offered for a richer evolution of insects and birds.

During the *Oligocene* the elevation of the land continued, the climate became much less moist, and the grazing herds extended their range.

The *Miocene* was the mammalian Golden Age and there were crowning examples of what Osborn calls "adaptive radiation." That is to say, mammals, like the reptiles before them, conquer every haunt of life. There are flying bats, volplaning parachutists, climbers in trees like sloths and squirrels, quickly moving hoofed mammals, burrowers like the moles, freshwater mammals, like duckmole and beaver, shore-frequenting seals and manatees, and open-sea cetaceans, some of which dive far more than full fathoms five. It is important to realise the perennial tendency of animals to conquer every corner and to fill every niche of opportunity, and to notice that this has been done by successive sets of animals in succeeding ages. *Most notably the mammals repeat all the experiments of reptiles on a higher turn of the spiral.* Thus arises what is called convergence, the superficial resemblance of unrelated types, like whales and fishes, the resemblance being due to the fact that the different types are similarly adapted to similar conditions of life. Professor H. F. Osborn points out that mammals may seek any one of the twelve different habitat-zones, and that in each of these there may be six quite different kinds of food. Living creatures penetrate everywhere like the overflowing waters of a great river in flood.

§ 3

The *Pliocene* period was a more strenuous time, with less genial climatic conditions, and with more intense competition. Old land bridges were broken and new ones made, and the geographical distribution underwent great changes. Professor R. S. Lull describes the *Pliocene* as "a period of great unrest." "Many migrations occurred the world over, new competitions arose, and the weaker stocks began to show the effects of the strenuous life. One momentous event seems to have occurred in the Pliocene, and that was the transformation of the precursor of humanity into man—the culmination of the highest line of evolution."

The *Pleistocene* period was a time of sifting. There was a continued elevation of the continental masses, and Ice Ages set in, relieved by less severe interglacial times when the ice-sheets retreated northwards for a time. Many types, like the mammoth, the woolly rhinoceros, the sabre-toothed tiger, the cave-lion, and the cave-bear, became extinct. Others which formerly had a wide range became restricted to the Far North or were left isolated here and there on the high mountains, like the Snow Mouse, which now occurs on isolated Alpine heights above the snow-line. Perhaps it was during this period that many birds of the Northern Hemisphere learned to evade the winter by the sublime device of migration.

Looking backwards we may quote Professor Schuchert again:

> "The lands in the Cenozoic began to bloom with more and more flowering plants and grand hardwood forests, the atmosphere is scented with sweet odours, a vast crowd of new kinds of insects appear, and the places of the once dominant reptiles of the lands and seas are taken by the mammals. Out of these struggles there rises a greater intelligence, seen in nearly all of the mammal stocks, but particularly in one, the monkey-ape-man. Brute man appears on the scene with the introduction of the last glacial climate, a most trying time for all things endowed with life, and finally there results the dominance of reasoning man over all his brute associates."

In man and human society the story of evolution has its climax.

The Ascent of Man

Man stands apart from animals in his power of building up general ideas and of using these in the guidance of his behaviour and the control of his conduct. This is essentially wrapped up with his development of language as an instrument of thought. Some animals have words, but man has language (Logos). Some animals show evidence of *perceptual* inference, but man often gets beyond this to *conceptual* inference (Reason). Many animals are affectionate and brave, self-forgetful and industrious, but man "thinks the ought," definitely guiding his conduct in the light of ideals, which in turn are wrapped up with the fact that he is "a social person."

Besides his big brain, which may be three times as heavy as

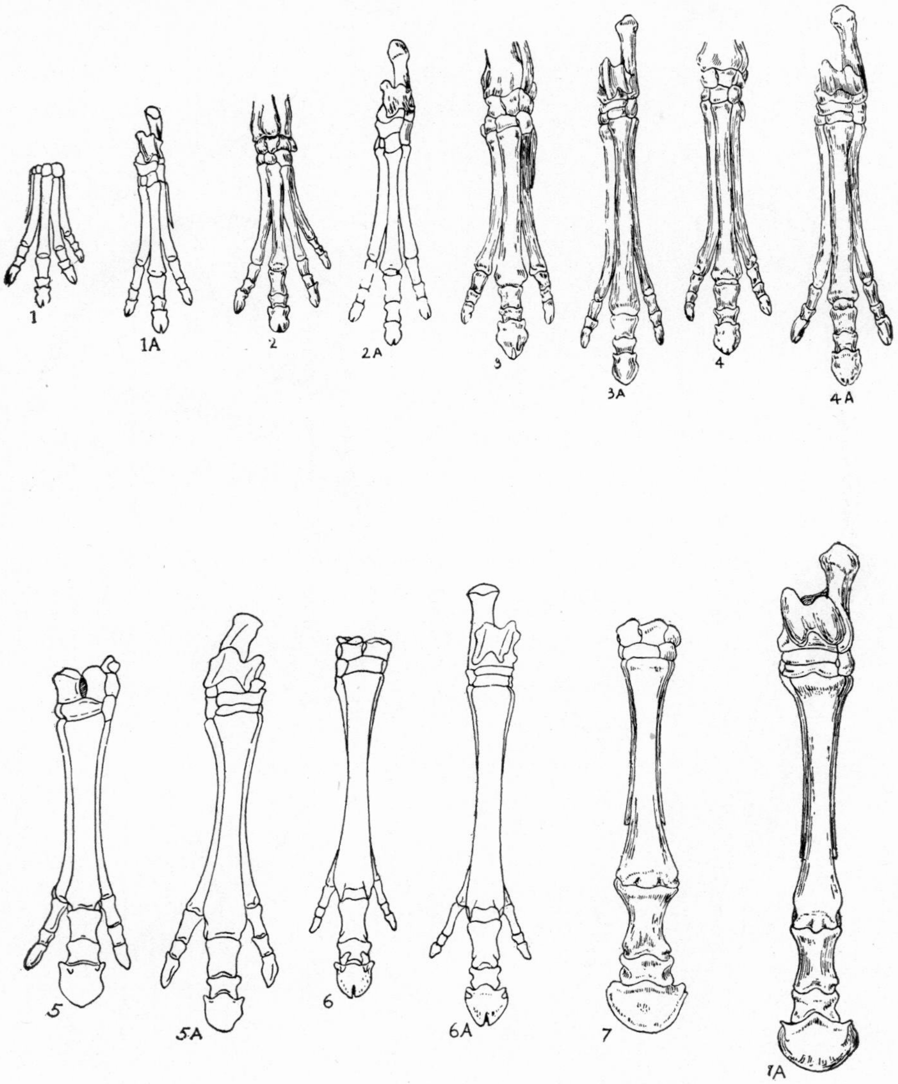

DIAGRAM SHOWING SEVEN STAGES IN THE EVOLUTION OF THE FORE-LIMBS AND HIND-LIMBS OF THE ANCESTORS OF THE MODERN HORSE, BEGINNING WITH THE EARLIEST KNOWN PREDECESSORS OF THE HORSE AND CULMINATING WITH THE HORSE OF TO-DAY

(*After Marsh and Lull.*)

1 and 1A, fore-limb and hind-limb of Eohippus; 2 and 2A, Orohippus; 3 and 3A, Mesohippus; 4 and 4A Hypohippus; 5 and 5A, Merychippus; 6 and 6A, Hipparion; 7 and 7A, the modern horse. Note how the toes shorten and disappear.

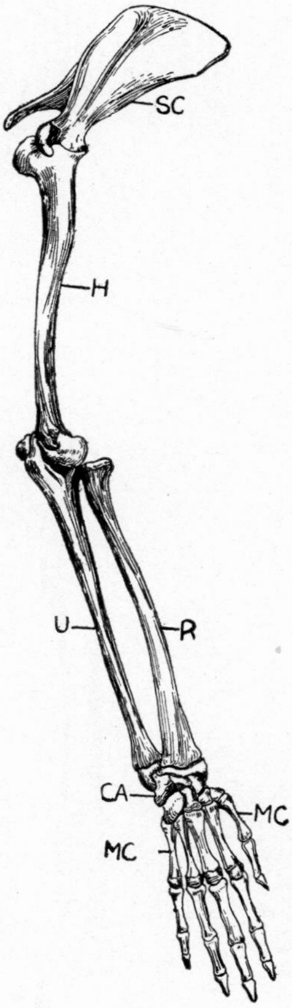

A. Fore-limb of Monkey

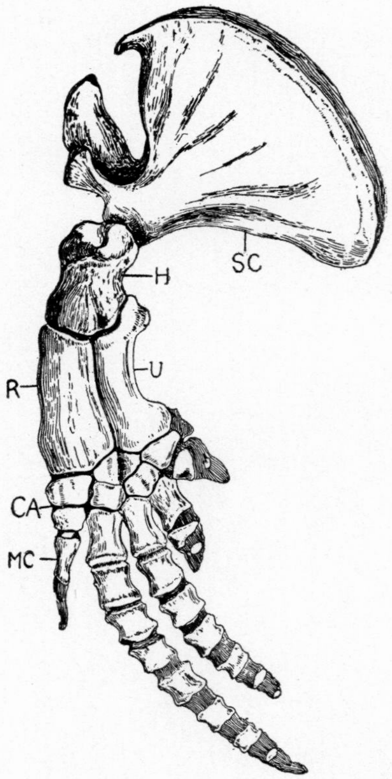

B. Fore-limb of Whale

WHAT IS MEANT BY HOMOLOGY? ESSENTIAL SIMILARITY OF ARCHITECTURE, THOUGH THE APPEARANCES MAY BE VERY DIFFERENT

This is seen in comparing these two fore-limbs, A, of Monkey, B, of Whale. They are as different as possible, yet they show the same bones, e.g. SC, the scapula or shoulder-blade; H, the humerus or upper arm: R and U, the radius and ulna of the fore-arm; CA, the wrist; MC, the palm; and then the fingers.

that of a gorilla, man has various physical peculiarities. He walks erect, he plants the sole of his foot flat on the ground, he has a chin and a good heel, a big forehead and a non-protrusive face, a relatively uniform set of teeth without conspicuous canines, and a relatively naked body.

But in spite of man's undeniable apartness, there is no doubt as to his solidarity with the rest of creation. There is an "all-pervading similitude of structure," between man and the Anthropoid Apes, though it is certain that it is not from any living form that he took his origin. None of the anatomical distinctions, except the heavy brain, could be called momentous. Man's body is a veritable museum of relics (vestigial structures) inherited from pre-human ancestors. In his everyday bodily life and in some of its disturbances, man's pedigree is often revealed. Even his facial expression, as Darwin showed, is not always human. Some fossil remains bring modern man nearer the anthropoid type.

It is difficult not to admit the ring of truth in the closing words of Darwin's *Descent of Man:*

> "We must, however, acknowledge, as it seems to me, that man, with all his noble qualities, with sympathy which feels for the most debased, with benevolence which extends not only to other men but to the humblest living creature, with his God-like intellect which has penetrated into the movements and constitution of the solar system—with all these exalted powers—man still bears in his bodily frame the indelible stamp of his lowly origin."

The Evolving System of Nature

There is another side of evolution so obvious that it is often overlooked, the tendency to link lives together in vital inter-relations. Thus flowers and their insect visitors are often vitally interlinked in mutual dependence. Many birds feed on berries and distribute the seeds. The tiny freshwater snail is the host of the juvenile stages of the liver-fluke of the sheep. The mosquito is the vehicle of malaria from man to man, and the tse-tse fly spreads sleeping sickness. The freshwater mussel cannot continue its race without the unconscious co-operation of the minnow, and the freshwater fish called the bitterling cannot continue its race without the unconscious co-operation of the mussel. There are numerous mutually beneficial partnerships between different kinds of creatures, and other inter-relations where the benefit is one-sided, as in the case of insects that make galls on plants. There are also among kindred animals many forms of colonies, communities, and societies. Nutritive chains bind long series of animals together, the cod feeding on the whelk, the whelk on the worm, the worm on the organic dust of the sea. There is a system of successive incarnations and matter is continually passing from one embodiment to another. These instances must suffice to illustrate the central biological idea of the web of life, the interlinked System of Animate Nature. Linnæus spoke of the Systema Naturæ, meaning the orderly hierarchy of classes, orders, families, genera, and species; but we owe to Darwin in particular some knowledge of a more dynamic Systema Naturæ, the network of vital inter-relations. This has become more and more complex as evolution has continued, and man's web is most complex of all. It means making Animate Nature more of a unity; it means an external method of registering steps of progress; it means an evolving set of sieves by which new variations are sifted, and living creatures are kept from slipping down the steep ladder of evolution.

Parasitism

It sometimes happens that the inter-relation established between one living creature and another works in a retrograde direction. This is the case with many thoroughgoing internal parasites which have sunk into an easygoing kind of life, utterly dependent on their host for food, requiring no exertions, running no risks, and receiving no spur to effort. Thus we see that evolution is not necessarily progressive; everything depends on the conditions in reference to which the living creatures have been evolved. When the conditions are too easygoing, the animal may be thoroughly well adapted to them—as a tapeworm certainly is—but it slips down the rungs of the ladder of evolution.

This is an interesting minor chapter in the story of evolution—the establishment of different kinds of parasites, casual and constant, temporary and lifelong, external hangers-on and internal unpaying boarders, those that live in the food-canal and depend on the host's food and those that inhabit the blood or the tissues and find their food there. It seems clear that ichneumon grubs and the like which hatch inside a caterpillar and eat it alive are not so much parasites as "beasts of prey" working from within.

But there are two sides to this minor chapter: there is the evolution of the parasite, and there is also the evolution of counteractive measures on the part of the host. Thus there is the maintenance of a bodyguard of wandering amœboid cells, which tackle the microbes invading the body and often succeed in overpowering and digesting them. Thus, again, there is the protective capacity the blood has of making antagonistic substances or "anti-bodies" which counteract poisons, including the poisons which the intruding parasites often make.

THE EVIDENCES OF EVOLUTION—HOW IT CAME ABOUT

§ 1

Progress in Evolution

There has often been slipping back and degeneracy in the course of evolution, but the big fact is that there has been progress. For millions of years Life has been slowly creeping upwards, and if we compare the highest animals—Birds and Mammals—with their predecessors, we must admit that they are more controlled, more masters of their fate, with more mentality. Evolution is on the whole *integrative;* that is to say, it makes against instability and disorder, and towards harmony and progress. Even in the rise of Birds and Mammals we can discern that the evolutionary process was making towards a fuller embodiment or expression of what Man values most—control, freedom, understanding, and love. The advance of animal life through the ages has been chequered, but on the whole it has been an advance towards increasing fullness, freedom, and fitness of life. In the study of this advance—the central fact of Organic Evolution—there is assuredly much for Man's instruction and much for his encouragement.

Evidences of Evolution

In all this, it may be said, the fact of evolution has been taken for granted, but what are the evidences? Perhaps it should be frankly answered that the idea of evolution, that the present is the child of the past and the parent of the future, cannot be *proved* as one may prove the Law of Gravitation. All that can be done is to show that it is a key—a way of looking at things—that fits the facts. There is no lock that it does not open.

But if the facts that the evolution theory vividly interprets be called the evidences of its validity, there is no lack of them. There is *historical* evidence; and what is more eloquent than the general fact that fishes emerge before amphibians, and these before reptiles, and these before birds, and so on? There are wonderfully complete fossil series, e.g. among cuttlefishes, in which we can almost see evolution in process. The pedigree of horse and elephant and crocodile is in general very convincing, though it is to be confessed that there are other cases in regard to which we have no light. Who can tell, for instance, how Vertebrates arose or from what origin?

There is *embryological* evidence, for the individual development often reads like an abbreviated recapitulation of the presumed evolution of the race. The mammal's visceral clefts are telltale evidence of remote aquatic ancestors, breathing by gills. Something is known in regard to the historical evolution of antlers in bygone ages; the Red Deer of to-day recapitulates at least the general outlines of the history. The individual development of an asymmetrical flatfish, like a plaice or sole, which rests and swims on one side, tells us plainly that its ancestors were symmetrical fishes.

There is what might be called *physiological* evidence, for many plants and animals are variable before our eyes, and evolution is going on around us to-day. This is familiarly seen among domesticated animals and cultivated plants, but there is abundant flux in Wild Nature. It need hardly be said that some organisms are very conservative, and that change need not be expected when a position of stable equilibrium has been secured.

There is also *anatomical* evidence of a most convincing quality. In the fore-limbs of backboned animals, say, the paddle of a turtle, the wing of a bird, the flipper of a whale, the foreleg of a horse, and the arm of a man; the same essential bones and muscles are used to such diverse results! What could it mean save blood relationship? And as to the two sets of teeth in whalebone whales, which never even cut the gum, is there any alternative but to regard them as relics of useful teeth which ancestral forms possessed? In short, the evolution theory is justified by the way in which it works.

§ 2

Factors in Evolution

If it be said "So much for the *fact* of evolution, but what of the *factors?*" the answer is not easy. For not only is the problem the greatest of all scientific problems, but the inquiry is still very young. The scientific study of evolution practically dates from the publication of *The Origin of Species* in 1859.

Heritable novelties or variations often crop up in living creatures, and these form the raw material of evolution. These variations are the outcome of expression of changes in the germ-cells that develop into organisms. But why should there be changes in the constitution of the germ-cells? Perhaps because the living material is very complex and inherently liable to change; perhaps because it is the vehicle of a multitude of hereditary items among which there are very likely to be reshufflings or rearrangements; perhaps because the germ-cells have very changeful surroundings (the blood, the body-cavity fluid, the sea-water); perhaps because deeply saturating outside influences, such as change of climate and habitat, penetrate through the body to its germ-cells and provoke them to vary. But we must be patient with the wearisome reiteration of "perhaps." Moreover, every many-celled organism reproduced in the usual way, arises from an egg-cell fertilised by a sperm-cell, and the changes involved in and preparatory to this fertilisation may make new permutations and combinations of the living items and hereditary qualities not only possible but necessary. It is something like shuffling a pack of cards, but the cards are living. As to the changes wrought on the body during its lifetime by peculiarities in nurture, habits, and surroundings, these dents or modifications are often very important for the individual, but it does not follow that they are directly important for the race, since it is not certain that they are transmissible.

Given a crop of variations or new departures or mutations, whatever the inborn novelties may be called, we have then to inquire how these are sifted. The sifting, which means the elimination of the relatively less fit variations and the selection of the relatively more fit, effected in many different ways in the course of the struggle for existence. The organism plays its new card in the game of life, and the consequences may determine survival. The relatively less fit to given conditions will tend to be eliminated, while the relatively more fit will tend to survive. If the variations are hereditary and reappear, perhaps increased in amount, generation after generation, and if the process of sifting continue consistently, the result will be the evolution of the species. The sifting process may be helped by various forms of "isolation" which lessen the range of free intercrossing between members of a species, e.g. by geographical barriers. Interbreeding of similar forms tends to make a stable stock; outbreeding among dissimilars tends to promote variability. But for an outline like this it is enough to suggest the general method of organic evolution: Throughout the ages organisms have been making tentatives— new departures of varying magnitude—and these tentatives have been tested. The method is that of testing all things and holding fast that which is good.

BIBLIOGRAPHY

(The following short list may be useful to readers who desire to have further books recommended to them.)

Clodd, *Story of Creation: A Plain Account of Evolution.*
Darwin, *Origin of Species, Descent of Man.*
Deperet, *Transformation of the Animal World* (Internat. Sci. Series).
Geddes and Thomson, *Evolution* (Home University Library).
Goodrich, *Evolution* (The People's Books).
Headley, *Life and Evolution.*
Hutchinson, H. Neville, *Extinct Monsters* (1892).
Lull, *Organic Evolution.*
McCabe, *A B C of Evolution.*
Metcalf, *Outline of the Theory of Organic Evolution.*
Osborn, H. F., *The Evolution of Life* (1921).
Thomson, *Darwinism and Human Life.*
Wallace, *Darwinism.*

III

ADAPTATIONS TO ENVIRONMENT

ADAPTATIONS TO ENVIRONMENT

WE saw in a previous chapter how the process of evolution led to a mastery of all the haunts of life. But it is necessary to return to these haunts or homes of animals in some detail, so as to understand the peculiar circumstances of each, and to see how in the course of ages of struggle all sorts of self-preserving and race-continuing adaptations or fitnesses have been wrought out and firmly established. Living creatures have spread over all the earth and in the waters under the earth; some of them have conquered the underground world and others the air. It is possible, however, as has been indicated, to distinguish six great haunts of life, each tenanted by a distinctive fauna, namely, the shore of the sea, the open sea, the depths of the sea, the fresh-waters, the dry land, and the air. In the deep sea there are no plants at all; in the air the only plants are floating bacteria, though there is a sense in which a tree is very aerial, and the orchid perched on its branches still more so; in the other four haunts there is a flora as well as a fauna—the two working into one another's hands in interesting and often subtle interrelations —the subject of a separate study.

I. THE SHORE OF THE SEA

The Seaweed Area

By the shore of the sea the zoologist means much more than the narrow zone between tide-marks; he means the whole of the relatively shallow, well-illumined, seaweed-growing shelf around the continents and continental islands. Technically, this is called the littoral area, and it is divisible into zones, each with its characteristic population. It may be noted that the green seaweeds are highest up on the shore; the brown ones come next; the beautiful red ones are lowest. All of them have got green chlorophyll, which enables them to utilise the sun's rays in photosynthesis (i.e. building up carbon compounds from air, water, and salts), but in the brown and red seaweeds the green pigment is masked by others. It is maintained by some botanists that these other pigments enable their possessors to make more of the scantier light in the deeper waters. However this may be, we must always think of the shore-haunt as the seaweed-growing area. Directly and indirectly the life of the shore animals is closely wrapped up with the seaweeds, which afford food and foothold, and temper the force of the waves. The minute fragments broken off from seaweeds and from the sea-grass (a flowering plant called Zostera) form a sort of nutritive sea-dust which is swept slowly down the slope from the shore, to form a very useful deposit in the quietness of deepish water. It is often found in the stomachs of marine animals living a long way offshore.

Conditions of Shore Life

The littoral area as defined is not a large haunt of life; it occupies only about 9 million square miles, a small fraction of the 197,000,000 of the whole earth's surface. But it is a very long haunt, some 150,000 miles, winding in and out by bay and fiord, estuary and creek. Where deep water comes close to cliffs there may be no shore at all; in other places the relatively shallow water, with seaweeds growing over the bottom, may extend outwards for miles. The nature of the shore varies greatly according to the nature of the rocks, according to what the streams bring down from inland, and according to the jetsam that is brought in by the tides. The shore is a changeful place; there is, in the upper reaches, a striking difference between "tide in" and "tide out"; there are vicissitudes due to storms, to freshwater floods, to

AN EIGHT-ARMED CUTTLEFISH OR OCTOPUS ATTACKING A SMALL CRAB

These molluscs are particularly fond of crustaceans, which they crunch with their parrot's beak-like jaws. Their salivary juice has a paralysing effect on their prey. To one side, below the eye, may be seen the funnel through which water is very forcibly ejected in the process of locomotion.

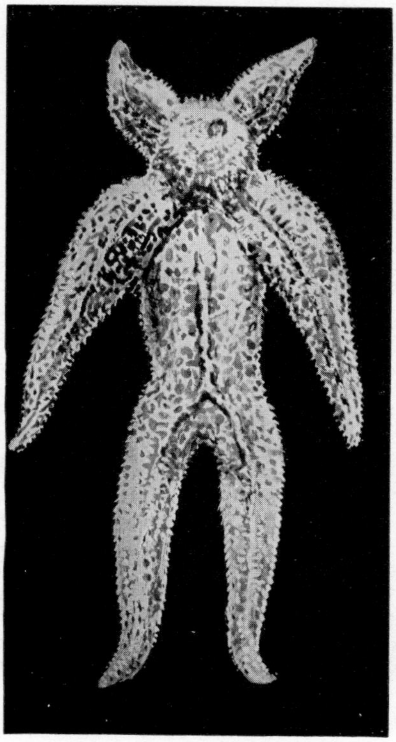

A COMMON STARFISH, WHICH HAS LOST THREE ARMS AND IS REGROWING THEM

The lowest arm is being regrown double.
(*After Professor W. C. McIntosh.*)

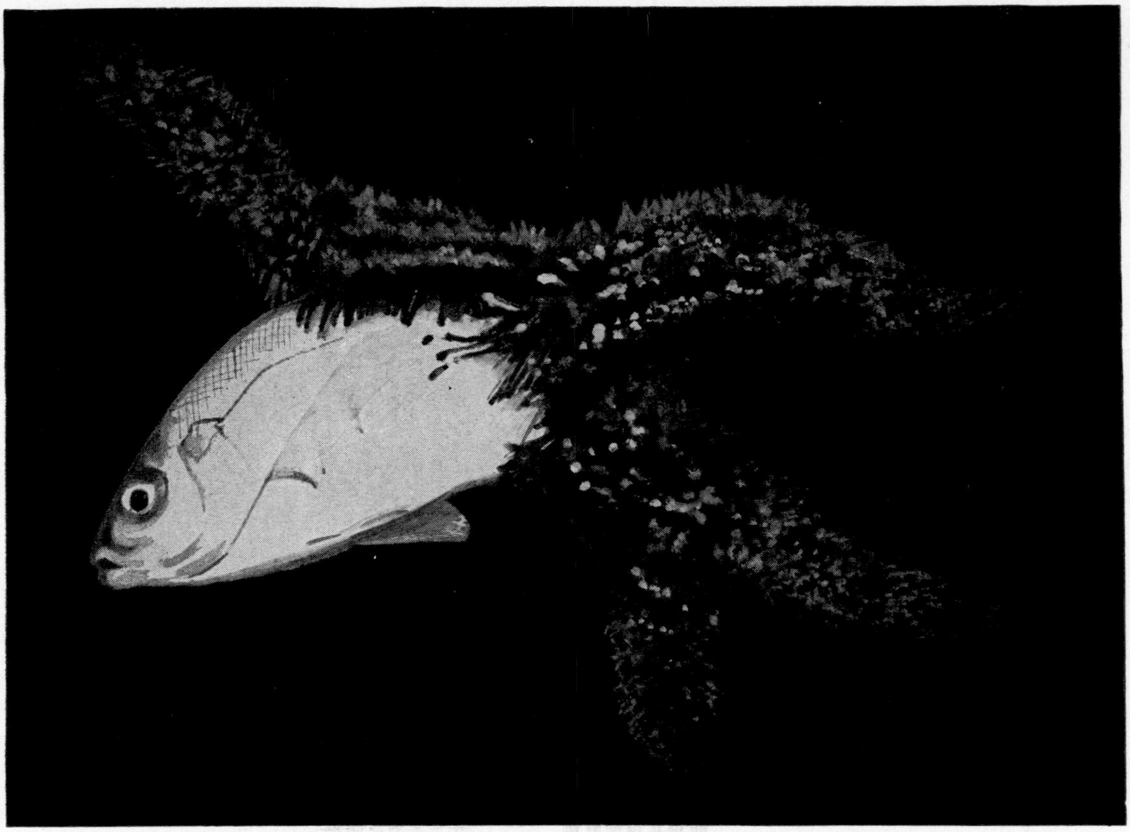

A PHOTOGRAPH SHOWING A STARFISH (*Asterias Forreri*) WHICH HAS CAPTURED A LARGE FISH

The suctorial tube-feet are seen gripping the fish firmly. (After an observation on the Californian coast.)

Photo: J. J. Ward, F.E.S.

THE PAPER NAUTILUS (ARGONAUTA), AN ANIMAL OF THE OPEN SEA

The delicate shell is made by the female only, and is used as a shelter for the eggs and young ones. It is secreted by two of the arms, not by the mantle as other mollusc shells are. It is a single-chambered shell, very different from that of the Pearly Nautilus.

wind-blown sand, and to slow changes of level, up and down. The shore is a very crowded haunt, for it is comparatively narrow, and every niche among the rocks may be precious.

Keen Struggle for Existence

It follows that the shore must be the scene of a keen struggle for existence—which includes all the answers-back that living creatures make to environing difficulties and limitations. There is struggle for food, accentuated by the fact that small items tend to be swept away by the outgoing tide or to sink down the slope to deep water. Apart from direct competition, e.g. between hungry hermit-crabs, it often involves hard work to get a meal. This is true even of apparently sluggish creatures. Thus the Crumb-of-Bread Sponge, or any other seashore sponge, has to lash large quantities of water through the intricate canal system of its body before it can get a sufficient supply of the microscopic organisms and organic particles on which it feeds. An index of the intensity of the struggle for food is afforded by the nutritive chains which bind animals together. The shore is almost noisy with the conjugation of the verb to eat in its many tenses. One pound of rock-cod requires for its formation ten pounds of whelk; one pound of whelk requires ten pounds of sea-worms; and one pound of worms requires ten pounds of sea-dust. Such is the circulation of matter, ever passing from one embodiment or incarnation to another.

Besides struggle for food there is struggle for foothold and for fresh air, struggle against the scouring tide and against the pounding breakers. The risk of dislodgment is often great and the fracture of limbs is a common accident. Of kinds of armour —the sea-urchin's hedgehog-like test, the crab's shard, the limpet's shell—there is great variety, surpassed only by that of weapons—the sea-anemone's stinging-cells, the sea-urchin's snapping-blades, the hermit-crab's forceps, the grappling tentacles and parrot's-beak jaws of the octopus.

Shifts for a Living

We get another glimpse of the intensity of the seashore struggle for existence in the frequency of "shifts for a living," adaptations of structure or of behaviour which meet frequently recurrent vicissitudes. The starfish is often in the dilemma of losing a limb or its life; by a reflex action it jettisons the captured arm and escapes. And what is lost is gradually regrown. The crab gets its leg broken past all mending; it casts off the leg across a weak breakage plane near the base, and within a preformed bandage which prevents bleeding a new leg is formed in miniature. Such is the adaptive device—more reflex than reflective—which is called self-mutilation or autotomy.

In another part of this book there is a discussion of camouflaging and protective resemblance; how abundantly these are illustrated on the shore! But there are other "shifts for a living." Some of the sand-hoppers and their relatives illustrate the puzzling phenomenon of "feigning death," becoming suddenly so motionless that they escape the eyes of their enemies. Cuttlefishes, by discharging sepia from their ink-bags, are able to throw dust in the eyes of their enemies. Some undisguised shore-animals, e.g. crabs, are adepts in a hide-and-seek game; some fishes, like the butterfish or gunnel, escape between stones where there seemed no opening and are almost uncatchable in their slipperiness. Subtlest of all, perhaps, is the habit some hermit-crabs have of entering into mutually beneficial partnership (commensalism) with sea-anemones, which mask their bearers and also serve as mounted batteries, getting transport as their reward and likewise crumbs from the frequently spread table. But enough has been said to show that the shore-haunt exhibits an extraordinary variety of shifts for a living.

Parental Care on the Shore

According to Darwin, the struggle for existence, as a big fact in the economy of Animate Nature, includes not only compe-

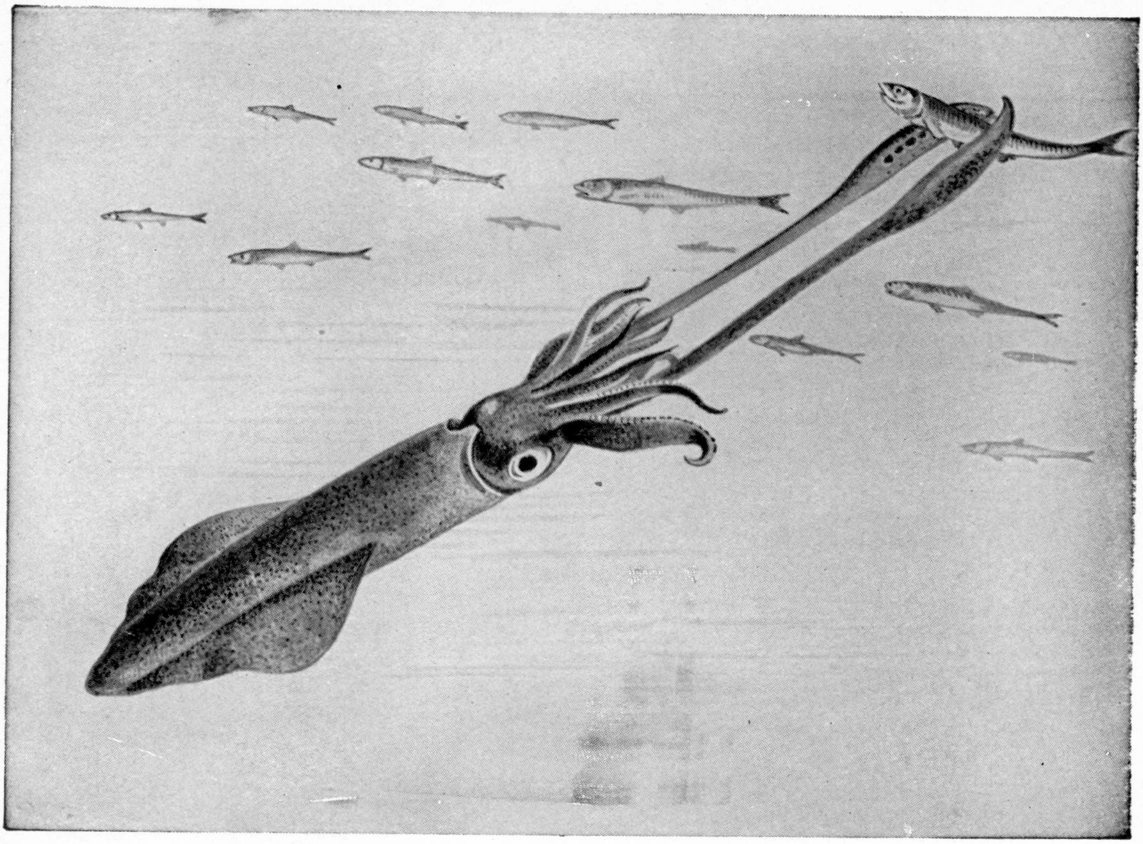

TEN-ARMED CUTTLEFISH OR SQUID IN THE ACT OF CAPTURING A FISH

The arms bear numerous prehensile suckers, which grip the prey. In the mouth there are strong jaws shaped like a parrot's beak. The cuttlefishes are molluscs and may be regarded as the highest of the backboneless or Invertebrate animals. Many occur near shore, others in the open sea, and others in the great depths.

GREENLAND WHALE

Showing the double blowhole or nostrils on the top of the head and the whalebone plates hanging down from the roof of the mouth.

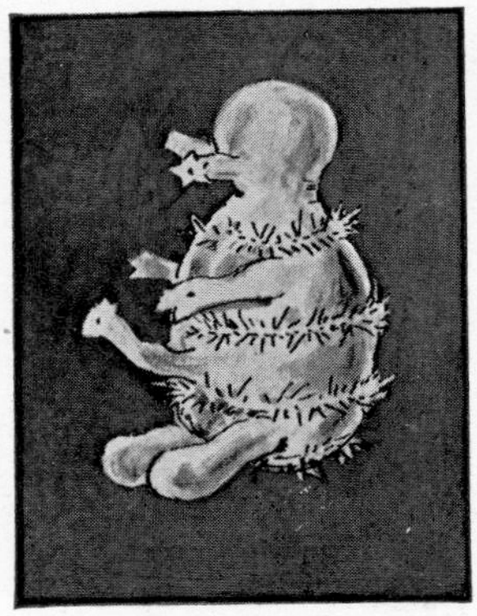

MINUTE TRANSPARENT EARLY STAGE OF A SEA-CUCUMBER

It swims in the open sea by means of girdles of microscopic cilia shown in the figure. After a period of free swimming and a remarkable metamorphosis, the animal settles down on the floor of the sea in relatively shallow water.

Photo: British Museum (Natural History)

AN INTRICATE COLONY OF OPEN-SEA ANIMALS (*Physophora Hydrostatica*) RELATED TO THE PORTUGUESE MAN-OF-WAR

There is great division of labor in the colony. At the top are floating and swimming "persons"; the long ones below are offensive "persons" bearing batteries of stinging cells; in the middle zone there are nutritive, reproductive, and other "persons." The color of the colony is a fine translucent blue. Swimmers and bathers are often badly stung by this strange animal and its relatives.

A SCENE IN THE GREAT DEPTHS

Showing a deep-sea fish of large gape, two feather-stars on the end of long stalks, a "sea-spider" (or Pycnogon) walking on lanky legs on the treacherous ooze, likewise a brittle-star, and some deep-sea corals.

tition but all the endeavours which secure the welfare of the offspring, and give them a good send-off in life. So it is without a jolt that we pass from struggle for food and foothold to parental care. The marine leech called Pontobdella, an interesting greenish warty creature fond of fixing itself to skate, places its egg-cocoons in the empty shell of a bivalve mollusc, and guards them for weeks, removing any mud that might injure their development. We have seen a British starfish with its fully-formed young ones creeping about on its body, though the usual mode of development for shore starfishes is that the young ones pass through a free-swimming larval period in the open water. The father sea-spider carries about the eggs attached to two of his limbs; the father sea-horse puts his mate's eggs into his breast pocket and carries them there in safety until they are hatched; the father stickleback of the shore-pools makes a seaweed nest and guards the eggs which his wives are induced to lay there; the father lumpsucker mounts guard over the bunch of pinkish eggs which his mate has laid in a nook of a rocky shore-pool, and drives off intruders with zest. He also aerates the developing eggs by frequent paddling with his pectoral fins and tail, as the Scots name Cock-paidle probably suggests. It is interesting that the salient examples of parental care in the shore-haunt are mostly on the male parent's side. But there is maternal virtue as well.

The fauna of the shore is remarkably *representative*—from unicellular Protozoa to birds like the oyster-catcher and mammals like the seals. Almost all the great groups of animals have apparently served an apprenticeship in the shore-hunt, and since lessons learned for millions of years sink in and become organically enregistered, it is justifiable to look to the shore as a great school in which were gained racial qualities of endurance, patience, and alertness.

II. THE OPEN SEA

In great contrast to the narrow, crowded, difficult conditions of the shore-haunt (littoral area) are the spacious, bountiful, and relatively easygoing conditions of the open sea (pelagic area), which means the well-lighted surface waters quite away from land. Many small organisms have their maximum abundance at about fifty fathoms, so that the word "surface" is to be taken generously. The light becomes very dim at 250 fathoms, and the open sea, as a zoological haunt, stops with the light. It is hardly necessary to say that the pelagic plants are more abundant near the surface, and that below a certain depth the population consists almost exclusively of animals. Not a few of the animals sink and rise in the water periodically; there are some that come near the surface by day, and others that come near the surface by night. Of great interest is the habit of the extremely delicate Ctenophores or "sea-gooseberries," which the splash of a wave would tear into shreds. Whenever there is any hint of a storm they sink beyond its reach, and "the ocean's surface must have remained flat as a mirror for many hours before they can be lured upwards from the calm of their deep retreat.

The Floating Sea-meadows

To understand the vital economy of the open sea, we must recognise the incalculable abundance of minute unicellular plants, for they form the fundamental food-supply. Along with these must also be included numerous microscopic animals which have got possession of chlorophyll, or have entered into internal partnership with unicellular Algæ (symbiosis). These green or greenish plants and animals are the *producers,* using the energy of the sunlight to help them in building up carbon compounds out of air, water, and salts. The animals which feed on the producers, or on other animals, are the *consumers.* Between the two come those open-sea bacteria that convert nitrogenous material, e.g. from dead plants or animals that other bacteria have rotted, into forms, e.g. nitrates, which plants can re-utilise. The importance of these *middlemen* is great in keeping "the circulation of matter" agoing.

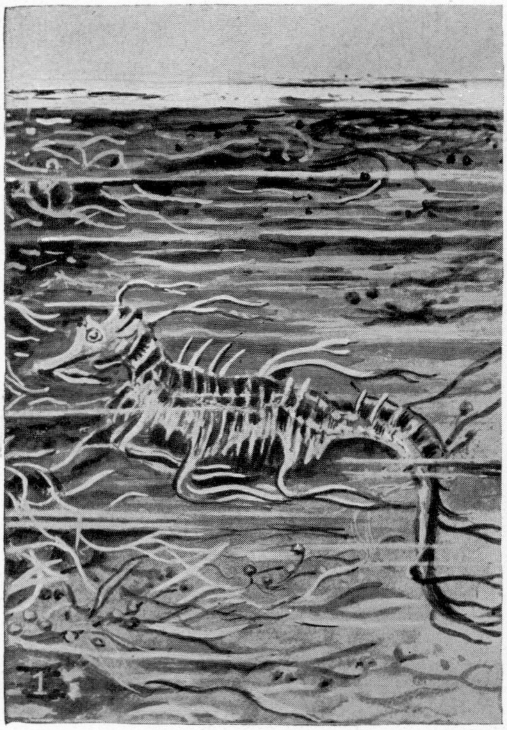

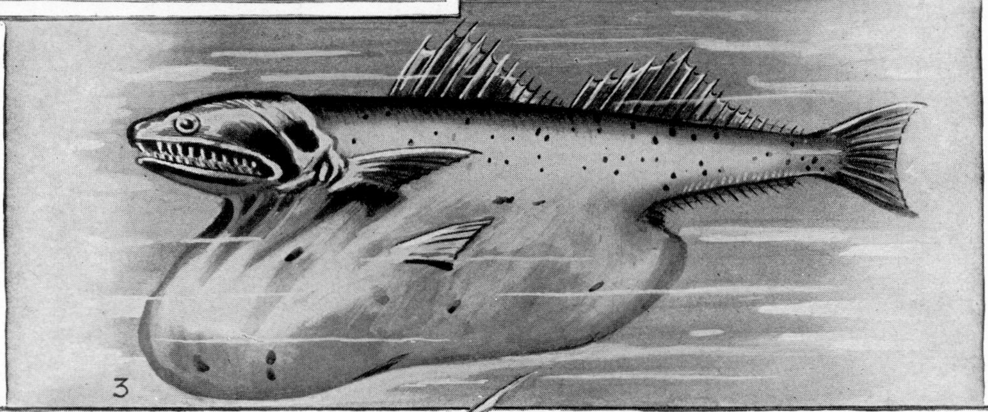

1. SEA-HORSE IN SARGASSO WEED. In its frond-like tags of skin and in its colouring this kind of sea-horse is well concealed among the floating seaweed of the so-called Sargasso Sea.

2. THE LARGE MARINE LAMPREYS (*PETROMYZON MARINUS*), WHICH MAY BE AS LONG AS ONE'S ARM, SPAWN IN FRESH WATER. Stones and pebbles, gripped in the suctorial mouth, are removed from a selected spot and piled around the circumference, so that the eggs, which are laid within the circle, are not easily washed away.

3. THE DEEP-SEA FISH *CHIASMODON NIGER* IS FAMOUS FOR ITS VORACITY. It sometimes manages to swallow a fish larger than itself, which causes an extraordinary protrusion of the stomach.

4. DEEP-SEA FISHES. Two of them—*Melanocetus murrayi* and *Melanocetus indicus*—are related to the Angler of British coasts, but adapted to life in the great abysses. They are very dark in colour, and delicately built; they possess well-developed luminous organs. The third form is called Chauliodus, a predatory animal with large gape and formidable teeth.

FLINTY SKELETON OF VENUS FLOWER BASKET (EUPLECTELLA), A JAPANESE DEEP-SEA SPONGE

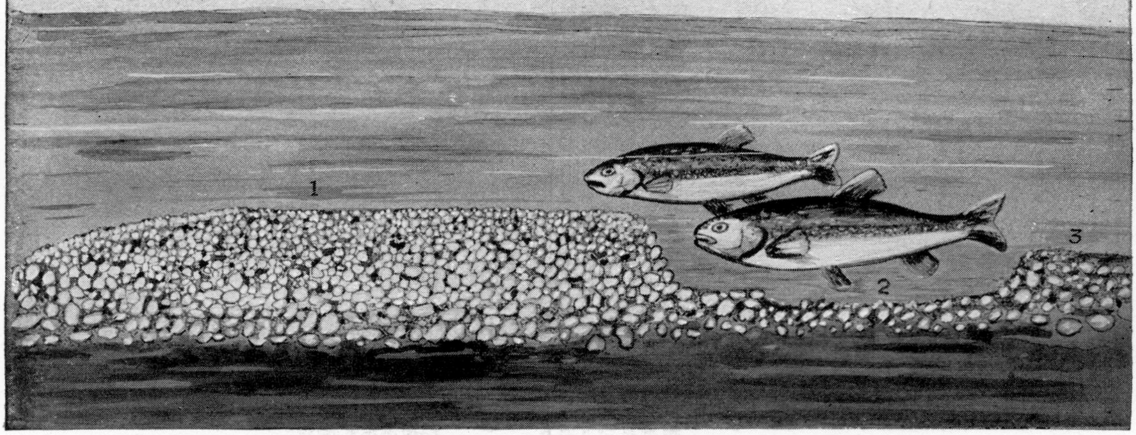

EGG DEPOSITORY OF *Semotilus Atromaculatus*

In the building of this egg depository, the male fish takes stones from the bottom of the stream, gripping them in his mouth, and heaps them up into the dam. In the egg depository he arranges the stones so that when the eggs are deposited in the interstices they are thoroughly protected, and cannot be washed down-stream.

1, dam of stones; 2, egg depository; 3, hillock of sand. The arrow shows the direction of the stream. Upper fish, male; lower, female.

The "floating sea-meadows," as Sir John Murray called them, are always receiving contributions from inshore waters, where the conditions are favourable for the prolific multiplication of unicellular Algæ, and there is also a certain amount of non-living sea-dust always being swept out from the seaweed and sea-grass area.

Swimmers and Drifters

The animals of the open sea are conveniently divided into the active swimmers (Nekton) and the more passive drifters (Plankton). The swimmers include whales great and small, such birds as the storm petrel, the fish-eating turtles and sea-snakes, such fishes as mackerel and herring, the winged snails or sea-butterflies on which whalebone whales largely feed, some of the active cuttles or squids, various open-sea prawns and their relatives, some worms like the transparent arrow-worm, and such active Protozoa as Noctiluca, whose luminescence makes the waves sparkle in the short summer darkness. Very striking as an instance of the insurgence of life are the sea-skimmers (Halobatidæ), wingless insects related to the water-measurers in the ditch. They are found hundreds of miles from land, skimming on the surface of the open sea, and diving in stormy weather. They feed on floating dead animals.

The drifters or easygoing swimmers—for there is no hard and fast line—are represented, for instance, by the flinty-shelled Radiolarians and certain of the chalk-forming animals (Globigerinid Foraminifera); by jellyfishes, swimming-bells, and Portuguese men-of-war; by the comb-bearers or Ctenophores; by legions of minute Crustaceans; by strange animals called Salps, related to the sedentary sea-squirts; and by some sluggish fishes like globe-fishes, which often float idly on the surface.

Open-sea animals tend to be delicately built, with a specific gravity near that of the sea-water, with adaptations, such as projecting filaments, which help flotation, and with capacities of rising and sinking according to the surrounding conditions. Many of them are luminescent, and many of them are very inconspicuous in the water owing to their transparency or their bluish colour. In both cases the significance is obscure.

Hunger and Love

Hunger is often very much in evidence in the open sea, especially in areas where the Plankton is poor. For there is great diversity in this respect, most of the Mediterranean, for instance, having a scanty Plankton as compared with the North Sea. In the South Pacific, west of Patagonia, there is said to be an immense "sea desert" where there is little Plankton, and therefore little in the way of fishes. The success of fisheries in the North, e.g. on the Atlantic cod-banks, is due to the richness of the floating sea-meadows and the abundance of the smaller constituents of the animal Plankton.

Hunger is plain enough when the Baleen Whale rushes through the water with open jaws, engulfing in the huge cavern of its mouth, where the pendent whalebone plates form a huge sieve, incalculable millions of small fry.

But there is love as well as hunger in the open sea. The maternal care exhibited by the whale reaches a very high level, and the delicate shell of the female Paper Nautilus or Argonaut, in which the eggs and the young ones are sheltered, may well be described as "the most beautiful cradle in the world."

Besides the permanent inhabitants of the open sea, there are the larval stages of many shore-animals which are there only for a short time. For there is an interesting give and take between the shore-haunt and the open sea. From the shore come nutritive contributions and minute organisms which multiply quickly in the open waters. But not less important is the fact that the open waters afford a safe cradle or nursery for many a delicate larva, e.g. of crab and starfish, acorn-shell and sea-urchin, which could not survive for a day in the rough-and-tumble conditions of the shore and the shallow water. After undergoing radical changes and gaining strength, the young creatures return to the shore in various ways.

III. THE DEEP SEA

Very different from all the other haunts are the depths of the sea, including the floor of the abysses and the zones of water near the bottom. This haunt, forever unseen, occupies more than a third of the earth's surface, and it is thickly peopled. It came into emphatic notice in connection with the mending of telegraph cables, but the results of the *Challenger* expedition (1873-6) gave the first impressive picture of what was practically a new world.

Physical Conditions

The average depth of the ocean is about two and a half miles; therefore, since many parts are relatively shallow, there must be enormous depths. A few of these, technically called "deeps," are about six miles deep, in which Mount Everest would be engulfed. There is enormous pressure in such depths; even at 2,500 fathoms it is two and a half tons on the square inch. The temperature is on and off the freezing-point of fresh water (28^0-34^0 Fahr.), due to the continual sinking down of cold water from the Poles, especially from the South. Apart from the fitful gleams of luminescent animals, there is utter darkness in the deep waters. The rays of sunlight are practically extinguished at 250 fathoms, though very sensitive bromogelatine plates exposed at 500 fathoms have shown faint indications even at that depth. It is a world of absolute calm and silence, and there is no scenery on the floor. A deep, cold, dark, silent, monotonous world!

Biological Conditions

While some parts of the floor of the abysses are more thickly peopled than others, there is no depth limit to the distribution of life. Wherever the long arm of the dredge has reached, animals have been found, e.g. Protozoa, sponges, corals, worms, starfishes, sea-urchins, sea-lilies, crustaceans, lamp-shells, molluscs, ascidians, and fishes—a very representative fauna. In the absence of light there can be no chlorophyll-possessing plants, and as the animals cannot all be eating one another there must be an extraneous source of food-supply. This is found in the sinking down of minute organisms which are killed on the surface by changes of temperature and other causes. What is left of them, before or after being swallowed, and of sea-dust and mineral particles of various kinds forms the diversified "ooze" of the sea-floor, a soft muddy precipitate, which is said to have in places the consistence of butter in summer weather.

There seems to be no bacteria in the abysses, so there can be no rotting. Everything that sinks down, even the huge carcase of a whale, must be nibbled away by hungry animals and digested, or else, in the case of most bones, slowly dissolved away. Of the whale there are left only the ear-bones, of the shark his teeth.

Adaptations to Deep-sea Life

In adaptation to the great pressure the bodies of deep-sea animals are usually very permeable, so that the water gets through and through them, as in the case of Venus' Flower Basket, a flinty sponge which a child's finger would shiver. But when the pressure inside is the same as that outside nothing happens. In adaptation to the treacherous ooze, so apt to smother, many of the active deep-sea animals have very long, stilt-like legs, and many of the sedentary types are lifted into safety on the end of long stalks which have their bases embedded in the mud. In adaptation to the darkness, in which there is only luminescence that eyes could use, there is a great development of tactility. The interesting problem of luminescence will be discussed elsewhere.

As to the origin of the deep-sea fauna, there seems no doubt

THE BITTERLING (*Rhodeus Amarus*)

A Continental fish which lays its eggs by means of a long ovipositor inside the freshwater mussel. The eggs develop inside the mollusc's gill-plates.

Photo: W. S. Berridge.

WOOLLY OPOSSUM CARRYING HER FAMILY

One of the young ones is clinging to its mother and has its long prehensile tail coiled round hers.

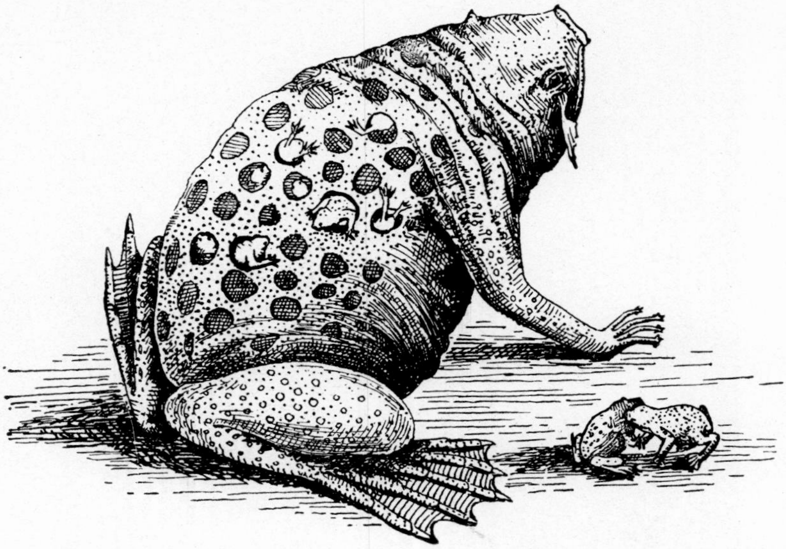

SURINAM TOAD (*Pipa Americana*) WITH YOUNG ONES HATCHING OUT OF LITTLE POCKETS ON HER BACK

STORM PETREL OR MOTHER CAREY'S CHICKEN
(*Procellaria Pelagica*)

This characteristic bird of the open sea does not come to land at all except to nest. It is the smallest web-footed bird, about four inches long. The legs are long and often touch the water as the bird flies. The storm petrel is at home in the Atlantic, and often nests on islands off the west coast of Britain.

that it has arisen by many contributions from the various shore-haunts. Following the down-drifting food, many shore-animals have in the course of many generations reached the world of eternal night and winter, and become adapted to its strange conditions. For the animals of the deep-sea are as fit, beautiful, and vigorous as those elsewhere. There are no slums in Nature.

IV. THE FRESH WATERS

Of the whole earth's surface the freshwaters form a very small fraction, about a hundredth, but they make up for their smallness by their variety. We think of deep lake and shallow pond, of the great river and the purling brook, of lagoon and swamp, and more besides. There is a striking resemblance in the animal population of widely separated freshwater basins: and this is partly because birds carry many small creatures on their muddy feet from one water-shed to another; partly because some of the freshwater animals are descended from types which make their way from the sea and the seashore through estuaries and marshes, and only certain kinds of constitution could survive the migration; and partly because some lakes are landlocked dwindling relics of ancient seas, and similar forms again would survive the change.

A typical assemblage of freshwater animals would include many Protozoa, like Amœbæ and the Bell-Animalcules, a representative of one family of sponges (Spongillidæ), the common Hydra, many unsegmented worms (notably Planarians and Nematodes), many Annelids related to the earthworms, many crustaceans, insects, and mites, many bivalves and snails, various fishes, a newt or two, perhaps a little mud-turtle or in warm countries a huge Crocodilian, various interesting birds like the water-ouzel or dipper, and mammals like the water-vole and the water-shrew.

Freshwater animals have to face certain difficulties, the greatest of which are drought, frost, and being washed away in times of flood. There is no more interesting study in the world than an inquiry into the adaptations by which freshwater animals overcome the difficulties of the situation. We cannot give more than a few illustrations.

(1) Drought is circumvented by the capacity that many freshwater animals have of lying low and saying nothing. Thus the African mudfish may spend half the year encased in the mud, and many minute crustaceans can survive being dried up for years. (2) Escape from the danger of being frozen hard in the pool is largely due to the almost unique property of water that it expands as it approaches the freezing-point. Thus the colder water rises to the surface and forms or adds to the protecting blanket of ice. The warmer water remains unfrozen at the bottom, and the animals live on. (3) The risk of being washed away, e.g. to the sea, is lessened by all sorts of gripping, grappling, and anchoring structures, and by shortening the juvenile stages when the risks are greatest.

V. THE DRY LAND

Over and over again in the history of animal life there have been attempts to get out of the water on to terra firma, and many of these have been successful, notably those made (1) by worms, (2) by air-breathing Arthropods, and (3) by amphibians.

In thinking of the conquest of the dry land by animals, we must recognise the indispensable rôle of plants in preparing the way. The dry ground would have proved too inhospitable had not terrestrial plants begun to establish themselves, affording food, shelter, and humidity. There had to be plants before there could be earthworms, which feed on decaying leaves and the like, but how soon was the debt repaid when the earthworms began their worldwide task of forming vegetable mould, opening up the earth with their burrows, circulating the soil by means of their castings, and bruising the particles in their gizzard—certainly the most important mill in the world.

Another important idea is that littoral haunts, both on the seashore and in the freshwaters, afforded the necessary apprenticeship and transitional experience for the more strenuous life on dry land. Much that was perfected on land had its beginnings on the shore. Let us inquire, however, what the passage from water to dry land actually implied. This has been briefly discussed in a previous article (on Evolution), but the subject is one of great interest and importance.

Difficulties and Results of the Transition from Water to Land

Leaving the water for dry land implied a loss in freedom of movement, for the terrestrial animal is primarily restricted to the surface of the earth. Thus it became essential that movements should be very rapid and very precise, needs with which we may associate the acquisition of fine cross-striped, quickly contracting muscles, and also, in time, their multiplication into very numerous separate engines. We exercise fifty-four muscles in the half-second that elapses between raising the heel of our foot in walking and planting it firmly on the ground again. Moreover, the need for rapid precisely controlled movements implied an improved nervous system, for the brain was a movement-controlling organ for ages before it did much in the way of thinking. The transition to terra firma also involved a greater compactness of body, so that there should not be too great friction on the surface. An animal like the jellyfish is unthinkable on land, and the elongated bodies of some land animals like centipedes and snakes are specially adapted so that they do not "sprawl." They are exceptions that prove the rule.

Getting on to dry land meant entering a kingdom where the differences between day and night, between summer and winter are more felt than in the sea. This made it advantageous to have protections against evaporation and loss of heat and other such dangers. Hence a variety of ways in which the surface of the body acquired a thickened skin, or a dead cuticle, or a shell, or a growth of hair, and so forth. In many cases there is an increase of the protection before the winter sets in, e.g. by growing thicker fur or by accumulating a layer of fat below the skin.

But the thickening or protection of the skin involved a partial or total loss of the skin as a respiratory surface. There is more oxygen available on dry land than in the water, but it is not so readily captured. Thus we see the importance of moist internal surfaces for capturing the oxygen which has been drawn into the interior of the body into some sort of lung. A unique solution was offered by Tracheate Arthropods, such as Peripatus, Centipedes, Millipedes, and Insects, where the air is carried to every hole and corner of the body by a ramifying system of air-tubes or tracheæ. In most animals the blood goes to the air, in insects the air goes to the blood. In the Robber-Crab, which has migrated from the shore inland, the dry air is absorbed by vascular tufts growing under the shelter of the gill-cover.

The problem of disposing of eggs or young ones is obviously much more difficult on land than in the water. For the water offers an immediate cradle, whereas on the dry land there were many dangers, e.g. of drought, extremes of temperature, and hungry sharp-eyed enemies, which had to be circumvented. So we find all manner of ways in which land animals hide their eggs or their young ones in holes and nests, on herbs and on trees. Some carry their young ones about after they are born, like the Surinam toad and the kangaroo, while others have prolonged the period of antenatal life during which the young ones develop in safety within their mother, and in very intimate partnership with her in the case of the placental mammals. It is very interesting to find that the pioneer animal called Peripatus, which bridges the gap between worms and insects, carries its young for almost a year before birth.

Enough has been said to show that the successive conquests of the dry land had great evolutionary results. It is hardly too much to say that the invasion which the Amphibians led was the

ALBATROSS: A CHARACTERISTIC PELAGIC BIRD OF THE SOUTHERN SEA

It may have a spread of wing of over 11 feet from tip to tip. It is famous for its extraordinary power of "sailing" round the ship without any apparent strokes of its wings.

beginning of better brains, more controlled activities, and higher expressions of family life.

VI. THE AIR

There are no animals thoroughly aerial, but many insects spend much of their adult life in the free air, and the swift hardly pauses in its flight from dawn to dusk of the long summer day, alighting only for brief moments at the nest to deliver insects to the young. All the active life of bats certainly deserves to be called aerial.

The air was the last haunt of life to be conquered, and it is interesting to inquire what the conquest implied. (1) It meant transcending the radical difficulty of terrestrial life which confines the creatures of the dry land to moving on one plane, the surface of the earth. But the power of flight brought its possessors back to the universal freedom of movement which water animals enjoy. When we watch a sparrow rise into the air just as the cat has completed her stealthy stalking, we see that flight implies an enormous increase of safety. (2) The power of flight also opened up new possibilities of following the prey, of exploring new territories, of prospecting for water. (3) Of great importance too was the practicability of placing the eggs and the young, perhaps in a nest, in some place inaccessible to most enemies. When one thinks of it, the rooks' nests swaying on the tree-tops express the climax of a brilliant experiment. (4) The crowning advantage was the possibility of migrating, of conquering time (by circumventing the arid summer and the severe winter) and of conquering space (by passing quickly from one country to another and sometimes almost girdling the globe). There are not many acquisitions that have meant more to their possessors than the power of flight. It was a key opening the doors of a new freedom.

The problem of flight, as has been said in a previous chapter, has been solved four times, and the solution has been different in each case. The four solutions are those offered by insects, extinct Pterodactyls, birds, and bats. Moreover, as has been pointed out, there have been numerous attempts at flight which remain glorious failures, notably the flying fishes, which take a great leap and hold their pectoral fins taut; the Flying Tree-Toad, whose webbed fingers and toes form a parachute; the Flying Lizard (*Draco volans*), which has its skin pushed out on five or six greatly elongated mobile ribs; and various "flying" mammals, e.g. Flying Phalangers and Flying Squirrels, which take great swooping leaps from tree to tree.

The wings of an insect are hollow flattened sacs which grow out from the upper parts of the sides of the second and third rings of the region called the thorax. They are worked by powerful muscles, and are supported, like a fan, by ribs of chitin, which may be accompanied by air-tubes, blood-channels, and nerves. The insect's body is lightly built and very perfectly aerated, and the principle of the insect's flight is the extremely rapid striking of the air by means of the lightly built elastic wings. Many an insect has over two hundred strokes of its wings in one *second.* Hence, in many cases, the familiar hum, comparable on a small scale to that produced by the rapidly revolving blades of an aeroplane's propeller. For a short distance a bee can outfly a pigeon, but few insects can fly far, and they are easily blown away or blown back by the wind. Dragon-flies and bees may be cited as examples of insects that often fly for two or three miles. But this is exceptional, and the usual shortness of insect flight is an important fact for man since it limits the range of insects like house-flies and mosquitoes which are vehicles of typhoid fever and malaria respectively. The most primitive insects (spring-tails and bristle-tails) show no trace of wings, while fleas and lice have become secondarily wingless. It is interesting to notice that some insects only fly once in their lifetime, namely, in connection with mating. The evolution of the insect's wing remains quite obscure, but it is probable that insects could run, leap, and parachute before they could actually fly.

The extinct Flying Dragons or Pterodactyls had their golden age in the Cretaceous era, after which they disappeared, leaving no descendants. A fold of skin was spread out from the sides of the body by the enormously elongated outermost finger (usually regarded as corresponding to our little finger); it was continued to the hind-legs and thence to the tail.

It is unlikely that the Pterodactyls could fly far, for they have at most a weak keel on their breastbone; on the other hand, some of them show a marked fusion of dorsal vertebræ, which, as in flying birds, must have served as a firm fulcrum for the stroke of the wings. The quaint creatures varied from the size of a sparrow up to a magnificent spread of 15-20 feet from tip to tip of the wings. They were the largest of all flying creatures.

The bird's solution of the problem of flight, which will be discussed separately, is centred in the feather, which forms a coherent vane for striking the air. In Pterodactyl and bat the wing is a web-wing or patagium, and a small web is to be seen on the front side of the bird's wing. But the bird's patagium is unimportant, and the bird's wing is on an evolutionary tack of its own—a fore-limb transformed for bearing the feathers of flight. Feathers are in a general way comparable to the scales of reptiles, but only in a general way, and no transition stage is known between the two. Birds evolved from a bipedal Dinosaur stock, as has been noticed already, and it is highly probable that they began their ascent by taking running leaps along the ground, flapping their scaly fore-limbs, and balancing themselves in kangaroo-like fashion with an extended tail. A second chapter was probably an arboreal apprenticeship, during which they made a fine art of parachuting—a persistence of which is to be seen in the pigeon "gliding" from the dovecot to the ground. It is in birds that the mastery of the air reaches its climax, and the mysterious "sailing" of the albatross and the vulture is surely the most remarkable locomotor triumph that has ever been achieved. Without any apparent stroke of the wings, the bird sails for half an hour at a time with the wind and against the wind, around the ship and in majestic spirals in the sky, probably taking advantage of currents of air of different velocities, and continually changing energy of position into energy of motion as it sinks, and energy of motion into energy of position as it rises. It is interesting to know that some dragon-flies are also able to "sail."

The web-wing of bats involves much more than the fore-arm. The double fold of skin begins on the side of the neck, passes along the front of the arm, skips the thumb, and is continued over the elongated palm-bones and fingers to the sides of the body again, and to the hind-legs, and to the tail if there is a tail. It is interesting to find that the bones of the bat's skeleton tend to be lightly built as in birds, that the breastbone has likewise a keel for the better insertion of the pectoral muscles, and that there is a solidifying of the vertebræ of the back, affording as in birds a firm basis for the wing action. Such similar adaptations to similar needs, occurring in animals not nearly related to one another, are called "convergences," and form a very interesting study. In addition to adaptations which the bat shares with the flying bird, it has many of its own. There are so many nerve-endings on the wing, and often also on special skin-leaves about the ears and nose, that the bat flying in the dusk does not knock against branches or other obstacles. Some say that it is helped by the echoes of its high-pitched voice, but there is no doubt as to its exquisite tactility. That it usually produces only a single young one at a time is a clear adaptation to flight, and similarly the sharp, mountain-top-like cusps on the back teeth are adapted in insectivorous bats for crunching insects.

Whether we think of the triumphant flight of birds, reaching a climax in migration, or of the marvel that a creature of the earth—as a mammal essentially is—should evolve such a mastery of the air as we see in bats, or even of the repeated but splendid failures which parachuting animals illustrate, we gain an impression of the insurgence of living creatures in their characteristic endeavour after fuller well-being.

We have said enough to show how well adapted many animals are to meet the particular difficulties of the haunt which they tenant. But difficulties and limitations are ever arising afresh, and so one fitness follows on another. It is natural, therefore, to pass to the frequent occurrence of protective resemblance, camouflage, and mimicry—the subject of the next article.

BIBLIOGRAPHY

Elmhirst, R., *Animals of the Shore.*
Flattely and Walton, *The Biology of the Shore* (1921).
Furneaux, *Life of Ponds and Streams.*
Hickson, S. J., *Story of Life in the Seas* and *Fauna of the Deep Sea.*
Johnstone, J., *Life in the Sea* (Cambridge Manual of Science).
Miall, L. C., *Aquatic Insects.*
Murray, Sir John, *The Ocean* (Home University Library).
Murray, Sir John and Hjort, Dr. J., *The Depths of the Ocean.*
Newbigin, M. I., *Life by the Sea Shore.*
Pycraft, W. P., *History of Birds.*
Scharff, R. F., *History of the European Fauna* (Contemp. Sci. Series).
Thomson, J. Arthur, *The Wonder of Life* (1914) and *The Haunts of Life* (1921).

IV

THE STRUGGLE FOR EXISTENCE

ANIMAL AND BIRD MIMICRY AND DISGUISE

§ 1

FOR every animal one discovers when observing carefully, there must be ten unseen. This is partly because many animals burrow in the ground or get in underneath things and into dark corners, being what is called cryptozoic or elusive. But it is partly because many animals put on disguise or have in some way acquired a garment of invisibility. This is very common among animals, and it occurs in many forms and degrees. The reason why it is so common is because the struggle for existence is often very keen, and the reasons why the struggle for existence is keen are four. First, there is the tendency to over-population in many animals, especially those of low degree. Second, there is the fact that the scheme of nature involves nutritive chains or successive incarnations, one animal depending upon another for food, and all in the long run on plants; thirdly, every vigorous animal is a bit of a hustler, given to insurgence and sticking out his elbows. There is a fourth great reason for the struggle for existence, namely, the frequent changefulness of the physical environment, which forces animals to answer back or die; but the first three reasons have most to do with the very common assumption of some sort of disguise. Even when an animal is in no sense a weakling, it may be very advantageous for it to be inconspicuous when it is resting or when it is taking care of its young. Our problem is the evolution of elusiveness, so far at least as that depends on likeness to surroundings, on protective resemblance to other objects, and in its highest reaches on true mimicry.

Colour Permanently Like That of Surroundings

Many animals living on sandy places have a light-brown colour, as is seen in some lizards and snakes. The green lizard is like the grass and the green tree-snake is inconspicuous among the branches. The spotted leopard is suited to the interrupted light of the forest, and it is sometimes hard to tell where the jungle ends and the striped tiger begins. There is no better case than the hare or the partridge sitting a few yards off on the ploughed field. Even a donkey grazing in the dusk is much more readily heard than seen.

The experiment has been made of tethering the green variety of Praying Mantis on green herbage, fastening them with silk threads. They escape the notice of birds. The same is true when the brown variety is tethered on withered herbage. But if the green ones are put on brown plants, or the brown ones on green plants, the birds pick them off. Similarly, out of 300 chickens in a field, 240 white or black and therefore conspicuous, 60 spotted and inconspicuous, 24 were soon picked off by crows, but only one of these was spotted. This was not the proportion that there should have been if the mortality had been fortuitous. There is no doubt that it often pays an animal to be like its habitual surroundings, like a little piece of scenery if the animal is not moving. It is safe to say that in process of time wide departures from the safest coloration will be wiped out in the course of Nature's ceaseless sifting.

But we must not be credulous, and there are three cautions to be borne in mind. (1) An animal may be very like its surroundings without there being any protection implied. The arrow-worms in the sea are as clear as glass, and so are many open-sea animals. But this is because their tissues are so watery, with a specific gravity near that of the salt water. And the invisibility does not save them, always or often, from being swallowed by larger animals that gather the harvest of the sea. (2) Among the cleverer animals it looks as if the creature sometimes sought out a spot where it was most inconspicuous. A spider may place itself

THE PRAYING MANTIS (*Mantis Religiosa*)

A very voracious insect with a quiet, unobstrusive appearance. It holds its formidable forelegs as if in the attitude of prayer; its movements are very slow and stealthy; and there is a suggestion of a leaf in the forewing. But there is no reason to credit the creature with conscious guile!

PROTECTIVE COLORATION: A WINTER SCENE IN NORTH SCANDINAVIA

Showing Variable Hare, Willow Grouse, and Arctic Fox, all white in winter and inconspicuous against the snow. But the white dress is also the dress that is physiologically best, for it loses least of the animal heat.

Photo: A. A. White.

THE VARIABLE MONITOR (*Varanus*)

The monitors are the largest of existing lizards, the Australian species represented in the photograph attaining a length of four feet. It has a brown colour with yellow spots, and in spite of its size it is not conspicuous against certain backgrounds, such as the bark of a tree.

in the middle of a little patch of lichen, where its self-effacement is complete. Perhaps it is more comfortable as well as safer to rest in surroundings the general colour of which is like that of the animal's body. (3) The fishes that live among the coral-reefs are startling in their brilliant coloration, and there are many different patterns. To explain this it has been suggested that these fishes are so safe among the mazy passages and endless nooks of the reefs, that they can well afford to wear any colour that suits their constitution. In some cases this may be true, but naturalists who have put on a diving suit and walked about among the coral have told us that each kind of fish is particularly suited to some particular place, and that some are suited for midday work and others for evening work. Sometimes there is a sort of Box and Cox arrangement by which two different fishes utilise the same corner at different times.

§ 2

Gradual Change of Colour

The common shore-crab shows many different colours and mottlings, especially when it is young. It may be green or grey, red or brown, and so forth, and it is often in admirable adjustment to the colour of the rock-pool where it is living. Experiments, which require extension, have shown that when the crab has moulted, which it has to do very often when it is young, the colour of the new shell tends to harmonise with the general colour of the rocks and seaweed. How this is brought about, we do not know. The colour does not seem to change till the next moult, and not then unless there is some reason for it. A full-grown shore-crab is well able to look after itself, and it is of interest to notice, therefore, that the variety of coloration is mainly among the small individuals, who have, of course, a much less secure position. It is possible, moreover, that the resemblance to the surroundings admits of more successful hunting, enabling the small crab to take its victim unawares.

Professor Poulton's experiments with the caterpillars of the small tortoise-shell butterfly showed that in black surroundings the pupæ tend to be darker, in white surroundings lighter, in gilded boxes golden; and the same is true in other cases. It appears that the surrounding colour affects the caterpillars through the skin during a sensitive period—the twenty hours immediately preceding the last twelve hours of the larval state. The result will tend to make the quiescent pupæ less conspicuous during the critical time of metamorphosis. The physiology of this sympathetic colouring remains obscure.

Seasonal Change of Colouring

The ptarmigan moults three times in the year. Its summer plumage is rather grouselike above, with a good deal of rufous brown; the back becomes much more grey in autumn; almost all the feathers of the winter plumage are white. That is to say, they develop without any pigment and with numerous gas-bubbles in their cells. Now there can be no doubt that this white winter plumage makes the ptarmigan very inconspicuous amidst the snow. Sometimes one comes within a few feet of the crouching bird without seeing it, and this garment of invisibility may save it from the hungry eyes of golden eagles.

Similarly the brown stoat becomes the white ermine, mainly by the growth of a new suit of white fur, and the same is true of the mountain hare. The ermine is all white except the black tip of its tail; the mountain hare in its winter dress is all white save the black tips of its ears. In some cases, especially in the mountain hare, it seems that individual hairs may turn white, by a loss of pigment, as may occur in man. According to Metchnikoff, the wandering amœboid cells of the body, called phagocytes, may creep up into the hairs and come back again with microscopic burdens of pigment. The place of the pigment is taken by gas-bubbles, and that is what causes the whiteness. In no animals is there any white *pigment;* the white *colour* is like that of snow or

Photo: W. S. Berridge, F.Z.S.

BANDED KRAIT: A VERY POISONOUS SNAKE WITH ALTERNATING YELLOW AND DARK BANDS

It is very conspicuous and may serve as an illustration of warning coloration. Perhaps, that is to say, its striking coloration serves as an advertisement, impressing other creatures with the fact that the Banded Krait should be left alone. It is very unprofitable for a snake to waste its venom on creatures it does not want.

Photos: W. S. Berridge, F.Z.S.

THE WARTY CHAMELEON

The upper photograph shows the Warty Chameleon inflated and conspicuous. At another time, however, with compressed body and adjusted coloration, the animal is very inconspicuous. The lower photograph shows the sudden protrusion of the very long tongue on a fly.

SEASONAL COLOUR-CHANGE: A SUMMER SCENE IN NORTH SCANDINAVIA

Showing a brown Variable Hare, Willow Grouse, and Arctic Fox, all inconspicuous in their coloration when seen in their natural surroundings.

foam, it is due to the complete reflection of the light from innumerable minute surfaces of crystals or bubbles.

The mountain hare may escape the fox the more readily because its whiteness makes it so inconspicuous against a background of snow; and yet, at other times, we have seen the creature standing out like a target on the dark moorland. So it cuts both ways. The ermine has almost no enemies except the gamekeeper, but its winter whiteness may help it to sneak upon its victims, such as grouse or rabbit, when there is snow upon the ground. In both cases, however, the probability is that the constitutional rhythm which leads to white hair in winter has been fostered and fixed for a reason quite apart from protection. The fact is that for a warm-blooded creature, whether bird or mammal, the physiologically best dress is a white one, for there is less radiation of the precious animal heat from white plumage or white pelage than from any other colour. The quality of warm-bloodedness is a prerogative of birds and mammals, and it means that the body keeps an almost constant temperature, day and night, year in and year out. This is effected by automatic internal adjustments which regulate the supply of heat, chiefly from the muscles, to the loss of heat, chiefly through the skin and from the lungs. The chief importance of this internal heat is that it facilitates the smooth continuance of the chemical processes on which life depends. If the temperature falls, as in hibernating mammals (whose warm-bloodedness is imperfect), the rate of the vital process is slowed down—sometimes dangerously. Thus we see how the white coat helps the life of the creature.

§ 3

Rapid Colour-change

Bony flat-fishes, like plaice and sole, have a remarkable power of adjusting their hue and pattern to the surrounding gravel and sand, so that it is difficult to find them even when we know that they are there. It must be admitted that they are also very quick to get a sprinkling of sand over their upturned side, so that only the eyes are left showing. But there is no doubt as to the exactness with which they often adjust themselves to be like a little piece of the substratum on which they lie; they will do this within limits in experimental conditions when they are placed on a quite artificial floor. As these fishes are very palatable and are much sought after by such enemies as cormorants and otters, it is highly probably that their power of self-effacement often saves their life. And it may be effected within a few minutes, in some cases within a minute.

In these self-effacing flat-fishes we know with some precision what happens. The adjustment of colour and pattern is due to changes in the size, shape, and position of mobile pigment-cells (chromatophores) and the skin. But what makes the pigment-cells change? The fact that a blind flat-fish does not change its colour gives us the first part of the answer. The colour and the pattern of the surroundings must affect the eye. The message travels by the optic nerve to the brain; from the brain, instead of passing down the spinal cord, the message travels down the chain of sympathetic ganglia. From these it passes along the nerves which comes out of the spinal cord and control the skin. Thus the message reaches the colour-cells in the skin, and before you have carefully read these lines the flat-fish has slipped on its Gyges ring and become invisible.

The same power of rapid colour-change is seen in cuttlefishes, where it is often an expression of nervous excitement, though it sometimes helps to conceal. It occurs with much sublety in the Æsop prawn, Hippolyte, which may be brown on a brown seaweed, green on sea-lettuce or sea-grass, red on red seaweed, and so on through an extensive repertory.

> According to the nature of the background, [Professor Gamble writes] so is the mixture of the pigments compounded so as to form a close reproduction both of its colour and its pattern. A sweep of the shrimp net detaches a bat-

Photo: J. J. Ward, F.E.S.

PROTECTIVE RESEMBLANCE

Hawk Moth, settled down on a branch, and very difficult to detect as long as it remains stationary. Note its remarkable sucking tongue, which is about twice the length of its body. The tongue can be quickly coiled up and put safely away beneath the lower part of the head.

WHEN ONLY A FEW DAYS OLD, YOUNG BITTERN BEGIN TO STRIKE THE SAME ATTITUDE AS THEIR PARENTS THRUSTING THEIR BILLS UPWARDS AND DRAWING THEIR BODIES UP SO THAT THEY RESEMBLE A BUNCH OF REEDS

The soft browns and blue-greens harmonise with the dull sheaths of the young reeds; the nestling bittern is thus completely camouflaged.

> talion of these sleeping prawns, and if we turn the motley into a dish and give a choice of seaweed, each variety after its kind will select the one with which it agrees in colour, and vanish. Both when young and when full-grown, the Æsop prawn takes on the colour of its immediate surroundings. At nightfall Hippolyte, of whatever colour, changes to a transparent azure blue: its stolidity gives place to a nervous restlessness; at the least tremor it leaps violently, and often swims actively from one food-plant to another. This blue fit lasts till daybreak, and is then succeeded by the prawn's diurnal tint.

Thus, Professor Gamble continues, the colour of an animal may express a nervous rhythm.

The Case of Chameleons

The highest level at which rapid colour-change occurs is among lizards, and the finest exhibition of it is among the chameleons. These quaint creatures are characteristic of Africa; but they occur also in Andalusia, Arabia, Ceylon, and Southern India. They are adapted for life on trees, where they hunt insects with great deliberateness and success. The protrusible tongue, ending in a sticky club, can be shot out for about seven inches in the common chameleon. Their hands and feet are split so that they grip the branches firmly, and the prehensile tail rivals a monkey's. When they wish they can make themselves very slim, contracting the body from side to side, so that they are not very readily seen. In other circumstances, however, they do not practise self-effacement, but the very reverse. They inflate their bodies, having not only large lungs, but air-sacs in connection with them. The throat bulges; the body sways from side to side; and the creature expresses its sentiments in a hiss. The power of colour-change is very remarkable, and depends partly on the contraction and expansion of the colour-cells (chromatophores) in the under-skin (or dermis) and partly on close-packed refractive granules and crystals of a waste-product called guanin. The repertory of possible colours in the common chameleon is greater than in any other animal except the Æsop prawn. There is a legend of a chameleon which was brown in a brown box, green in a green box, and blue in a blue box, and died when put into one lined with tartan; and there is no doubt that one and the same animal has a wide range of colours. The so-called "chameleon" (*Anolis*) of North America is so sensitive that a passing cloud makes it change its emerald hue.

There is no doubt that a chameleon may make itself more inconspicuous by changing its colour, being affected by the play of light on its eyes. A bright-green hue is often seen on those that are sitting among strongly illumined green leaves. But the colour also changes with the time of day and with the animal's moods. A sudden irritation may bring about a rapid change; in other cases the transformation comes about very gradually. When the colour-change expresses the chameleon's feelings it might be compared to blushing, but that is due to an expansion of the arteries of the face, allowing more blood to get into the capillaries of the under-skin. The case of the chameleon is peculiarly interesting because the animal has two kinds of tactics—self-effacement on the one hand and bluffing on the other. There can be little doubt that the power of colour-change sometimes justifies itself by driving off intruders. Dr. Cyril Crossland observed that a chameleon attacked by a fox-terrier "turned round and opened its great pink mouth in the face of the advancing dog, at the same time rapidly changing colour, becoming almost black. This ruse succeeded every time, the dog turning off at once." In natural leafy surroundings the startling effect would be much greater—a sudden throwing off of the mantle of invisibility and the exposure of a conspicuous black body with a large red mouth.

§ 4

Likeness to Other Things

Dr. H. O. Forbes tells of a flat spider which presents a striking resemblance to a bird's dropping on a leaf. Years after he

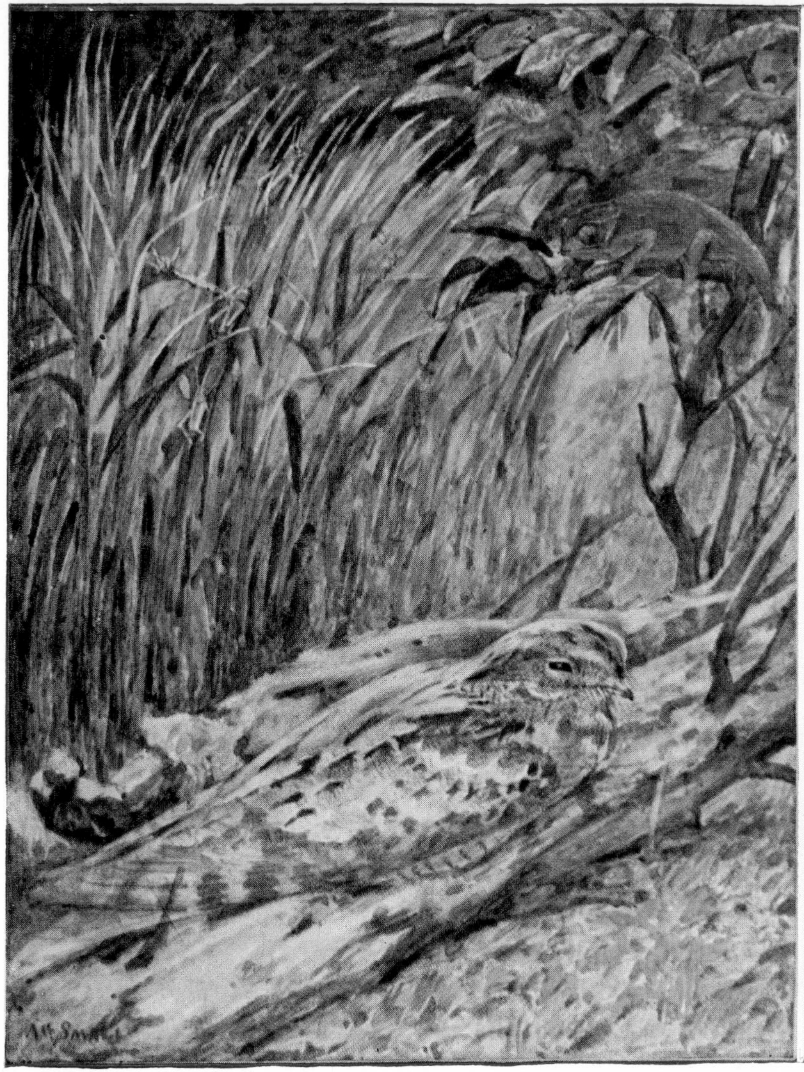

A. PROTECTIVE COLORATION OR CAMOUFLAGING, GIVING ANIMALS A GARMENT OF INVISIBILITY

At the foot of the plate is a Nightjar, with plumage like bark and withering leaves; to the right, resting on a branch, is shown a Chameleon in a green phase amid green surroundings; the insects on the reeds are Locusts; while a green Frog, merged into its surroundings, rests on a leaf near the centre at the top of the picture.

B. ANOTHER EXAMPLE OF PROTECTIVE COLORATION OR CAMOUFLAGE

A shore scene showing Trout in the pool almost invisible against their background. The Stone Curlews, both adult and young, are very inconspicuous among the stones on the beach.

first found it he was watching in a forest in the Far East when his eye fell on a leaf before him which had been blotched by a bird. He wondered idly why he had not seen for so long another specimen of the bird-dropping spider (*Ornithoscatoides decipiens*), and drew the leaf towards him. Instantaneously he got a characteristic sharp nip; it was the spider after all! Here the colour-resemblance was enhanced by a form-resemblance.

But why should it profit a spider to be like a bird-dropping? Perhaps because it thereby escapes attention; but there is another possibility. It seems that some butterflies, allied to our Blues, are often attracted to excrementitious material, and the spider Dr. Forbes observed had actually caught its victim. This is borne out by a recent observation by Dr. D. G. H. Carpenter, who found a Uganda bug closely resembling a bird-dropping on sand. The bug actually settled down on a bird-dropping on sand, and caught a blue butterfly which came to feed there!

Some of the walking-stick insects, belonging to the order of crickets and grasshoppers (Orthoptera), have their body elongated and narrow, like a thin dry branch, and they have a way of sticking out their limbs at abrupt and diverse angles, which makes the resemblance to twigs very close indeed. Some of these quaint insects rest through the day and have the remarkable habit of putting themselves into a sort of kataleptic state. Many creatures turn stiff when they get a shock, or pass suddenly into new surroundings, like some of the sand-hoppers when we lay them on the palm of our hand; but these twig-insects put themselves into this strange state. The body is rocked from side to side for a short time, and then it stiffens. An advantage may be that even if they were surprised by a bird or a lizard, they will not be able to betray themselves by even a tremor. Disguise is perfected by a remarkable habit, a habit which leads us to think of a whole series of different ways of lying low and saying nothing which are often of life-preserving value. The top end of the series is seen when a fox plays 'possum.

The leaf-butterfly ***Kallima,*** conspicuously coloured on its upper surface, is like a withered leaf when it settles down and shows the under side of its wings. Here, again, there is precise form-resemblance, for the nervures on the wings are like the mid-rib and side veins on a leaf, and the touch of perfection is given in the presence of whitish spots which look exactly like the discolorations produced by lichens on leaves. An old entomologist, Mr. Jenner Weir, confessed that he repeatedly pruned off a caterpillar on a bush in mistake for a superfluous twig, for many brownish caterpillars fasten themselves by their posterior claspers and by an invisible thread of silk from their mouth, and project from the branch at a twig-like angle. An insect may be the very image of a sharp prickle or a piece of soft moss; a spider may look precisely like a tiny knob on a branch or a fragment of lichen; one of the sea-horses (*Phyllopteryx*) has frond-like tassels on various parts of its body, so that it looks extraordinarily like the seaweeds among which it lives. In a few cases, e.g. among spiders, it has been shown that animals with a special protective resemblance to something else seek out a position where this resemblance tells, and there is urgent need for observations bearing on this selection of environment.

§ 5

Mimicry in the True Sense

It sometimes happens that in one and the same place there are two groups of animals not very nearly related which are "doubles" of one another. Investigation shows that the members of the one group, *always in the majority,* are in some way specially protected, e.g. by being unpalatable. They are the "mimicked." The members of the other group, *always in the minority,* have not got the special protection possessed by the others. They are the "mimickers," though the resemblance is not, of course, associated with any conscious imitation. The theory is that the mimickers live on the reputation of the mimicked. If the mimicked are left alone

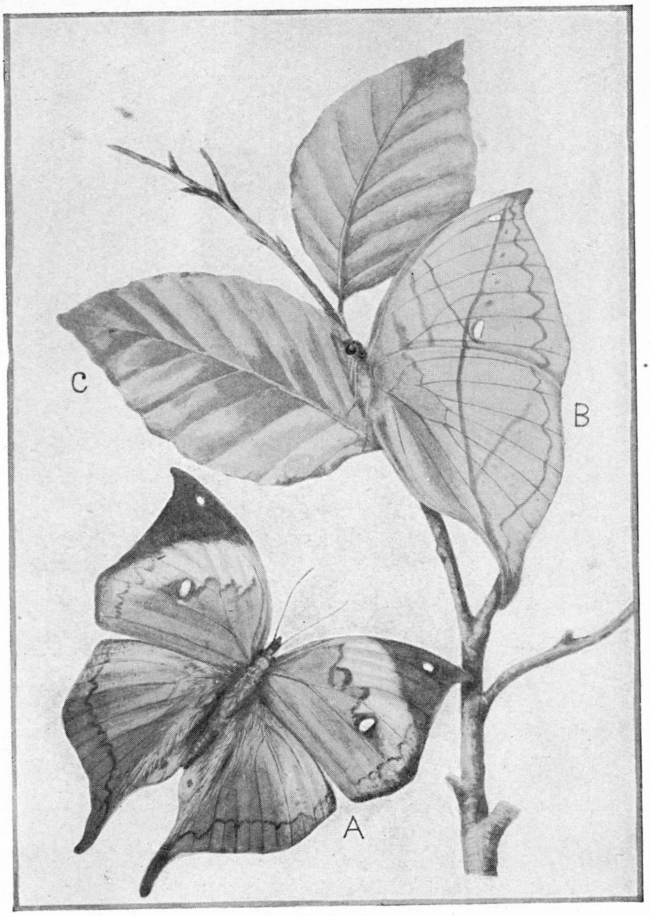

DEAD-LEAF BUTTERFLY (*Kallima Inachis*) FROM INDIA

It is conspicuous on its upper surface, but when it settles down on a twig and shows the underside of its wings it is practically invisible. The colouring of the under surface of the wings is like that of the withering leaf; there are spots like fungas spots; and the venation of the wings suggests the midrib and veins of the leaf. A, showing upper surface; B, showing under surface; C, a leaf.

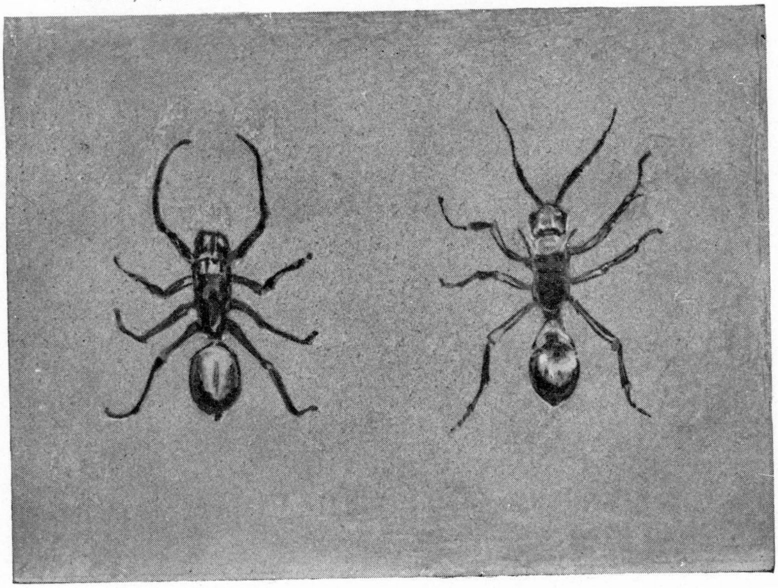

PROTECTIVE RESEMBLANCE BETWEEN A SMALL SPIDER (*to the left*) AND AN ANT (*to the right*)

As ants are much dreaded, it is probably profitable to the spider to be like an ant. It will be noted that the spider has four pairs of legs and no feelers, whereas the ant has three pairs of legs and a pair of feelers.

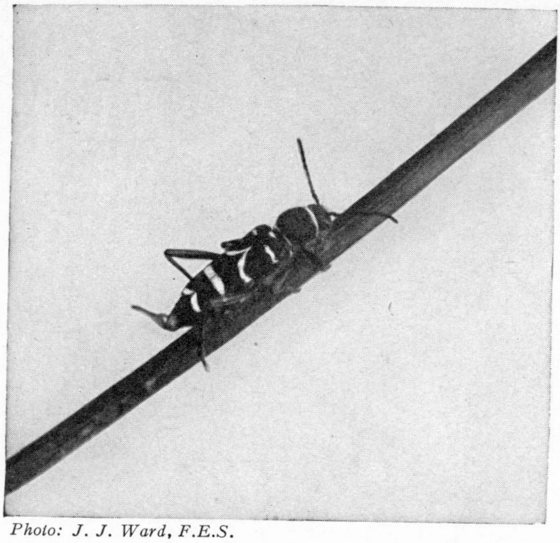

Photo: J. J. Ward, F.E.S.

THE WASP BEETLE, WHICH, WHEN MOVING AMONGST THE BRANCHES GIVES A WASP-LIKE IMPRESSION

HERMIT-CRAB WITH PARTNER SEA-ANEMONES

Hermit-crabs hide their soft tail in the shell or a whelk or some other sea-snail. But some hermit-crabs place sea-anemones on the back of their borrowed shell. The sea-anemones mask the hermit-crab and their tentacles can sting. As for the sea-anemones, they are carried about by the hermit-crab and they get crumbs from its table. This kind of mutually beneficial external partnership is called commensalism, i.e. eating at the same table.

Photo: G. P. Duffus.

CUCKOO-SPIT

The white mass in the centre of the picture is a soapy froth which the young frog-hopper makes, and within which it lies safe both from the heat of the sun and almost all enemies. After sojourning for a time in the cuckoo-spit, the frog-hopper becomes a winged insect.

by birds because they have a reputation for unpalatability, or because they are able to sting, the mimickers survive—although they are palatable and stingless. They succeed, not through any virtue of their own, but because of their resemblance to the mimicked, for whom they are mistaken. There are many cases of mimetic resemblance so striking and so subtle that it seems impossible to doubt that the thing works; there are other cases which are rather far-fetched, and may be somewhat of the nature of coincidences. Thus although Mr. Bates tells us that he repeatedly shot humming-bird moths in mistake for humming-birds, we cannot think that this is a good illustration of mimicry. What is needed for many cases is what is forthcoming for some, namely, experimental evidence, e.g. that the unpalatable mimicked butterflies are left in relative peace while similar palatable butterflies are persecuted. It is also necessary to show that the mimickers do actually consort with the mimicked. Some beetles and moths are curiously wasplike, which may be a great advantage; the common drone-fly is superficially like a small bee; some harmless snakes are very like poisonous species; and Mr. Wallace maintained that the powerful "friar-birds" of the Far East are mimicked by the weak and timid orioles. When the model is unpalatable or repulsive or dangerous, and the mimic the reverse, the mimicry is called "Batesian" (after Mr. Bates), but there is another kind of mimicry called Müllerian (after Fritz Müller) where the mimic is also unpalatable. The theory in this case is that the mimicry serves as mutual assurance, the members of the ring getting on better by consistently presenting the same appearance, which has come to mean to possible enemies a signal, *Noli me tangere* ("Leave me alone"). There is nothing out of the question in this theory, but it requires to be taken in a critical spirit. It leads us to think of "warning colours," which are the very opposite of the disguises which we are now studying. Some creatures like skunks, magpies, coral-snakes, cobras, brightly coloured tree-frogs are obtrusive rather than elusive, and the theory of Alfred Russel Wallace was that the flaunting conspicuousness serves as a useful advertisement, impressing itself on the memories of inexperienced enemies, who soon learn to leave creatures with "warning colours" alone. In any case it is plain that an animal which is as safe as a wasp or a coral-snake can afford to wear any suit of clothes it likes.

Masking

The episode in Scottish history called "The Walking Wood of Birnam," when the advancing troop masked their approach by cutting down branches of the trees, has had its counterpart in many countries. But it is also enacted on the seashore. There are many kinds of crabs that put on disguise with what looks like deliberateness. The sand-crab takes a piece of seaweed, nibbles at the end of it, and then rubs it on the back of the carapace or on the legs so that it fixes to the bristles. As the seaweed continues to live, the crab soon has a little garden on its back which masks the crab's real nature. It is most effective camouflaging, but if the crab continues to grow it has to moult, and that means losing the disguise. It is then necessary to make a new one. The crab must have on the shore something corresponding to a reputation; that is to say, other animals are clearly or dimly aware that the crab is a voracious and combative creature. How useful to the crab, then, to have its appearance cloaked by a growth of innocent seaweed, or sponge, or zoophyte. It will enable the creature to sneak upon its victims or to escape the attention of its own enemies.

If a narrow-beaked crab is cleaned artificially it will proceed to clothe itself again, the habit has become instinctive; and it must be admitted that while a particular crab prefers a particular kind of seaweed for its dress, it will cover itself with unsuitable and even conspicuous material, such as pieces of coloured cloth, if nothing better is available. The disguise differs greatly, for one crab is masked by a brightly coloured and unpalatable sponge densely packed with flinty needles; another cuts off the tunic of a sea-squirt and throws it over its shoulders; another trundles about a bivalve shell. The facts recall the familiar case of the hermit-crab, which protects its soft tail by tucking it into the empty shell of a periwinkle or a whelk or some other sea-snail, and that case leads on to the elaboration known as commensalism, where the hermit-crab fixes sea-anemones on the back of its borrowed house. The advantage here is beyond that of masking, for the sea-anemone can sting, which is a useful quality in a partner. That this second advantage may become the main one is evident in several cases where the sea-anemone is borne, just like a weapon, on each of the crustacean's great claws. Moreover, as the term commensalism (eating at the same table) suggests, the partnership is *mutually* beneficial. For the sea-anemone is carried about by the hermit-crab, and it doubtless gets its share of crumbs from its partner's frequent meals. There is a very interesting sidelight on the mutual benefit in the case of a dislodged sea-anemone which sulked for a while and then waited in a state of preparedness until a hermit-crab passed by and touched it. Whereupon the sea-anemone griped and slowly worked itself up on to the back of the shell.

§ 6

Other Kinds of Elusiveness

There are various kinds of disguise which are not readily classified. A troop of cuttlefish swimming in the sea is a beautiful sight. They keep time with one another in their movements and they show the same change of colour almost at the same moment. They are suddenly attacked, however, by a small shark, and then comes a simultaneous discharge of sepia from their inkbags. There are clouds of ink in the clear water, for, as Professor Hickson puts it, the cuttlefishes have thrown dust in the eyes of their enemies. One can see a newborn cuttlefish do this a minute after it escapes from the egg.

Very beautiful is the way in which many birds, like our common chaffinch, disguise the outside of their nest with moss and lichen and other trifles felted together, so that the cradle is as inconspicuous as possible. There seems to be a touch of art in fastening pieces of spider's web on the outside of a nest!

How curious is the case of the tree-sloth of South American forests, that walks slowly, back downwards, along the undersides of the branches, hanging on by its long, curved fingers and toes. It is a nocturnal animal, and therefore not in special danger, but when resting during the day it is almost invisible because its shaggy hair is so like certain lichens and other growths on the branches. But the protective resemblance is enhanced by the presence of a green alga, which actually lives on the surface of the sloth's hairs—an alga like the one that makes tree-stems and gate-posts green in damp weather.

There is no commoner sight in the early summer than the cuckoo-spit on the grasses and herbage by the wayside. It is conspicuous and yet it is said to be left severely alone by almost all creatures. In some way it must be a disguise. It is a sort of soap made by the activity of small frog-hoppers while they are still in the wingless larval stage, before they begin to hop. The insect pierces with its sharp mouth-parts the skin of the plant and sucks in sweet sap which by and by overflows over its body. It works its body up and down many times, whipping in air, which mixes with the sugary sap, reminding one of how "whipped egg" is made. But along with the sugary sap and the air, there is a little ferment from the food-canal and a little wax from glands on the skin, and the four things mixed together make a kind of soap which lasts through the heat of the day.

There are many other modes of disguise besides those which we have been able to illustrate. Indeed, the biggest fact is that there are so many, for it brings us back to the idea that life is not an easy business. It is true, as Walt Whitman says, that animals do not sweat and whine about their condition; perhaps it is true, as he says, that not one is unhappy over the whole earth. But there is another truth, that this world is not a place for the unlit lamp and the ungirt loin, and that when a creature has not armour or weapons or cleverness it must find some path of safety or go back. One of these paths of safety is disguise, and we have illustrated its evolution.

V
THE ASCENT OF MAN

THE ASCENT OF MAN

§ 1

NO one thinks less of Sir Isaac Newton because he was born as a very puny infant, and no one should think less of the human race because it sprang from a stock of arboreal mammals. There is no doubt as to man's apartness from the rest of creation when he is seen at his best—"a little lower than the angels, crowned with glory and honour." "What a piece of work is a man! How noble in reason! How infinite in faculty! in form and moving how express and admirable! in action how like an angel! in apprehension so like a God." Nevertheless, all the facts point to his affiliation to the stock to which monkeys and apes also belong. Not, indeed, that man is descended from any living ape or monkey; it is rather that he and they have sprung from a common ancestry—are branches of the same stem. This conclusion is so momentous that the reasons for accepting it must be carefully considered. They were expounded with masterly skill in Darwin's *Descent of Man* in 1871—a book which was but an expansion of a chapter in *The Origin of Species* (1859).

Anatomical Proof of Man's Relationship with a Simian Stock

The anatomical structure of man is closely similar to that of the anthropoid apes—the gorilla, the orang, the chimpanzee, and the gibbon. Bone for bone, muscle for muscle, blood-vessel for blood-vessel, nerve for nerve, man and ape agree. As the conservative anatomist, Sir Richard Owen, said, there is between them "an all-pervading similitude of structure." Differences, of course, there are, but they are not momentous except man's big brain, which may be three times as heavy as that of a gorilla. The average human brain weighs about 48 ounces; the gorilla brain does not exceed 20 ounces at its best. The capacity of the human skull is never less than 55 cubic inches; in the orang and the chimpanzee the figures are 26 and 27½ respectively. We are not suggesting that the most distinctive features of man are such as can be measured and weighed, but it is important to notice that the main seat of his mental powers is physically far ahead of that of the highest of the anthropoid apes.

Man alone is thoroughly erect after his infancy is past; his head weighted with the heavy brain does not droop forward as the ape's does; with his erect attitude there is perhaps to be associated his more highly developed vocal organs. Compared with an anthropoid ape, man has a bigger and more upright forehead, a less protrusive face region, smaller cheek-bones and eyebrow ridges, and more uniform teeth. He is almost unique in having a chin. Man plants the sole of his foot flat on the ground, his big toe is usually in a line with the other toes, and he has a better heel than any monkey has. The change in the shape of the head is to be thought of in connection with the enlargement of the brain, and also in connection with the natural reduction of the muzzle region when the hand was freed from being an organ of support and became suited for grasping the food and conveying it to the mouth.

Everyone is familiar in man's clothing with traces of the past persisting in the present, though their use has long since disappeared. There are buttons on the back of the waist of the morning coat to which the tails of the coat used to be fastened up, and there are buttons, occasionally with buttonholes, at the wrist which were once useful in turning up the sleeve. The same is true of man's body, which is a veritable museum of relics. Some

Photo: New York Zoological Park.

CHIMPANZEE, SITTING

The head shows certain facial characteristics, e.g. the beetling eyebrow ridges, which were marked in the Neanderthal race of men. Note the shortening of the thumb and the enlargement of the big toe.

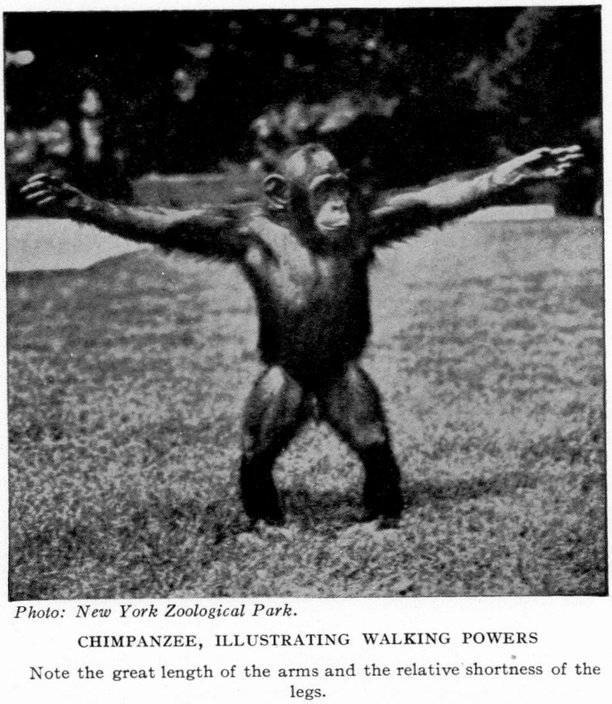

Photo: New York Zoological Park.

CHIMPANZEE, ILLUSTRATING WALKING POWERS

Note the great length of the arms and the relative shortness of the legs.

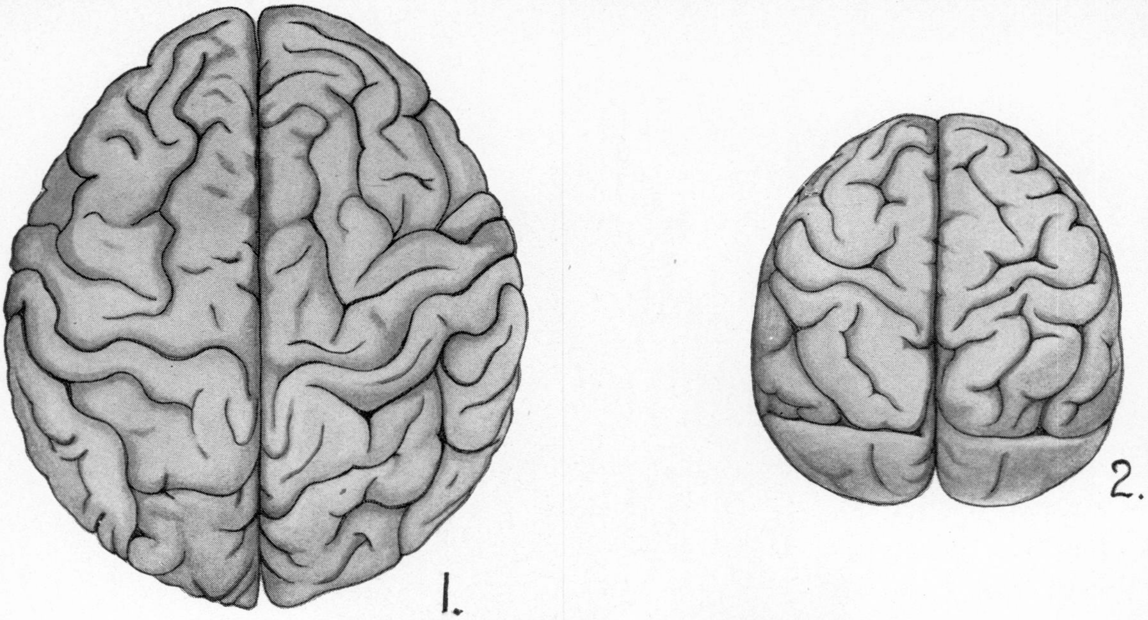

SURFACE VIEW OF THE BRAINS OF MAN (1) AND CHIMPANZEE (2)

The human brain is much larger and heavier, more dome-like, and with much more numerous and complicated convolutions.

Photo: New York Zoological Park.

SIDE-VIEW OF CHIMPANZEE'S HEAD.

(Compare with opposite picture.)

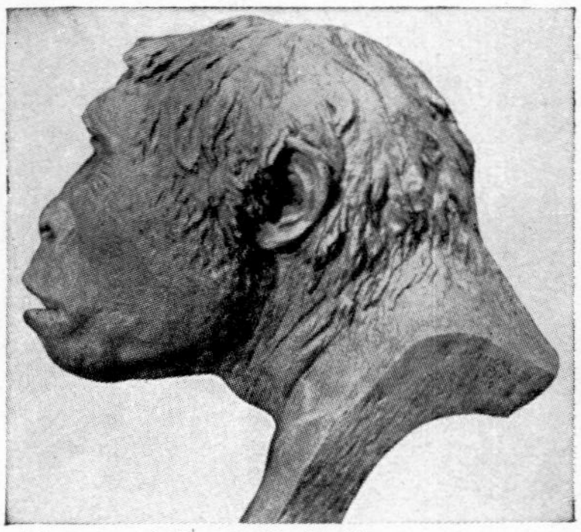

After a model by J. H. McGregor.

PROFILE VIEW OF HEAD OF PITHECANTHROPUS, THE JAVA APE MAN, RECONSTRUCTED FROM THE SKULL-CAP.

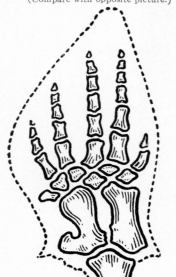

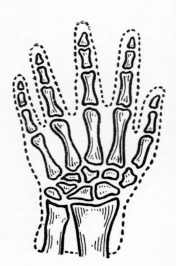

THE FLIPPER OF A WHALE AND THE HAND OF A MAN

In the bones and in their arrangement there is a close resemblance in the two cases, yet the outcome is very different. The multiplication of finger joints in the whale is a striking feature.

anatomists have made out a list of over a hundred of these *vestigial* structures, and though this number is perhaps too high, there is no doubt that the list is long. In the inner upper corner of the eye there is a minute tag—but larger in some races than in others—which is the last dwindling relic of the third eyelid, used in cleaning the front of the eye, which most mammals possess in a large and well-developed form. It can be easily seen, for instance, in ox and rabbit. In man and in monkeys it has become a useless vestige, and the dwindling must be associated with the fact that the upper eyelid is much more mobile in man and monkeys than in the other mammals. The vestigial third eyelid in man is enough of itself to prove his relationship with the mammals, but it is only one example out of many. Some of these are discussed in the article dealing with the human body, but we may mention the vestigial muscles going to the ear-trumpet, man's dwindling counterpart of the skin-twitching muscle which we see a horse use when he jerks a fly off his flanks, and the short tail which in the seven-weeks-old human embryo is actually longer than the leg. Without committing ourselves to a belief in the entire uselessness of the vermiform appendix, which grows out as a blind alley at the junction of the small intestine with the large, we are safe in saying that it is a dwindling structure—the remains of a blind gut which must have been capacious and useful in ancestral forms. In some mammals, like the rabbit, the blind gut is the bulkiest structure in the body, and bears the vermiform appendix at its far end. In man the appendix alone is left, and it tells its tale. It is interesting to notice that it is usually longer in the orang than in man, and that it is very variable, as dwindling structures tend to be. One of the unpleasant expressions of this variability is the liability to go wrong: hence appendicitis. Now these vestigial structures are, as Darwin said, like the unsounded, i.e. functionless, letters in words, such as the *o* in "leopard," the *b* in "doubt," the *g* in "reign." They are of no use, but they tell us something of the history of the words. So do man's vestigial structures reveal his pedigree. They must have an historical or evolutionary significance. No other interpretation is possible.

Some men, oftener than women, show on the inturned margin of the ear-trumpet or pinna, a little conical projection of great interest. It is a vestige of the tip of the pointed ear of lower mammals, and it is well named *Darwin's point.* It was he who described it as a "surviving symbol of the stirring times and dangerous days of man's animal youth."

§ 2

Physiological Proof of Man's Relationship with a Simian Stock

The everyday functions of the human body are practically the same as those of the anthropoid ape, and similar disorders are common to both. Monkeys may be infected with certain microbes to which man is peculiarly liable, such as the bacillus of tuberculosis. Darwin showed that various human gestures and facial expressions have their counterparts in monkeys. The sneering curl of the upper lip, which tends to expose the canine tooth, is a case in point, though it may be seen in many other mammals besides monkeys—in dogs, for instance, which are at some considerable distance from the simian branch to which man's ancestors belonged.

When human blood is transfused into a dog or even a monkey, it behaves in a hostile way to the other blood, bringing about a destruction of the red blood corpuscles. But when it is transfused into a chimpanzee there is an harmonious mingling of the two. This is a very literal demonstration of man's blood-relationship with the higher apes. But there is a finer form of the same experiment. When the blood-fluid (or serum) of a rabbit, which has had human blood injected into it, is mingled with human blood, it forms a cloudy precipitate. It forms almost as marked a precipitate when it is mingled with the blood of an anthropoid ape. But when it is mingled with the blood of an American mon-

THE GORILLA, INHABITING THE FOREST TRACT OF THE GABOON IN AFRICA

A full-grown individual stands about 5 feet high. The gait is shuffling, the strength enormous, the diet mainly vegetarian, the temper rather ferocious.

key there is only a slight clouding after a considerable time and no actual precipitate. When it is added to the blood of one of the distantly related "half-monkeys" or lemurs there is no reaction or only a very weak one. With the blood of mammals off the simian line altogether there is no reaction at all. Thus, as a distinguished anthropologist, Professor Schwalbe, has said: "We have in this not only a proof of the literal blood-relationship between man and apes, but the degree of relationship with the different main groups of apes can be determined beyond possibility of mistake." We can imagine how this modern line of experiment would have delighted Darwin.

Embryological Proof of Man's Relationship with a Simian Stock

In his individual development, man does in some measure climb up his own genealogical tree. Stages in the development of the body during its nine months of ante-natal life are closely similar to stages in the development of the anthropoid embryo. Babies born in times of famine or siege are sometimes, as it were, imperfectly finished, and sometimes have what may be described as monkeyish features and ways. A visit to an institution for the care of children who show arrested, defective, or disturbed development leaves one sadly impressed with the risk of slipping down the rungs of the steep ladder of evolution; and even in adults the occurrence of serious nervous disturbance, such as "shell-shock," is sometimes marked by relapses to animal ways. It is a familiar fact that a normal baby reveals the past in its surprising power of grip, and the careful experiments of Dr. Louis Robinson showed that an infant three weeks old could support its own weight for over two minutes, holding on to a horizontal bar. "In many cases no sign of distress is evinced and no cry uttered, until the grasp begins to give way." This persistent grasp probably points back to the time when the baby had to cling to its arboreal mother. The human tail is represented in the adult by a fusion of four or five vertebræ forming the "coccyx" at the end of the backbone, and is normally concealed beneath the flesh, but in the embryo the tail projects freely and is movable. Up to the sixth month of the ante-natal sleep the body is covered, all but the palms and soles, with longish hair (the lanugo), which usually disappears before birth. This is a stage in the normal development, which is reasonably interpreted as a recapitulation of a stage in the racial evolution. We draw this inference when we find that the unborn offspring of an almost hairless whale has an abundant representation of hairs; we must draw a similar inference in the case of man.

It must be noticed that there are two serious errors in the careless statement often made that man in his development is at one time like a little fish, at a later stage like a little reptile, at a later stage like a little primitive mammal, and eventually like a little monkey. The first error here is that the comparison should be made with *embryo*-fish, *embryo*-reptile, *embryo*-mammal, and so on. It is in the making of the embryos that the great resemblance lies. When the human embryo shows the laying down of the essential vertebrate characters, such as brain and spinal cord, then it is closely comparable to the embryo of a lower vertebrate at a similar stage. When, at a subsequent stage, its heart, for instance, is about to become a four-chambered mammalian heart, it is closely comparable to the heart of, let us say, a turtle, which never becomes more than three-chambered. The point is that in the making of the organs of the body, say brain and kidneys, the embryo of man pursues a path closely corresponding to the path followed by the embryos of other backboned animals lower in the scale, but at successive stages it parts company with these, with the lowest first and so on in succession. A human embryo is never like a little reptile, but the developing organs pass through stages which very closely resemble the corresponding stages in lower types which are in a general way ancestral.

The second error is that every kind of animal, man included,

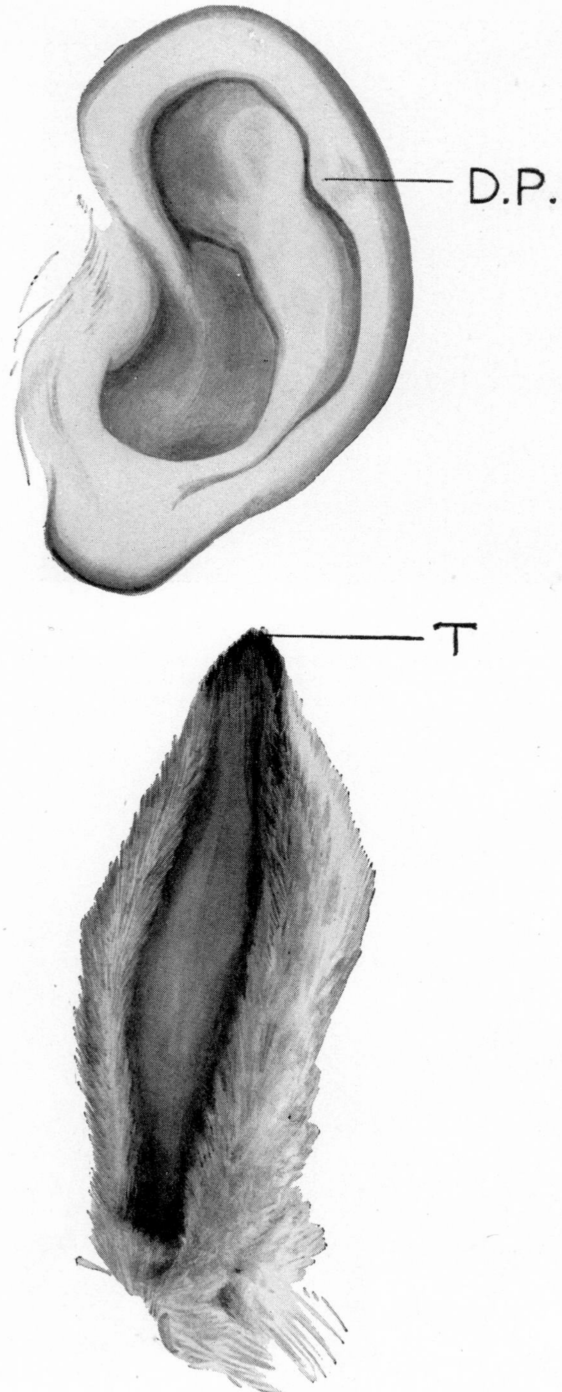

"DARWIN'S POINT" ON HUMAN EAR (MARKED D.P.)

It corresponds to the tip (T) of the ear of an ordinary mammal, as shown in the hare's ear below. In the young orang the part corresponding to Darwin's point is still at the tip of the ear.

Photo: J. Russell & Sons.

PROFESSOR SIR ARTHUR KEITH, M.D., LL.D., F.R.S.

Conservator of the Museum and Hunterian Professor, Royal College of Surgeons of England. One of the foremost living anthropologists and a leading authority on the antiquity of man.

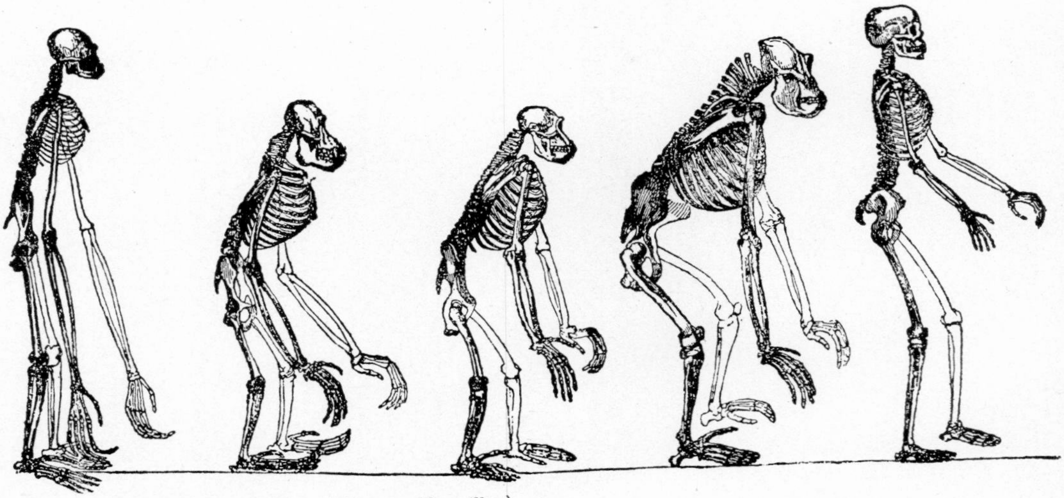

After T. H. Huxley (by permission of Messrs. Macmillan).

SKELETONS OF THE GIBBON, ORANG, CHIMPANZEE, GORILLA, MAN

Photographically reduced from diagrams of the natural size (except that of the gibbon, which was twice as large as nature) drawn by Mr. Waterhouse Hawkins from specimens in the Museum of the Royal College of Surgeons.

has from the first a certain individuality, with peculiar characteristics which are all its own. This is expressed by the somewhat difficult word *specificity,* which just means that every species is itself and no other. So in the development of the human embryo, while there are close resemblances to the embryos of apes, monkeys, other mammals, and even, at earlier stages still, to the embryos of reptile and fish, it has to be admitted that we are dealing from first to last with a human embryo with peculiarities of its own.

Every human being begins his or her life as a single cell—a fertilised egg-cell, a treasure-house of all the ages. For in this living microcosm, only a small fraction ($\frac{1}{125}$) of an inch in diameter, there is condensed—who can imagine how?—all the natural inheritance of man, all the legacy of his parentage, of his ancestry, of his long pre-human pedigree. Darwin called the pinhead brain of the ant the most marvellous atom of matter in the world, but the human ovum is more marvellous still. It has more possibilities in it than any other thing, yet without fertilisation it will die. The fertilised ovum divides and redivides; there results a ball of cells and a sack of cells; gradually division of labour becomes the rule; there is a laying down of nervous system and food-canal, muscular system and skeleton, and so proceeds what is learnedly called differentiation. Out of the apparently simple there emerges the obviously complex. As Aristotle observed more than two thousand years ago, in the developing egg of the hen there soon appears the beating heart! There is nothing like this in the non-living world. But to return to the developing human embryo, there is formed from and above the embryonic food-canal a skeletal rod, which is called the notochord. It thrills the imagination to learn that this is the only supporting axis that the lower orders of the backboned race possess. The curious thing is that it does not become the backbone, which is certainly one of the essential features of the vertebrate race. The notochord is the supporting axis of the pioneer backboned animals, namely the Lancelets and the Round-mouths (Cyclostomes), such as the Lamprey. They have no backbone in the strict sense, but they have this notochord. It can easily be dissected out in the lamprey—a long gristly rod. It is surrounded by a sheath which becomes the backbone of most fishes and of all higher animals. The interesting point is that although the notochord is only a vestige in the adults of these types, it is never absent from the embryo. It occurs even in man, a short-lived relic of the primeval supporting axis of the body. It comes and then it goes, leaving only minute traces in the adult. We cannot say that it is of any use, unless it serves as a stimulus to the development of its substitute, the backbone. It is only a piece of preliminary scaffolding, but there is no more eloquent instance of the living hand of the past.

One other instance must suffice of what Professor Lull calls the wonderful changes wrought in the dark of the ante-natal period, which recapitulate in rapid abbreviation the great evolutionary steps which were taken by man's ancestors "during the long night of the geological past." On the sides of the neck of the human embryo there are four pairs of slits, the "visceral clefts," openings from the beginning of the food-canals to the surface. There is no doubt as to their significance. They correspond to the gill-slits of fishes and tadpoles. Yet in reptiles, birds, and mammals they have no connection with breathing, which is their function in fishes and amphibians. Indeed, they are not of any use at all, except that the first becomes the Eustachian tube bringing the ear-passage into connection with the back of the mouth, and that the second and third have to do with the development of a curious organ called the thymus gland. Persistent, nevertheless, these gill-slits are, recalling even in man an aquatic ancestry of many millions of years ago.

When all these lines of evidence are considered, they are seen to converge in the conclusion that man is derived from a simian stock of mammals. He is solidary with the rest of creation. To quote the closing words of Darwin's *Descent of Man:*

> We must, however, acknowledge, as it seems to me, that man with all his noble qualities, with sympathy which feels for the most debased, with benevolence which extends not only to other men but to the humblest living creature, with his God-like intellect, which has penetrated into the movements and constitution of the solar system—with all these exalted powers—man still bears in his bodily frame the indelible stamp of his lowly origin.

We should be clear that this view does not say more than that man sprang from a stock common to him and to the higher apes. Those who are repelled by the idea of man's derivation from a simian type should remember that the theory implies rather more than this, namely, that man is the outcome of a genealogy which has implied many millions of years of experimenting and sifting —the groaning and travailing of a whole creation. Speaking of man's mental qualities, Sir Ray Lankester says: "They justify the view that man forms a new departure in the gradual unfolding of Nature's predestined plan." In any case, we have to try to square our views with the facts, not the facts with our views, and while one of the facts is that man stands unique and apart, the other is that man is a scion of a progressive simian stock. Naturalists have exposed the pit whence man has been digged and the rock whence he has been hewn, but it is surely a heartening encouragement to know that it is an ascent, not a descent, that we have behind us. There is wisdom in Pascal's maxim:

> It is dangerous to show man too plainly how like he is to the animals, without, at the same time, reminding him of his greatness. It is equally unwise to impress him with his greatness and not with his lowliness. It is worse to leave him in ignorance of both. But it is very profitable to recognise the two facts.

§ 3

Man's Pedigree

The facts of anatomy, physiology, and embryology, of which we have given illustrations, all point to man's affiliation with the order of monkeys and apes. To this order is given the name Primates, and our first and second question must be when and whence the Primates began. The rock record answers the first question: the Primates emerged about the dawn of the Eocene era, when grass was beginning to cover the earth with a garment. Their ancestral home was in the north in both hemispheres, and then they migrated to Africa, India, Malay, and South America. In North America the Primates soon became extinct, and the same thing happened later on in Europe. In this case, however, there was a repeopling from the South (in the Lower Miocene) and then a second extinction (in the Upper Pliocene) before man appeared. There is considerable evidence in support of Professor R. S. Lull's conclusion, that in Southern Asia, Africa, and South America the evolution of Primates was continuous since the first great southward migration, and there is, of course, an abundant modern representation of Primates in these regions to-day.

As to the second question: Whence the Primates sprang, the answer must be more conjectural. But it is a reasonable view that Carnivores and Primates sprang from a common Insectivore stock, the one order diverging towards flesh-eating and hunting on the ground, the other order diverging towards fruit-eating and arboreal habits. There is no doubt that the Insectivores (including shrews, tree-shrews, hedgehog, mole, and the like) were very plastic and progressive mammals.

What followed in the course of ages was the divergence of branch after branch from the main Primate stem. First there diverged the South American monkeys on a line of their own, and then the Old World monkeys, such as the macaques and

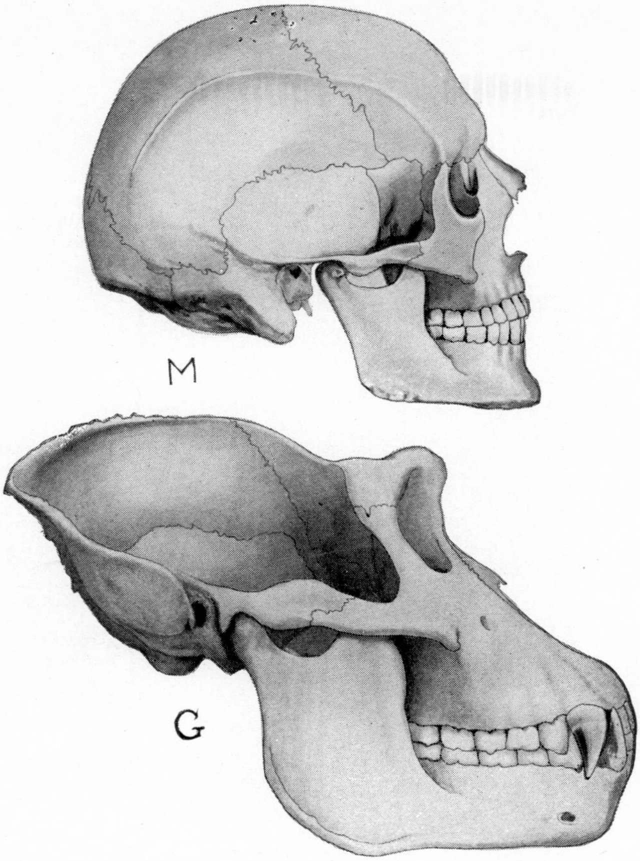

SIDE-VIEW OF SKULL OF MAN (M) AND GORILLA (G)

Notice in the gorilla's skull the protrusive face region, the big eyebrow ridges, the much less domed cranial cavity, the massive lower jaw, the big canine teeth. Notice in man's skull the well-developed forehead, the domed and spacious cranial cavity, the absence of any snout, the chin process, and many other marked differences separating the human skull from the ape's.

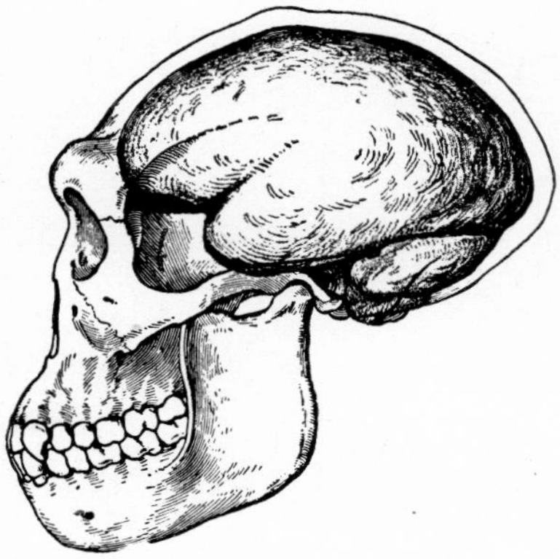

THE SKULL AND BRAIN-CASE OF PITHECANTHROPUS, THE JAVA APE-MAN, AS RESTORED BY J. H. McGREGOR FROM THE SCANTY REMAINS

The restoration shows the low, retreating forehead and the prominent eyebrow ridges.

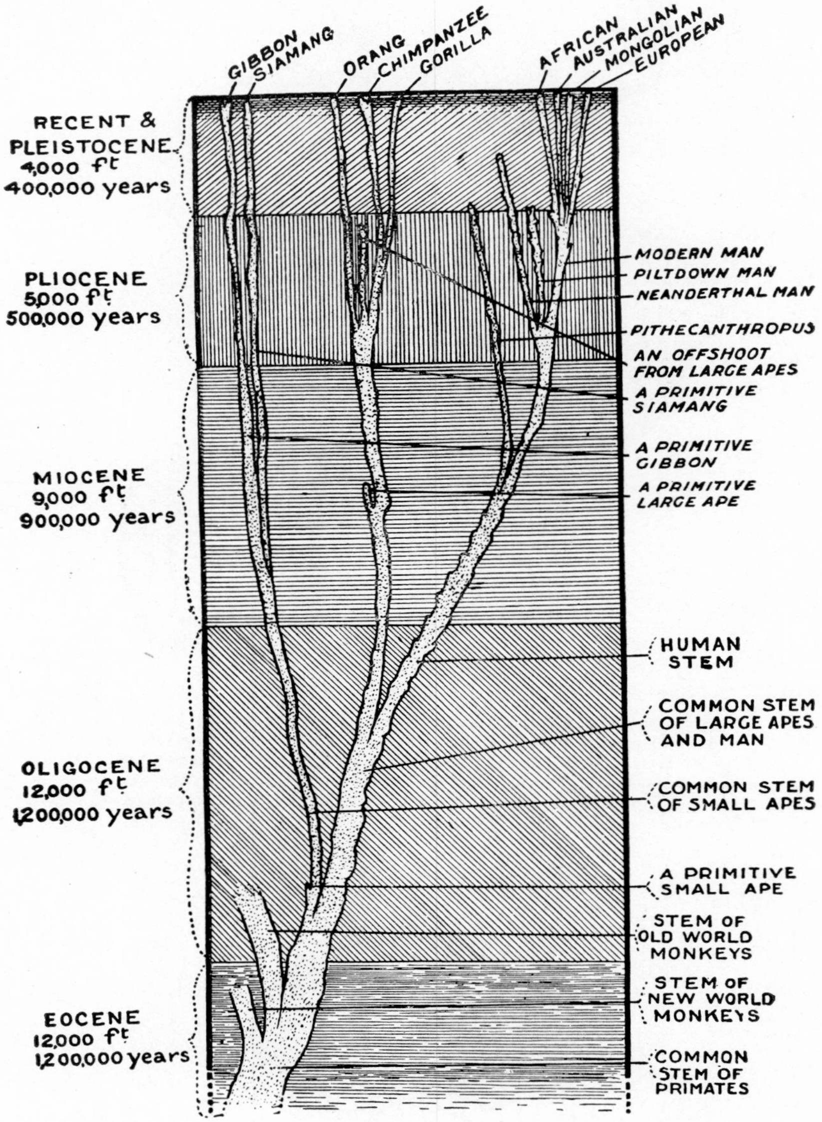

SUGGESTED GENEALOGICAL TREE OF MAN AND ANTHROPOID APES

From Sir Arthur Keith; the lettering to the right has been slightly simplified.

baboons. Ages passed and the main stems gave off (in the Oligocene period) the branch now represented by the small anthropoid apes—the gibbon and the siamang. Distinctly later there diverged the branch of the large anthropoid apes—the gorilla, the chimpanzee, and the orang. That left a generalised humanoid stock separated off from all monkeys and apes, and including the immediate precursors of man. When this sifting out of a generalised humanoid stock took place remains very uncertain, some authorities referring it to the Miocene, others to the early Pliocene. Some would estimate its date at half a million years ago, others at two millions! The fact is that questions of chronology do not as yet admit of scientific statement.

We are on firmer, though still uncertain, ground when we state the probability that it was in Asia that the precursors of man were separated off from monkeys and apes, and began to be terrestrial rather than arboreal. Professor Lull points out that Asia is nearest to the oldest known human remains (in Java), and that Asia was the seat of the most ancient civilisations and the original home of many domesticated animals and cultivated plants. The probability is that the cradle of the human race was in Asia.

Man's Arboreal Apprenticeship

At this point it will be useful to consider man's arboreal apprenticeship and how he became a terrestrial journeyman. Professor Wood Jones has worked out very convincingly the thesis that man had no direct four-footed ancestry, but that the Primate stock to which he belongs was from its first divergence arboreal. He maintains that the leading peculiarities of the immediate precursors of man were wrought out during a long arboreal apprenticeship. The first great gain of arboreal life on bipedal erect lines (not after the quadrupedal fashion of tree-sloths, for instance) was the emancipation of the hand. The foot became the supporting and branch-gripping member, and the hand was set free to reach upward, to hang on by, to seize the fruit, to lift it and hold it to the mouth, and to hug the young one close to the breast. The hand thus set free has remained plastic—a generalised, not a specialised member. Much has followed from man's "handiness."

The arboreal life had many other consequences. It led to an increased freedom of movement of the thigh on the hip joint, to muscular arrangements for balancing the body on the leg, to making the backbone a supple yet stable curved pillar, to a strongly developed collar-bone which is only found well-formed when the fore-limb is used for more than support, and to a power of "opposing" the thumb and the big toe to the other digits of the hand and foot—an obvious advantage for branch-gripping. But the evolution of a free hand made it possible to dispense with protrusive lips and gripping teeth. Thus began the recession of the snout region, the associated enlargement of the brain-box, and the bringing of the eyes to the front. The overcrowding of the teeth that followed the shortening of the snout was one of the taxes on progress of which modern man is often reminded in his dental troubles.

Another acquisition associated with arboreal life was a greatly increased power of turning the head from side to side—a mobility very important in locating sounds and in exploring with the eyes. Furthermore, there came about a flattening of the chest and of the back, and the movements of the midriff (or diaphragm) came to count for more in respiration than the movements of the ribs. The sense of touch came to be of more importance and the sense of smell of less; the part of the brain receiving tidings from hand and eye and ear came to predominate over the part for receiving olfactory messages. Finally, the need for carrying the infant about among the branches must surely have implied an intensification of family relations, and favoured the evolution of gentleness.

Photo: New York Zoological Park.

THE GIBBON IS LOWER THAN THE OTHER APES AS REGARDS ITS SKULL AND DENTITION, BUT IT IS HIGHLY SPECIALIZED IN THE ADAPTATION OF ITS LIMBS TO ARBOREAL LIFE

Photo: New York Zoological Park.

THE ORANG HAS A HIGH ROUNDED SKULL AND A LONG FACE

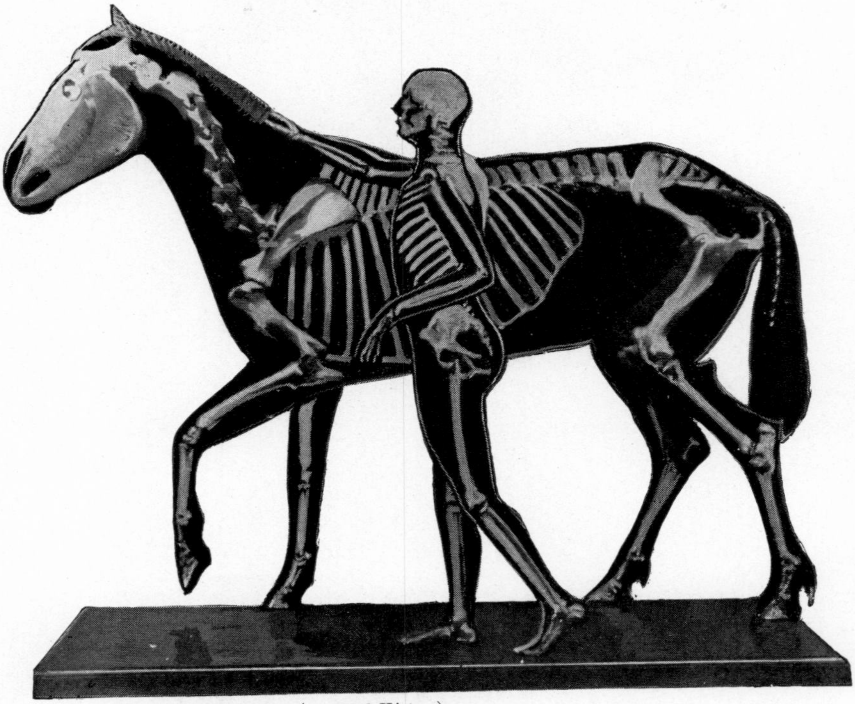

Photo: British Museum (Natural History).

COMPARISONS OF THE SKELETONS OF HORSE AND MAN

Bone for bone, the two skeletons are like one another, though man is a biped and the horse a quadruped. The backbone in man is mainly vertical; the backbone in the horse is horizontal except in the neck and the tail. Man's skull is mainly in a line with the backbone; the horse's at an angle to it. Both man and horse have seven neck vertebræ. Man has five digits on each limb; the horse has only one digit well developed on each limb.

It may be urged that we are attaching too much importance to the arboreal apprenticeship, since many tree-loving animals remain to-day very innocent creatures. To this reasonable objection there are two answers, first that in its many acquisitions the arboreal evolution of the *humanoid* precursors of man prepared the way for the survival of a *human* type marked by a great step in brain-development; and second that the passage from the humanoid to the human was probably associated with *a return to mother earth.*

According to Professor Lull, to whose fine textbook, *Organic Evolution* (1917), we are much indebted, "climatic conditions in Asia in the Miocene or early Pliocene were such as to compel the descent of the prehuman ancestor from the trees, a step which was absolutely essential to further human development." Continental elevation and consequent aridity led to a dwindling of the forests, and forced the ape-man to come to earth. "And at the last arose the man."

According to Lull, the descent from the trees was associated with the assumption of a more erect posture, with increased liberation and plasticity of the hand, with becoming a hunter, with experiments towards clothing and shelter, with an exploring habit, and with the beginning of communal life.

It is a plausible view that the transition from the humanoid to the human was effected by a discontinuous variation of considerable magnitude, what is nowadays called a *mutation,* and that it had mainly to do with the brain and the vocal organs. But given the gains of the arboreal apprenticeship, the stimulus of an enforced descent to terra firma, and an evolving brain and voice, we can recognise accessory factors which helped success to succeed. Perhaps the absence of great physical strength prompted reliance on wits; the prolongation of infancy would help to educate the parents in gentleness; the strengthening of the feeling of kinship would favour the evolution of family and social life—of which there are many anticipations at lower levels. There is much truth in the saying: "Man did not make society, society made man."

A continuation of the story will deal with the emergence of the primitive types of man and the gradual ascent of the modern species.

§ 4

Tentative Men

So far the story has been that of the sifting out of a humanoid stock and of the transition to human kind, from the ancestors of apes and men to the man-ape, and from the man-ape to man. It looks as if the sifting-out process had proceeded further, for there were several human branches that did not lead on to the modern type of man.

1. The first of these is represented by the scanty fossil remains known as *Pithecanthropus erectus,* found in Java in fossiliferous beds which date from the end of the Pliocene or the beginning of the Pleistocene era. Perhaps this means half a million years ago, and the remains occurred along with those of some mammals which are now extinct. Unfortunately the remains of Pithecanthropus the Erect consisted only of a skull-cap, a thigh-bone, and two back teeth, so it is not surprising that experts should differ considerably in their interpretation of what was found. Some have regarded the remains as those of a large gibbon, others as those of a pre-human ape-man, and others as those of a primitive man off the main line of ascent. According to Sir Arthur Keith, Pithecanthropus was "a being human in stature, human in gait, human in all its parts, save its brain." The thigh-bone indicates a height of about 5 feet 7 inches, one inch less than the average height of the men of to-day. The skull-cap indicates a low, flat forehead, beetling brows, and a capacity about two-thirds of the modern size. The remains were found by Dubois, in 1894, in Trinil in Central Java.

2. The next offshoot is represented by the Heidelberg man

A RECONSTRUCTION OF THE JAVA MAN

(*Pithecanthropus erectus.*)

(*Homo heidelbergensis*), discovered near Heidelberg in 1907 by Dr. Schoetensack. But the remains consisted only of a lower jaw and its teeth. Along with this relic were bones of various mammals, including some long since extinct in Europe, such as elephant, rhinoceros, bison, and lion. The circumstances indicate an age of perhaps 300,000 years ago. There were also very crude flint implements (or eoliths). But the teeth are human teeth, and the jaw seems transitional between that of an anthropoid ape and that of man. Thus there was no chin. According to most authorities the lower jaw from the Heidelberg sand-pit must be regarded as a relic of a primitive type off the main line of human ascent.

3. It was in all probability in the Pliocene that there took origin the Neanderthal species of man, *Homo neanderthalensis,* first known from remains found in 1856 in the Neanderthal ravine near Düsseldorf. According to some authorities Neanderthal man was living in Europe a quarter of a million years ago. Other specimens were afterwards found elsewhere, e.g. in Belgium ("the men of Spy"), in France, in Croatia, and at Gibraltar, so that a good deal is known of Neanderthal man. He was a loose-limbed fellow, short of stature and of slouching gait, but a skilful artificer, fashioning beautifully worked flints with a characteristic style. He used fire; he buried his dead reverently and furnished them with an outfit for a long journey; and he had a big brain. But he had great beetling, ape-like eyebrow ridges and massive jaws, and he showed "simian characters swarming in the details of his structure." In most of the points in which he differs from modern man he approaches the anthropoid apes, and he must be regarded as a low type of man off the main line. Huxley regarded the Neanderthal man as a low form of the modern type, but expert opinion seems to agree rather with the view maintained in 1864 by Professor William King of Galway, that the Neanderthal man represents a distinct species off the main line of ascent. He disappeared with apparent suddenness (like some aboriginal races to-day) about the end of the Fourth Great Ice Age; but

there is evidence that before he ceased to be there had emerged a successor rather than a descendant—the modern man.

4. Another offshoot from the main line is probably represented by the Piltdown man, found in Sussex in 1912. The remains consisted of the walls of the skull, which indicate a large brain, and a high forehead without the beetling eyebrows of the Neanderthal man and Pithecanthropus. The "find" included a tooth and part of a lower jaw, but these perhaps belong to some ape, for they are very discrepant. The Piltdown skull represents the most ancient human remains as yet found in Britain, and Dr. Smith Woodward's establishment of a separate genus Eoanthropus expresses his conviction that the Piltdown man was off the line of the evolution of the modern type. If the tooth and piece of lower jaw belong to the Piltdown skull, then there was a remarkable combination of ape-like and human characters. As regards the brain, *inferred* from the skull-walls, Sir Arthur Keith says:

> All the essential features of the brain of modern man are to be seen in the brain cast. There are some which must be regarded as primitive. There can be no doubt that it is built on exactly the same lines as our modern brains. A few minor alterations would make it in all respects a modern brain. . . . Although our knowledge of the human brain is limited—there are large areas to which we can assign no definite function—we may rest assured that a brain which was shaped in a mould so similar to our own was one which responded to the outside world as ours does. Piltdown man saw, heard, felt, thought, and dreamt much as we do still.

And this was 150,000 years ago at a modern estimate, and some would say half a million.

There is neither agreement nor certainty as to the antiquity of man, except that the modern type was distinguishable from its collaterals hundreds of thousands of years ago. The general impression left is very grand. In remote antiquity the Primate

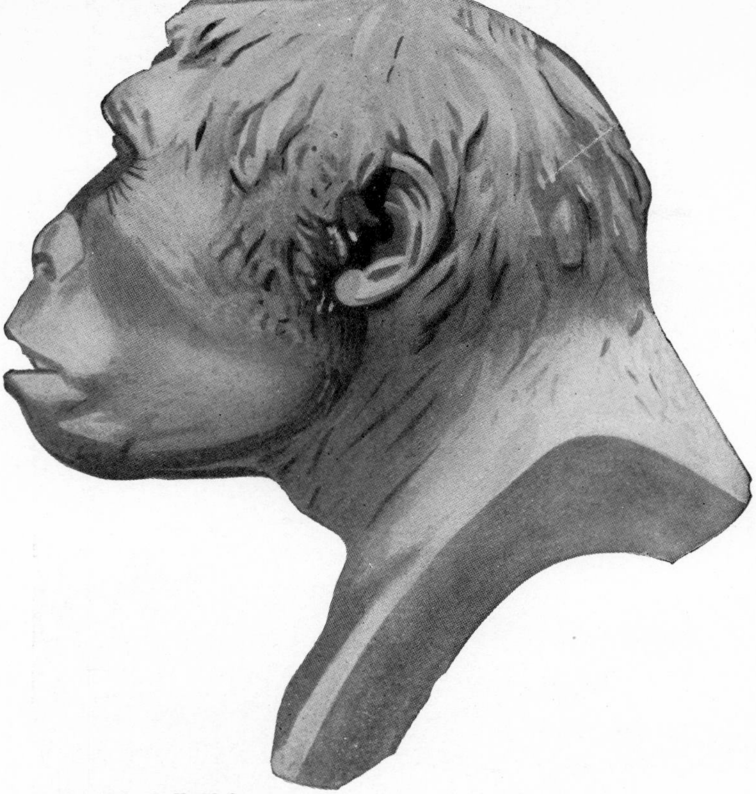

After a model by J. H. McGregor.

PROFILE VIEW OF THE HEAD OF PITHECANTHROPUS, THE JAVA APE-MAN—AN EARLY OFFSHOOT FROM THE MAIN LINE OF MAN'S ASCENT

The animal remains found along with the skull-cap, thigh-bone, and two teeth of Pithecanthropus seem to indicate the lowest Pleistocene period, perhaps 500,000 years ago.

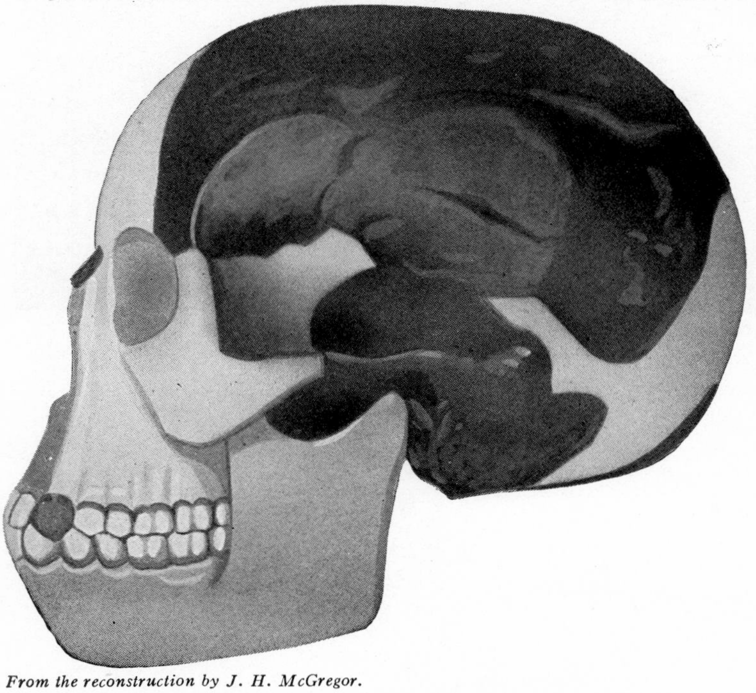

From the reconstruction by J. H. McGregor.

PILTDOWN SKULL. THE DARK PARTS ONLY ARE PRESERVED, NAMELY PORTIONS OF THE CRANIAL WALLS AND THE NASAL BONES

Some authorities include a canine tooth and part of the lower jaw which were found close by. The remains were found in 1912 in Thames gravels in Sussex, and are usually regarded as vastly more ancient than those of Neanderthal Man. It has been suggested that Piltdown Man lived 100,000 to 150,000 years ago, in the Third Interglacial period.

Reproduced by permission from Osborn's "Men of the Old Stone Age."

SAND-PIT AT MAUER, NEAR HEIDELBERG: DISCOVERY SITE OF THE JAW OF HEIDELBERG MAN

a—b. "Newer loess," either of Third Interglacial or of Postglacial times.
b—c. "Older loess" (sandy loess), of the close of Second Interglacial times.
c—f. The "sands of Mauer."
d—e. An intermediate layer of clay.

The white cross (X) indicates the spot at the base of the "sands of Mauer" at which the jaw of Heidelberg was discovered.

stem diverged from the other orders of mammals; it sent forth its tentative branches, and the result was a tangle of monkeys; ages passed and the monkeys were left behind, while the main stem, still probing its way, gave off the Anthropoid apes, both small and large. But they too were left behind, and the main line gave off other experiments—indications of which we know in Java, at Heidelberg, in the Neanderthal, and at Piltdown. None of these lasted or was made perfect. They represent *tentative* men who had their day and ceased to be, our predecessors rather than our ancestors. Still, the main stem goes on evolving, and who will be bold enough to say what fruit it has yet to bear!

Primitive Men

Ancient skeletons of men of the modern type have been found in many places, e.g. Combe Capelle in Dordogne, Galley Hill in Kent, Cro-Magnon in Périgord, Mentone on the Riviera; and they are often referred to as "Cave-men" or "men of the Early Stone Age." They had large skulls, high foreheads, well-marked chins, and other features such as modern man possesses. They were true men at last—that is to say, like ourselves! The spirited pictures they made on the walls of caves in France and Spain show artistic sense and skill. Well-finished statuettes representing nude female figures are also known. The elaborate burial customs point to a belief in life after death. They made stone implements—knives, scrapers, gravers, and the like, of the type known as Palæolithic, and these show interesting gradations of skill and peculiarities of style. The "Cave-men" lived between the third and fourth Ice Ages, along with cave-bear, cave-lion, cave-hyæna, mammoth, woolly rhinoceros, Irish elk, and other mammals now extinct—taking us back to 30,000–50,000 years ago, and many would say much more. Some of the big-brained skulls of these Palæolithic cave-men show not a single feature that could be called primitive. They show teeth which in size and form are exactly the same as those of a thousand generations afterwards—and suffering from gumboil too! There seems little doubt that these vigorous Palæolithic Cave-men of Europe were living for a while contemporaneously with the men of Neanderthal, and it is possible that they directly or indirectly hastened the disappearance of their more primitive collaterals. Curiously enough, however, they had not themselves adequate lasting power in Europe, for they seem for the most part to have dwindled away, leaving perhaps stray present-day survivors in isolated districts. The probability is that after their decline Europe was repeopled by immigrants from Asia. It cannot be said that there is any inherent biological necessity for the decline of a vigorous race—many animal races go back for millions of years—but in mankind the historical fact is that a period of great racial vigour and success is often followed by a period of decline, sometimes leading to practical disappearance as a definite race. The causes of this waning remain very obscure—sometimes environmental, sometimes constitutional, sometimes competitive. Sometimes the introduction of a new parasite, like the malaria organism, may have been to blame.

After the Ice Ages had passed, perhaps 25,000 years ago, the Palæolithic culture gave place to the Neolithic. The men who made rudely dressed but often beautiful stone implements were succeeded or replaced by men who made polished stone implements. The earliest inhabitants of Scotland were of this Neolithic culture, migrating from the Continent when the ice-fields of the Great Glaciation had disappeared. Their remains are often associated with the "Fifty-foot Beach" which, though now high and dry, was the seashore in early Neolithic days. Much is known about these men of the polished stones. They were hunters, fowlers, and fishermen; without domesticated animals or agriculture; short folk, two or three inches below the present standard; living an active strenuous life. Similarly, for the south, Sir Arthur Keith pictures for us a Neolithic community at Coldrum in Kent, dating from about 4,000 years ago—a few ticks of the

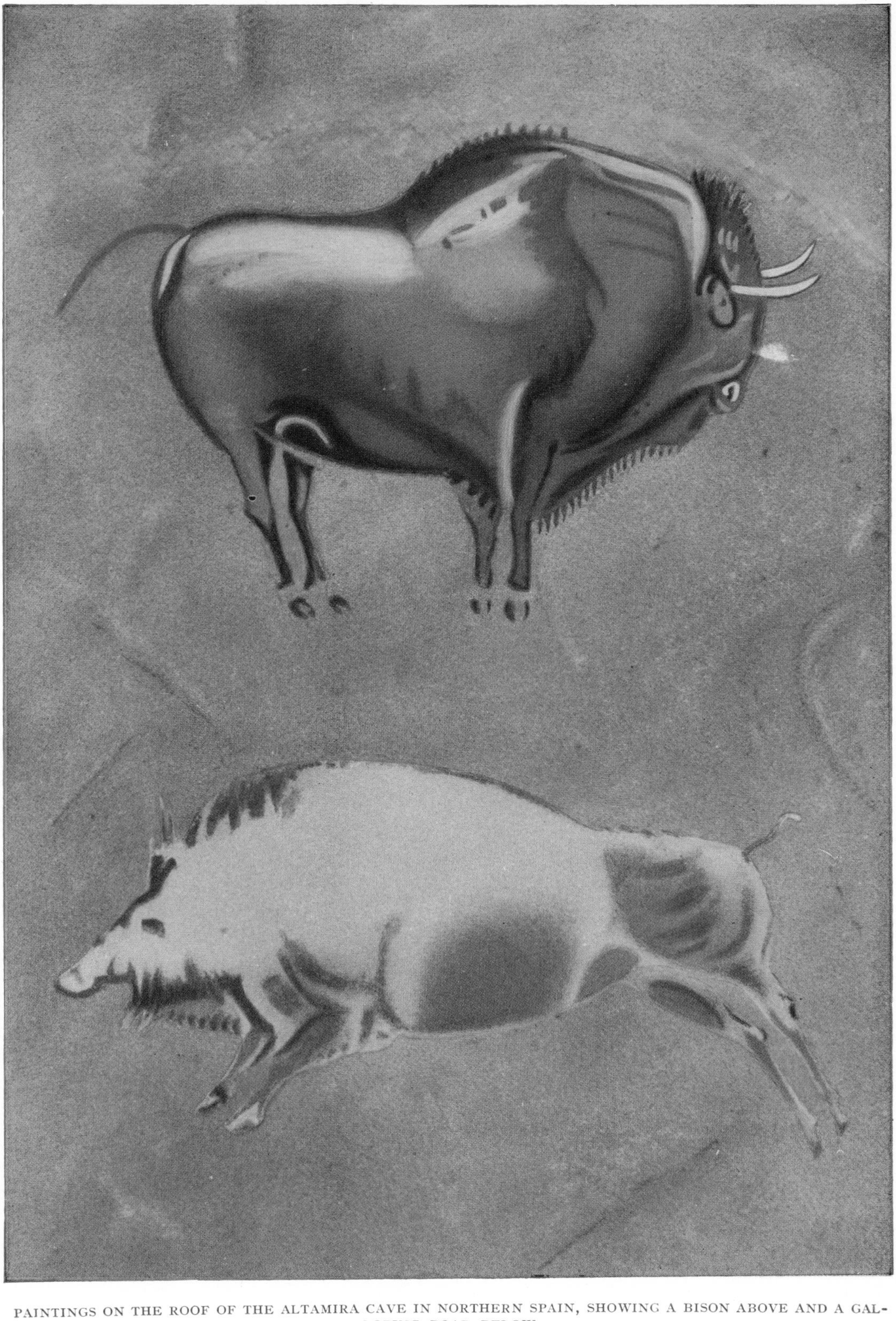

PAINTINGS ON THE ROOF OF THE ALTAMIRA CAVE IN NORTHERN SPAIN, SHOWING A BISON ABOVE AND A GALLOPING BOAR BELOW

The artistic drawings, over 2 feet in length, were made by the Reindeer Men or "Cromagnards" in the time of the Upper or Post-Glacial Pleistocene, before the appearance of the Neolithic men.

geological clock. It consisted, in this case, of agricultural pioneers, men with large heads and big brains, about two inches shorter in stature than the modern British average (5 ft. 8 in.), with better teeth and broader palates than men have in these days of soft food, with beliefs concerning life and death similar to those that swayed their contemporaries in Western and Southern Europe. Very interesting is the manipulative skill they showed on a large scale in erecting standing stones (probably connected with calendar-keeping and with worship), and on a small scale in making daring operations on the skull. Four thousand years ago is given as a probable date for that early community in Kent, but evidences of Neolithic man occur in situations which demand a much greater antiquity—perhaps 30,000 years. And man was not young then!

We must open one more chapter in the thrilling story of the Ascent of Man—the Metal Ages, which are in a sense still continuing. Metals began to be used in the late Polished Stone (Neolithic) times, for there were always overlappings. Copper came first, Bronze second, and Iron last. The working of copper in the East has been traced back to the fourth millennium B.C., and there was also a very ancient Copper Age in the New World. It need hardly be said that where copper is scarce, as in Britain, we cannot expect to find much trace of a Copper Age.

The ores of different metals seem to have been smelted together in an experimental way by many prehistoric metallurgists, and bronze was the alloy that rewarded the combination of tin with copper. There is evidence of a more or less definite Bronze Age in Egypt and Babylonia, Greece and Europe.

It is not clear why iron should not have been the earliest metal to be used by man, but the Iron Age dates from about the middle of the second millennium B.C. From Egypt the usage spread through the Mediterranean region to North Europe, or it may have been that discoveries made in Central Europe, so rich in iron-mines, saturated southwards, following for instance, the route of the amber trade from the Baltic. Compared with stone, the metals afforded much greater possibilities of implements, instruments, and weapons, and their discovery and usage had undoubtedly great influence on the Ascent of Man. Occasionally, however, on his descent.

Retrospect

Looking backwards, we discern the following stages: (1) The setting apart of a Primate stock, marked off from other mammals by a tendency to big brains, a free hand, gregariousness, and good-humoured talkativeness. (2) The divergence of marmosets and New World monkeys and Old World monkeys, leaving a stock—an anthropoid stock—common to the present-day and extinct apes and to mankind. (3) From this common stock the Anthropoid apes diverged, far from ignoble creatures, and a humanoid stock was set apart. (4) From the latter (we follow Sir Arthur Keith and other authorities) there arose what may be called, without disparagement, tentative or experimental men, indicated by Pithecanthropus "the Erect," the Heidelberg man, the Neanderthalers, and, best of all, the early men of the Sussex Weald—hinted at by the Piltdown skull. It matters little whether particular items are corroborated or disproved—e.g. whether the Heidelberg man came before or after the Neanderthalers—the general trend of evolution remains clear. (5) In any case, the result was the evolution of *Homo sapiens, the man we are*—a quite different fellow from the Neanderthaler. (6) Then arose various stocks of primitive men, proving everything and holding fast to that which is good. There were the Palæolithic peoples, with rude stone implements, a strong vigorous race, but probably, in most cases, supplanted by fresh experiments. These may have arisen as shoots from the growing point of the old race, or as a fresh offshoot from more generalised members at a lower level. This is the eternal possible victory alike of aristocracy and democracy. (7) Palæolithic men were involved in the

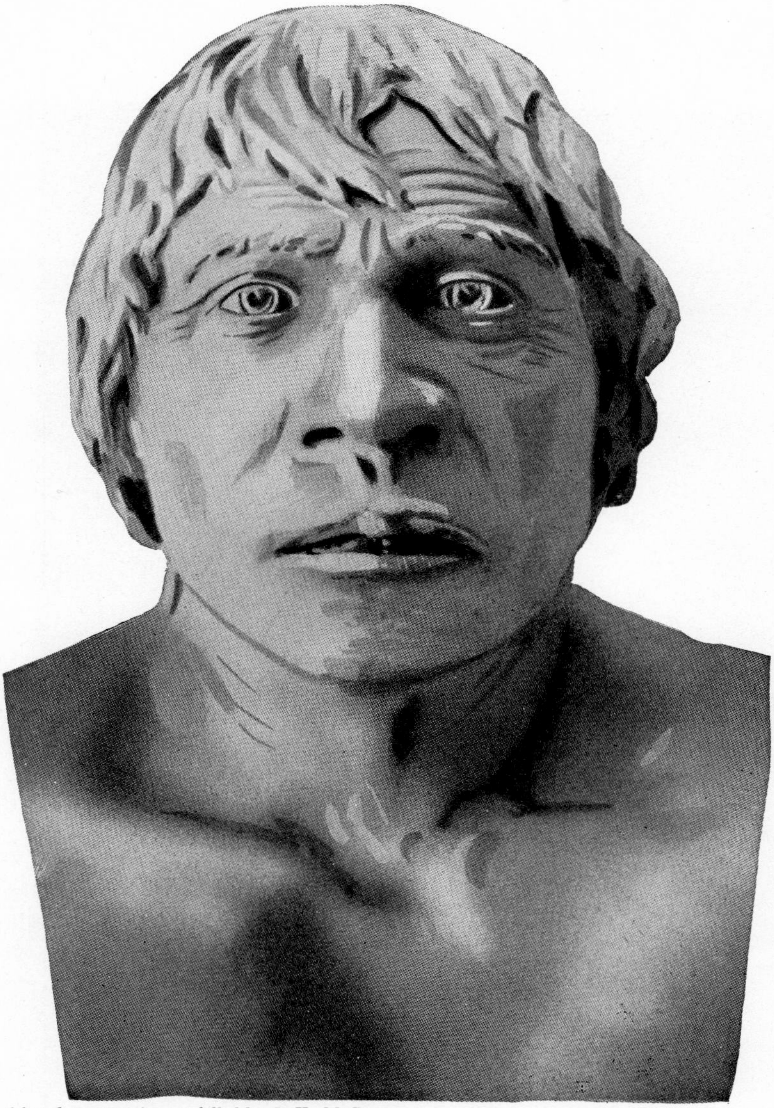

After the restoration modelled by J. H. McGregor.

PILTDOWN MAN, PRECEDING NEANDERTHAL MAN, PERHAPS 100,000 TO 150,000 YEARS AGO

After the restoration modelled by J. H. McGregor.

THE NEANDERTHAL MAN OF LA CHAPELLE-AUX-SAINTS

The men of this race lived in Europe from the Third Interglacial period through the Fourth Glacial. They disappeared somewhat suddenly, being replaced by the Modern Man type, such as the Cromagnards. Many regard the Neanderthal Men as a distinct species.

succession of four Great Ice Ages or Glaciations, and it may be that the human race owes much to the alternation of hard times and easy times—glacial and interglacial. When the ice-fields cleared off Neolithic man had his innings. (8) And we have closed the story, in the meantime, with the Metal Ages.

It seems not unfitting that we should at this point sound another note—that of the man of feeling. It is clear in William James's words:

> Bone of our bone, and flesh of our flesh, are these half-brutish prehistoric brothers. Girdled about with the immense darkness of this mysterious universe even as we are, they were born and died, suffered and struggled. Given over to fearful crime and passion, plunged in the blackest ignorance, preyed upon by hideous and grotesque delusions, yet steadfastly serving the profoundest of ideals in their fixed faith that existence in any form is better than non-existence, they ever rescued triumphantly from the jaws of ever imminent destruction the torch of life which, thanks to them, now lights the world for us.

Races of Mankind

Given a variable stock spreading over diverse territory, we expect to find it splitting up into varieties which may become steadied into races or incipient species. Thus we have races of hive-bees, "Italians," "Punics," and so forth; and thus there arose races of men. Certain types suited certain areas, and periods of in-breeding tended to make the distinctive peculiarities of each incipient race well-defined and stable. When the original peculiarities, say, of negro and Mongol, Australian and Caucasian, arose as brusque variations or "mutations," then they would have great staying power from generation to generation. They would not be readily swamped by intercrossing or averaged off. Peculiarities and changes of climate and surroundings, not to speak of other change-producing factors, would provoke new departures from age to age, and so fresh racial ventures were made. Moreover, the occurrence of out-breeding when two races met, in peace or in war, would certainly serve to induce fresh starts. Very important in the evolution of human races must have been the alternating occurrence of periods of in-breeding (endogamy), tending to stability and sameness, and periods of out-breeding (exogamy), tending to changefulness and diversity.

Thus we may distinguish several more or less clearly defined primitive races of mankind—notably the African, the Australian, the Mongolian, and the Caucasian. The woolly-haired African race includes the negroes and the very primitive bushmen. The wavy- to curly-haired Australian race includes the Jungle Tribes of the Deccan, the Vedda of Ceylon, the Jungle Folk or Semang, and the natives of unsettled parts of Australia—all sometimes slumped together as "Pre-Dravidians." The straight-haired Mongols include those of Tibet, Indo-China, China, and Formosa, those of many oceanic islands, and of the north from Japan to Lapland. The Caucasians include Mediterraneans, Semites, Nordics, Afghans, Alpines, and many more.

There are very few corners of knowledge more difficult than that of the Races of Men, the chief reason being that there has been so much movement and migration in the course of the ages. One physical type has mingled with another, inducing strange amalgams and novelties. If we start with what might be called "zoological" races or strains differing, for instance, in their hair (woolly-haired Africans, straight-haired Mongols, curly- or wavy-haired Pre-Dravidians and Caucasians), we find these replaced by *peoples* who are mixtures of various races, "brethren by civilisation more than by blood." As Professor Flinders Petrie has said, the only meaning the term "race" now can have is that of a group of human beings whose type has been unified by their rate of assimilation exceeding the rate of change produced by the infiltration of foreign elements. It is probable, however, that the progress of precise anthropology will make it possible to distinguish the various racial "strains" that make up

RESTORATION BY A. FORESTIER OF THE RHODESIAN MAN WHOSE SKULL WAS DISCOVERED IN 1921

Attention may be drawn to the beetling eyebrow ridges, the projecting upper lip, the large eye-sockets, the well-poised head, the strong shoulders.

The squatting figure is crushing seeds with a stone, and a crusher is lying on the rock to his right.

RESTORATION BY A. FORESTIER OF THE RHODESIAN MAN WHOSE SKULL WAS DISCOVERED IN 1921

The figure in the foreground, holding a staff, shows the erect attitude and the straight legs. His left hand holds a flint implement. On the left, behind the sitting figure, is seen the entrance to the cave. This new Rhodesian cave-man may be regarded as a southern representative of a Neanderthal race, or as an extinct type intermediate between the Neanderthal Men and the Modern Man type.

any people. For the human sense of race is so strong that it convinces us of reality even when scientific definition is impossible. It was this the British sailor expressed in his answer to the question "What is a Dago?" "Dagoes," he replied, "is anything wot isn't our sort of chaps."

Steps in Human Evolution

Real men arose, we believe, by variational uplifts of considerable magnitude which led to big and complex brains and to the power of reasoned discourse. In some other lines of mammalian evolution there were from time to time great advances in the size and complexity of the brain, as is clear, for instance, in the case of horses and elephants. The same is true of birds as compared with reptiles, and everyone recognises the high level of excellence that has been attained by their vocal powers. How these great cerebral advances came about we do not know, but it has been one of the main trends of animal evolution to improve the nervous system. Two suggestions may be made. First, the prolongation of the period of ante-natal life, in intimate physiological partnership with the mother, may have made it practicable to start the higher mammal with a much better brain than in the lower orders, like Insectivores and Rodents, and still more Marsupials, where the period before birth (gestation) is short. Second, we know that the individual development of the brain is profoundly influenced by the internal secretions of certain ductless glands notably the thyroid. When this organ is not functioning properly the child's brain development is arrested. It may be that increased production of certain hormones—itself, of course, to be accounted for—may have stimulated brain development in man's remote ancestors.

Given variability along the line of better brains and given a process of discriminate sifting which would consistently offer rewards to alertness and foresight, to kin-sympathy and parental care, there seems no great difficulty in imagining how Man would evolve. We must not think of an Aristotle or a Newton except as fine results which justify all the groaning and travailing; we must think of average men, of primitive peoples to-day, and of our forbears long ago. We must remember how much of man's advance is dependent on the external registration of the social heritage, not on the slowly changing natural inheritance.

Looking backwards it is impossible, we think, to fail to recognise progress. There is a ring of truth in the fine description Æschylus gave of primitive men that—

> first, beholding they beheld in vain, and, hearing, heard not, but, like shapes in dreams, mixed all things wildly down the tedious time, nor knew to build a house against the sun with wicketed sides, nor any woodwork knew, but lived like silly ants, beneath the ground, in hollow caves unsunned. There came to them no steadfast sign of winter, nor of spring flower-perfumed, nor of summer full of fruit, but blindly and lawlessly they did all things.

Contrast this picture with the position of man to-day. He has mastered the forces of Nature and is learning to use their resources more and more economically; he has harnessed electricity to his chariot and he has made the ether carry his messages. He tapped supplies of material which seemed for centuries unavailable, having learned, for instance, how to capture and utilise the free nitrogen of the air. With his telegraph and "wireless" he has annihilated distance, and he has added to his navigable kingdom the depths of the sea and the heights of the air. He has conquered one disease after another, and the young science of heredity is showing him how to control in his domesticated animals and cultivated plants the nature of the generations yet unborn. With all his faults he has his ethical face set in the right direction. The main line of movement is towards the fuller embodiment of the true, the beautiful, and the good in healthy lives which are increasingly a satisfaction in themselves.

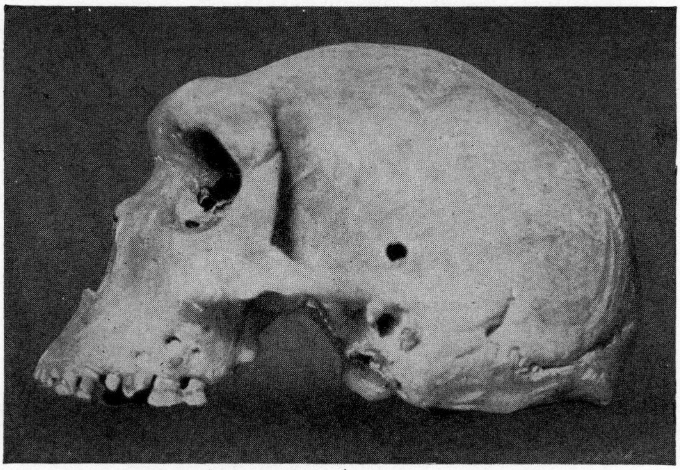

Photo: British Museum (Natural History).

SIDE-VIEW OF A PREHISTORIC HUMAN SKULL DISCOVERED IN 1921 IN BROKEN HILL CAVE, NORTHERN RHODESIA

Very striking are the prominent eyebrow ridges and the broad massive face. The skull looks less domed than that of modern man, but its cranial capacity is far above the lowest human limit. The teeth are interesting in showing marked rotting or "caries," hitherto unknown in prehistoric skulls. In all probability the Rhodesian man was an African representative of the extinct Neanderthal species hitherto known only from Europe.

After the restoration modelled by J. H. McGregor.

A CROMAGNON MAN OR CROMAGNARD, REPRESENTATIVE OF A STRONG ARTISTIC RACE LIVING IN THE SOUTH OF FRANCE IN THE UPPER PLEISTOCENE, PERHAPS 25,000 YEARS AGO

They seemed to have lived for a while contemporaneously with the Neanderthal Men, and there may have been interbreeding. Some Cromagnards probably survive, but the race as a whole declined, and there was repopulation of Europe from the East.

Reproduced by permission from Osborn's "Men of the Old Stone Age."

PHOTOGRAPH SHOWING A NARROW PASSAGE IN THE CAVERN OF FONT-DE-GAUME ON THE BEUNE

Throughout the cavern the walls are crowded with engravings; on the left wall, shown in the photograph, are two painted bison. In the great gallery there may be found not less than eighty figures—bison, reindeer, and mammoths. A specimen of the last is reproduced below.

A MAMMOTH DRAWN ON THE WALL OF THE FONT-DE-GAUME CAVERN

The mammoth age was in the Middle Pleistocene, while Neanderthal Men still flourished, probably far over 30,000 years ago.

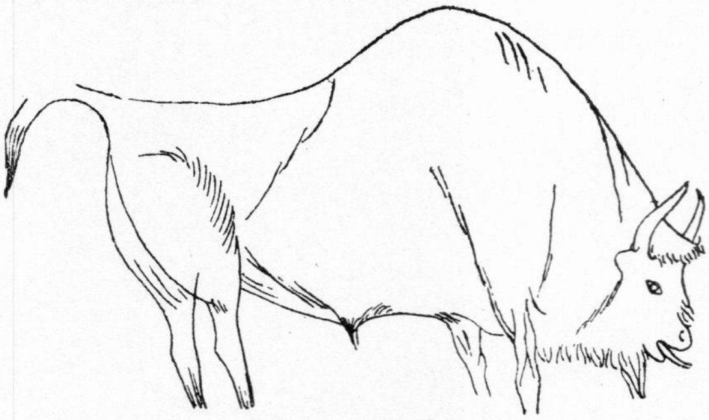

A GRAZING BISON, DELICATELY AND CAREFULLY DRAWN, ENGRAVED ON A WALL OF THE ALTAMIRA CAVE, NORTHERN SPAIN

This was the work of a Reindeer Man or Cromagnard, in the Upper or Post-Glacial Pleistocene, perhaps 25,000 years ago. Firelight must have been used in making these cave drawings and engravings.

Factors in Human Progress

Many, we believe, were the gains that rewarded the arboreal apprenticeship of man's ancestors. Many, likewise, were the results of leaving the trees and coming down to the solid earth—a transition which marked the emergence of more than tentative men. What great steps followed?

Some of the greatest were—the working out of a spoken language and of external methods of registration; the invention of tools; the discovery of the use of fire; the utilisation of iron and other metals; the taming of wild animals such as dog and sheep, horses and cattle; the cultivation of wild plants such as wheat and rice; and the irrigation of fields. All through the ages necessity has been the mother of invention and curiosity its father; but perhaps we miss the heart of the matter if we forget the importance of some leisure time—wherein to observe and think. If our earth had been so clouded that the stars were hidden from men's eyes the whole history of our race would have been different. For it was through his leisure-time observations of the stars that early man discovered the regularity of the year and got his fundamental impressions of the order of Nature—on which all his science is founded.

If we are to think clearly of the factors of human progress we must recall the three great biological ideas—the living organism, its environment, and its functioning. For man these mean (1) the living creature, the outcome of parents and ancestors, a fresh expression of a bodily and mental inheritance; (2) the surroundings, including climate and soil, the plants and animals these allow; and (3) the activities of all sorts, occupations and habits, all the actions and reactions between man and his milieu. In short, we have to deal with FOLK, PLACE, WORK; the *Famille, Lieu, Travail* of the LePlay school.

As to FOLK, human progress depends on intrinsic racial qualities—notably health and vigour of body, clearness and alertness of mind, and an indispensable sociality. The most powerful factors in the world are clear ideas in the minds of energetic men of good will. The differences in bodily and mental health which mark races, and stocks within a people, just as they mark individuals, are themselves traceable back to germinal variations or mutations, and to the kind of sifting to which the race or stock has been subjected. Easygoing conditions are not only without stimulus to new departures, they are without the sifting which progress demands.

As to PLACE, it is plain that different areas differ greatly in their material resources and in the availability of these. Moreover, even when abundant material resources are present, they will not make for much progress unless the climate is such that they can be readily utilised. Indeed, climate has been one of the great factors in civilisation, here stimulating and there depressing energy, in one place favouring certain plants and animals important to man, in another place preventing their presence. Moreover, climate has slowly changed from age to age.

As to WORK, the form of a civilisation is in some measure dependent on the primary occupations, whether hunting or fishing, farming or shepherding; and on the industries of later ages which have a profound moulding effect on the individual at least. We cannot, however, say more than that the factors of human progress have always had these three aspects, Folk, Place, Work, and that if progress is to continue on stable lines it must always recognise the essential correlation of fitter folk in body and mind; improved habits and functions, alike in work and leisure; and bettered surroundings in the widest and deepest sense.

BIBLIOGRAPHY

DARWIN, CHARLES, *Descent of Man.*
HADDON, A. C., *Races of Men.*
HADDON, A. C., *History of Anthropology*
KEANE, A. H., *Man Past and Present.*
KEITH, ARTHUR, *Antiquity of Man.*

LULL, R. S., *Organic Evolution.*
McCABE, JOSEPH, *Evolution of Civilization.*
MARETT, R. R., *Anthropology* (Home University Library).
OSBORN, H. F., *Men of the Early Stone Age.*
SOLLAS, W. J., *Ancient Hunters and their Modern Representatives.*
TYLOR, E. B., *Anthropology and Primitive Culture.*

VI

EVOLUTION GOING ON

EVOLUTION GOING ON

EVOLUTION, as we have seen in a previous chapter, is another word for race-history. It means the ceaseless process of Becoming, linking generation to generation of living creatures. The Doctrine of Evolution states the fact that the present is the child of the past and the parent of the future. It comes to this, that the living plants and animals we know are descended from ancestors on the whole simpler, and these from others likewise simpler, and so on, back and back—till we reach the first living creatures, of which, unfortunately, we know nothing. Evolution is a process of racial change in a definite direction, whereby new forms arise, take root, and flourish, alongside of or in the place of their ancestors, which were in most cases rather simpler in structure and behaviour.

The rock-record, which cannot be wrong, though we may read it wrongly, shows clearly that there was once a time in the history of the Earth when the only backboned animals were Fishes. Ages passed, and there evolved Amphibians, with fingers and toes, scrambling on to dry land. Ages passed, and there evolved Reptiles, in bewildering profusion. There were fish-lizards and sea-serpents, terrestrial dragons and flying dragons, a prolific and varied stock. From the terrestrial Dinosaurs it seems that Birds and Mammals arose. In succeeding ages there evolved all the variety of Birds and all the variety of Mammals. Until at last arose the Man. The question is whether similar processes of evolution are still going on.

We are so keenly aware of rapid changes in mankind, though

these concern the social heritage much more than the flesh-and-blood natural inheritance, that we find no difficulty in the idea that evolution is going on in mankind. We know the contrast between modern man and primitive man, and we are convinced that in the past, at least, progress has been a reality. That degeneration may set in is an awful possibility—involution rather than evolution—but even if going back became for a time the rule, we cannot give up the hope that the race would recover itself and begin afresh to go forward. For although there have been retrogressions in the history of life, continued through unthinkably long ages, and although great races, the Flying Dragons for instance, have become utterly extinct, leaving no successors whatsoever, we feel sure that there has been on the whole a progress towards nobler, more masterful, more emancipated, more intelligent, and *better* forms of life—a progress towards what mankind at its best has always regarded as best, i.e. affording most enduring satisfaction. So we think of evolution going on in mankind, evolution chequered by involution, but on the whole *progressive evolution.*

Evolutionary Prospect for Man

It is not likely that man's body will admit of *great* change, but there is room for some improvement, e.g. in the superfluous length of the food-canal and the overcrowding of the teeth. It is likely, however, that there will be constitutional changes, e.g. of prolonged youthfulness, a higher standard of healthfulness, and a greater resistance to disease. It is justifiable to look forward to great improvements in intelligence and in control. The potentialities of the human brain, as it is, are far from being utilised to the full, and new departures of promise are of continual occurrence. What is of great importance is that the new departures or variations which emerge in fine children should be fostered, not nipped in the bud, by the social environment, education included. The evolutionary prospect for man is promising.

PHOTOGRAPH OF A MEDIAN SECTION THROUGH THE SHELL OF THE PEARLY NAUTILUS

It is only the large terminal chamber that is occupied by the animal.

PHOTOGRAPH OF THE ENTIRE SHELL OF THE PEARLY NAUTILUS

The headquarters of the Nautilus are in the Indian and Pacific Oceans. They sometimes swim at the surface of the sea, but they usually creep slowly about on the floor of comparatively shallow water.

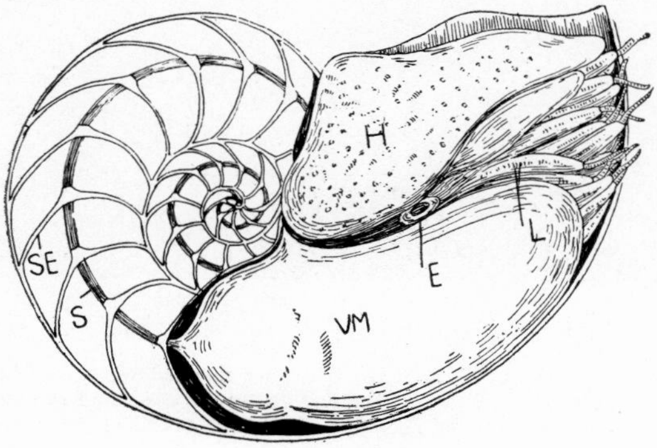

NAUTILUS

A section through the Pearly Nautilus, *Nautilus pompilius*, common from Malay to Fiji. The shell is often about 9 inches long. The animal lives in the last chamber only, but a tube (S) runs through the empty chambers, perforating the partitions (SE). The bulk of the animal is marked VM; the eye is shown at E; a hood is marked H; round the mouth there are numerous lobes (L) bearing protrusible tentacles, some of which are shown. When the animal is swimming near the surface the tentacles radiate out in all directions, and it has been described as "a shell with something like a cauliflower sticking out of it." The Pearly Nautilus is a good example of a conservative type, for it began in the Triassic Era. But the family of Nautiloids to which it belongs illustrates very vividly what is meant by a dwindling race. The Nautiloids began in the Cambrian, reached their golden age in the Silurian, and began to decline markedly in the Carboniferous. There are 2,500 extinct or fossil species of Nautiloids, and only 4 living to-day.

Photo: W. S. Berridge.

SHOEBILL

A bird of a savage nature, never mixing with other marsh birds. According to Dr. Chalmers Mitchell, it shows affinities to herons, storks, pelicans, and gannets, and is a representative of a type equal to both herons and storks and falling between the two.

But it is very important to realise that among plant and animals likewise, *Evolution is going on.*

The Fountain of Change: Variability

On an ordinary big clock we do not readily see that even the minute hand is moving, and if the clock struck only once in a hundred years we can conceive of people arguing whether the hands did really move at all. So it often is with the changes that go on from generation to generation in living creatures. The flux is so slow, like the flowing of a glacier, that some people fail to be convinced of its reality. And it must, of course, be admitted that some kinds of living creatures, like the Lamp-shell *Ligula* or the Pearly Nautilus, hardly change from age to age, whereas others, like some of the birds and butterflies, are always giving rise to something new. The Evening Primrose among plants, and the Fruit-fly, Drosophila, among animals, are well-known examples of organisms which are at present in a sporting or mutating mood.

Certain dark varieties of moth, e.g. of the Peppered Moth, are taking the place of the paler type in some parts of England, and the same is true of some dark forms of Sugar-bird in the West Indian islands. Very important is the piece of statistics worked out by Professor R. C. Punnett, that "if a population contains .001 per cent of a new variety, and if that variety has even a 5 per cent selection advantage over the original form, the latter will almost completely disappear in less than a hundred generations." This sort of thing has been going on all over the world for untold ages, and the face of animate nature has consequently changed.

We are impressed by striking novelties that crop up—a clever dwarf, a musical genius, a calculating boy, a cock with a 10 ft. tail, a "wonder-horse" with a mane reaching to the ground, a tailless cat, a white blackbird, a copper beech, a Greater Celandine with much cut up leaves; but this sort of mutation is common, and smaller, less brusque variations are commoner still. *They form the raw materials of possible evolution.* We are actually standing before an apparently inexhaustible fountain of change. This is evolution going on.

The Sporting Jellyfish

It is of interest to consider a common animal like the jellyfish Aurelia. It is admirably suited for a leisurely life in the open sea, where it swims about by contracting its saucer-shaped body, thus driving water out from its concavity. By means of millions of stringing cells on its four frilled lips and on its marginal tentacles it is able to paralyse and lasso minute crustaceans and the like, which it then wafts into its mouth. It has a very eventful life-history, for it has in its early youth to pass through a fixed stage, fastened to rock or seaweed, but it is a successful animal, well suited for its habitat, and practically cosmopolitan in its distribution. It is certainly an old-established creature. Yet it is very variable in colour and in size, and even in internal structure. Very often it is the size of a saucer or a soup-plate, but giants over two feet in diameter are well known. Much more important, however, than variation in colour and size are the inborn changes in structure. Normally a jellyfish has its parts in four or multiples of four. Thus it has four frilled lips, four tufts of digestive filaments in its stomach, and four brightly coloured reproductive organs. It has eight sense-organs round the margin of its disc, eight branched and eight unbranched radial canals running from the central stomach to a canal round the circumference. The point of giving these details is just this, that every now and then we find a jellyfish with its parts in sixes, fives, or threes, and with a multitude of minor idiosyncrasies. *Even in the well-established jellyfish there is a fountain of change.*

§ 1

Evolution of Plants

It is instructive to look at the various kinds of cabbages, such as cauliflower and Brussels sprouts, kale and curly greens, and remember that they are all scions of the not very promising wild cabbage found on our shores. And are not all the aristocrat apple-trees of our orchards descended from the plebeian crab-apple of the roadside? We know far too little about the precise origin of our cultivated plants, but there is no doubt that after man got a hold of them he took advantage of their variability to establish race after race, say, of rose and chrysanthemum, of potato and cereal. The evolution of cultivated plants is continuing before our eyes, and the creations of Mr. Luther Burbank, such as the stoneless plum and the primus berry, the spineless cactus and the Shasta daisy, are merely striking instances of what is always going on.

There is reason to believe that the domestic dog has risen three times, from three distinct ancestors—a wolf, a jackal, and a coyote. So a multiple pedigree must be allowed for in the case of the dog, and the same is true in regard to some other domesticated animals. But the big fact is the great variety of breeds that man has been able to fix, after he once got started with a domesticated type. There are over 200 well-marked breeds of domestic pigeons, and there is very strong evidence that all are descended from the wild rock-dove, just as the numerous kinds of poultry are descended from the jungle-fowl of some parts of India and the Malay Islands. Even more familiar is the way in which man has, so to speak, unpacked the complex fur of the wild rabbit, and established all the numerous colour-varieties which we see among domestic rabbits. And apart from colour-varieties there are long-haired Angoras and quaint lop-eared forms, and many more besides. All this points to evolution going on.

The Romance of the Wheat

It is well-known that Neolithic man grew wheat, and some authorities have put the date of the first wheat harvest at between fifteen thousand and ten thousand years ago. The ancient civilisations of Babylonia, Egypt, Crete, Greece, and Rome were largely based on wheat, and it is highly probable that the first great wheatfields were in the fertile land between the Tigris and the Euphrates. The oldest Egyptian tombs that contain wheat, which, by the way, never germinates after its millennia of rest, belong to the First Dynasty, and are about six thousand years old. But there must have been a long history of wheat before that.

Now it is a very interesting fact that the almost certain ancestor of the cultivated wheat is at present living on the arid and rocky slopes of Mount Hermon. It is called *Triticum hermonis,* and it is varying notably to-day, as it did long ago when it gave rise to the emmer, which was cultivated in the Neolithic Age and is the ancestor of all our ordinary wheats. We must think of Neolithic man noticing the big seeds of this Hermon grass, gathering some of the heads, breaking the brittle spikelet-bearing axis in his fingers, knocking off the rough awns or bruising the spikelets in his hand till the glumes or chaff separated off and could be blown away, chewing a mouthful of the seeds—and resolving to sow and sow again.

That was the beginning of a long story, in the course of which man took advantage of the numerous variations that cropped up in this sporting stock and established one successful race after another on his fields. Virgil refers in the "Georgics" to the gathering of the largest and fullest ears of wheat in order to get good seed for another sowing, but it was not till the first quarter of the nineteenth century that the great step was taken, by men like Patrick Sheriff of Haddington, of deliberately selecting individual ears of great excellence and segregating their progeny from mingling with mediocre stock. This is the method which has been followed with remarkable success in modern times.

One of the factors that assisted the Allies in overcoming the food crisis in the darkest period of the war was the virtue of Marquis Wheat, a very prolific, early ripening, hard red spring wheat

THE WALKING-FISH OR MUD-SKIPPER (PERIOPHTHALMUS), COMMON AT THE MOUTHS OF RIVERS IN TROPICAL AFRICA, ASIA, AND NORTH-WEST AUSTRALIA

It skips about by means of its strong pectoral fins on the mud-flats; it jumps from stone to stone hunting small shore-animals; it climbs up the roots of the mangrove-trees. The close-set eyes protrude greatly and are very mobile. The tail seems to help in respiration.

Photo: "The Times."

THE AUSTRALIAN MORE-PORK OR PODARGUS

A bird with a frog-like mouth, allied to the British Nightjar. Now in the London Zoological Gardens.

The capacious mouth is well suited for engulfing large insects such as locusts and mantises, which are mostly caught on the trees. During the day the More-pork or Frogmouth sleeps upright on a branch, and its mottled brown plumage makes it almost invisible.

PELICAN'S BILL, ADAPTED FOR CATCHING AND STORING FISHES

There is an enormous dilatable sac beneath the lower jaw.

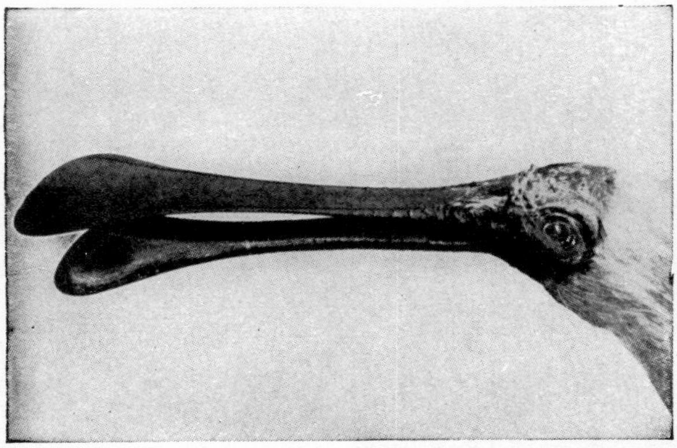

SPOONBILL'S BILL, ADAPTED FOR SIFTING THE MUD AND CATCHING THE SMALL ANIMALS, E.G. FISHES, CRUSTACEANS, INSECT LARVÆ, WHICH LIVE THERE

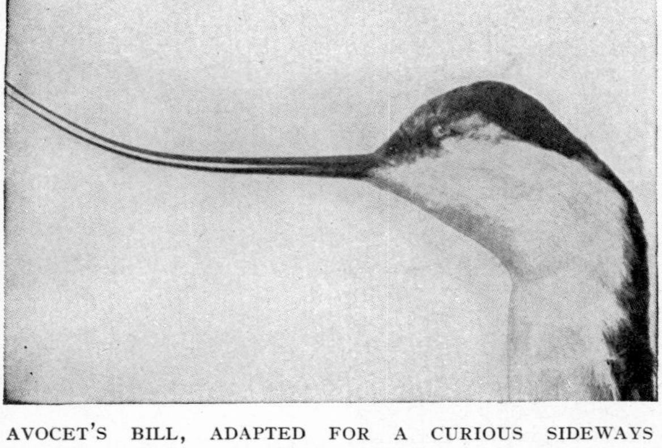

AVOCET'S BILL, ADAPTED FOR A CURIOUS SIDEWAYS SCOOPING IN THE SHORE-POOLS AND CATCHING SMALL ANIMALS

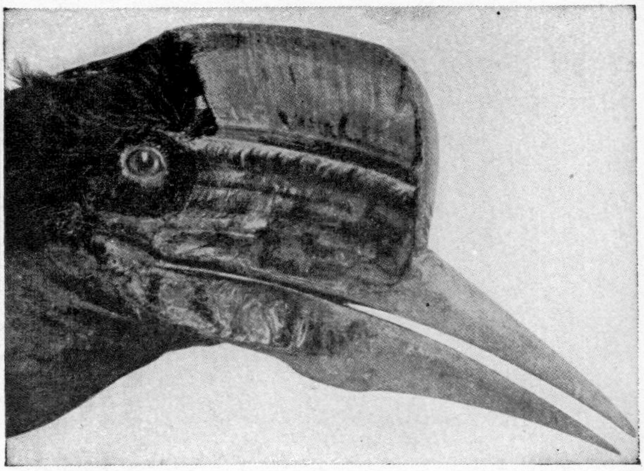

HORNBILL'S BILL, ADAPTED FOR EXCAVATING A NEST IN A TREE, AND ALSO FOR SEIZING AND BREAKING DIVERSE FORMS OF FOOD, FROM MAMMALS TO TORTOISES, FROM ROOTS TO FRUITS

The use of the helmet or casque is obscure.

FALCON'S BILL, ADAPTED FOR SEIZING, KILLING, AND TEARING SMALL MAMMALS AND BIRDS

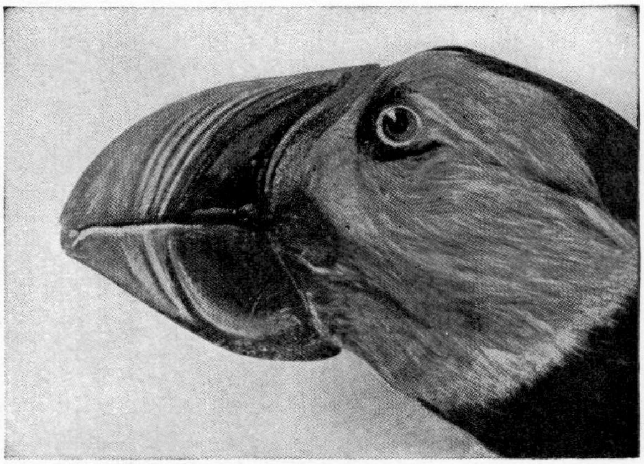

PUFFIN'S BILL, ADAPTED FOR CATCHING SMALL FISHES NEAR THE SURFACE OF THE SEA, AND FOR HOLDING THEM WHEN CAUGHT AND CARRYING THEM TO THE NEST

The scaly covering is moulted in the autumn.

with excellent milling and baking qualities. It is now the dominant spring wheat in Canada and the United States, and it has enormously increased the real wealth of the world in the last ten years (1921). Now our point is simply that this Marquis Wheat is a fine example of evolution going on. In 1917 upwards of 250,000,000 bushels of this wheat were raised in North America, and in 1918 upwards of 300,000,000 bushels; yet the whole originated from a single grain planted in an experimental plot at Ottawa by Dr. Charles E. Saunders so recently as the spring of 1903.

We must not dwell too long on this particular instance of evolution, though it has meant much to our race. We wish, however, following Professor Buller's *Essays on Wheat* (1919), to explain the method by which this good seed was discovered. From one we may learn all. The parent of Marquis Wheat on the male side was the mid-Europe Red Fife—a first-class cereal. The parent on the female side was less promising, a rather nondescript, not pure-bred wheat, called Red Calcutta, which was imported from India into Canada about thirty years ago. The father was part of a cargo that came from the Baltic to Glasgow, and was happily included in a sample sent on to David Fife in Ontario about 1842. From one kernel of this sample David Fife started his stock of Red Fife, which was crossed by Dr. Saunders with Hard Red Calcutta. The result of the cross was a medley of types, nearly a hundred varieties altogether, and it was in scrutinising these that Dr. Saunders hit upon Marquis. He worked steadily through the material, studying head after head of what resulted from sowing, and selecting out those that gave most promise. Each of the heads selected was propagated; most of the results were rejected; the elect were sifted again and yet again, and finally Marquis Wheat emerged, rich in constructive possibilities, probably the most valuable food-plant in the world. It is like a romance to read that "the first crop of the wheat that was destined within a dozen years to overtax the mightiest elevators in the land was stored away in the winter of 1904-5 in a paper packet no larger than an envelope."

Thus from the Wild Wheat of Mount Hermon there evolved one of the most important food-plants of the world. This surely is ***Evolution going on.***

§ 2

Changes in the Animal Life of a Country

Nothing gives us a more convincing impression of evolution in being than a succession of pictures of the animal life of a country in different ages. Dr. James Ritchie, a naturalist of distinction, has written a masterly book, *The Influence of Man on Animal Life in Scotland* (1920), in which we get this succession of pictures. "Within itself," he says, "a fauna is in a constant state of uneasy restlessness, an assemblage of creatures which in its parts ebbs and flows as one local influence or another plays upon it." There are temporary and local changes, endless disturbances and readjustments of the "balance of nature." One year there is a plague of field-voles, perhaps next year "grouse disease" is rife; in one place there is huge increase of starlings, in another place of rabbits; here cockchafers are in the ascendant, and there the moles are spoiling the pasture. "But while the parts fluctuate, the fauna as a whole follows a path of its own. As well as internal tides which swing to and fro about an average level, there is a drift which carries the fauna bodily along an 'irretraceable course.'" This is partly due to considerable changes of climate, for climate calls the tune to which living creatures dance, but it is also due to new departures among the animals themselves. We need not go back to the extinct animals and lost faunas of past ages—for Britain has plenty of relics of these—which "illustrate the reality of the faunal drift," but it may be very useful, in illustration of evolution in being, to notice what has happened in Scotland since the end of the Great Ice Age.

Some nine thousand years ago or more, certain long-headed,

LIFE-HISTORY OF A FROG

1, Before hatching; 2, newly hatched larvæ hanging on to water-weed; 3, with external gills; 4, external gills are covered over and are absorbed; 5, limbless larva about a month old with internal gills; 6, tadpole with hind-legs, about two months old; 7, with the fore-limbs emerging; 8, with all four legs free; 9, a young frog, about three months old, showing the almost complete absorption of the tail and the change of the tadpole mouth into a frog mouth.

Photo: J. J. Ward, F.E.S.

HIND-LEG OF WHIRLIGIG BEETLE WHICH HAS BECOME BEAUTIFULLY MODIFIED FOR AQUATIC LOCOMOTION

The flattened tips form an expanding "fan" or paddle, which opens and closes with astonishing rapidity. The closing of the "fan," like the "feathering" of an oar, reduces friction when the leg is being moved forwards for the next stroke.

THE BIG ROBBER-CRAB (*Birgus Latro*), THAT CLIMBS THE COCO-NUT PALM AND BREAKS OFF THE NUTS

It occurs on islands in the Indian Ocean and Pacific, and is often found far above sea-level. It is able to breathe dry air. One is seen emerging from its burrow, which is often lined with coco-nut fibre. The empty coco-nut shell is sometimes used by the Robber-Crab for the protection of its tail.

square-jawed, short-limbed, but agile hunters and fishermen, whom we call Neolithic Man, established themselves in Scotland. What was the state of the country then?

> It was a country of swamps, low forests of birch, alder, and willow, fertile meadows, and snow-capped mountains. Its estuaries penetrated further inland than they now do, and the sea stood at the level of the Fifty-Foot Beach. On its plains and in its forests roamed many creatures which are strange to the fauna of to-day—the Elk and the Reindeer, Wild Cattle, the Wild Boar and perhaps Wild Horses, a fauna of large animals which paid toll to the European Lynx, the Brown Bear and the Wolf. In all likelihood, the marshes resounded to the boom of the Bittern and the plains to the breeding calls of the Crane and the Great Bustard.

Such is Dr. Ritchie's initial picture.

Now what happened in this kingdom of Caledonia which Neolithic Man had found? He began to introduce domesticated animals, and that meant a thinning of the ranks of predacious creatures. "Safety first" was the dangerous motto in obedience to which man exterminated the lynx, the brown bear, and the wolf. Other creatures, such as the great auk, were destroyed for food, and others like the marten for their furs. Small pests were destroyed to protect the beginnings of agriculture; larger animals like the boar were hunted out of existence; others, like the pearl-bearing river-mussels, yielded to subtler demands. No doubt there was protection also—protection for sport, for utility, for æsthetic reasons, and because of humane sentiments; even wholesome superstitions have safeguarded the robin redbreast and the wren. There were introductions too—the rabbit for utility, the pheasant for sport, and the peacock for amenity. And every introduction, every protection, every killing out had its far-reaching influences.

But if we are to picture the evolution going on, we must think also of man's indirect interference with animal life. He destroyed the forests, he cultivated the wild, he made bridges, he allowed aliens, like rats and cockroaches, to get in unawares. Of course, he often did good, as when he drained swamps and got rid of the mosquitoes which once made malaria rife in Scotland.

What has been the net result? Not, as one might think for a moment, a reduction in the *number* of different kinds of animals. Fourteen or so species of birds and beasts have been banished from Scotland since man interfered, but as far as numbers go they have been more than replaced by deliberate introductions like fallow deer, rabbit, squirrel, and pheasant, and by accidental introductions like rats and cockroaches. But the change is rather in *quality* than in quantity; the smaller have taken the place of the larger, rather paltry pigmies of noble giants. Thus we get a vivid idea that evolution, especially when man interferes, is not necessarily progressive. That depends on the nature of the sieves with which the living materials are sifted. As Dr. Ritchie well says, the standard of the wild fauna as regards size has fallen and is falling, and it is not in size only that there is loss, there is a deterioration of quality. "For how can the increase of Rabbits and Sparrows and Earthworms and Caterpillars, and the addition of millions of Rats and Cochroaches and Crickets and Bugs, ever take the place of those fine creatures round the memories of which the glamour of Scotland's past still plays—the Reindeer and the Elk, the Wolf, the Brown Bear, the Lynx, and the Beaver, the Bustard, the Crane, the Bumbling Bittern, and many another, lost or disappearing." Thus we see again that evolution is going on.

§ 3

The Adventurers

All through the millions of years during which animals have tenanted the earth and the waters under the earth, there has been a search for new kingdoms to conquer, for new corners in which to make a home. And this still goes on. *It has been and is one of the methods of evolution to fill every niche of opportunity.* There is a spider that lives inside a pitcher-plant, catching some of the inquisitive insects which slip down the treacherous internal surface of the trap. There is another that makes its home in crevices among the rocks on the shore of the Mediterranean, or even in empty tubular shells, keeping the water out, more or less successfully, by spinning threads of silk across the entrance to its retreat. The beautiful brine-shrimp, *Artemia salina,* that used to occur in British salterns has found a home in the dense waters of the Great Salt Lake of Utah. Several kinds of earthworms have been found up trees, and there is a fish, Arges, that climbs on the stones of steep mountain torrents of the Andes. The intrepid explorers of the *Scotia* voyage found quite a number of Arctic terns spending our winter within the summer of the Antarctic Circle—which means girdling the globe from pole to pole; and every now and then there are incursions of rare birds, like Pallas's Sand-grouse, into Britain, just as if they were prospecting in search of a promised land. Twice or thrice the distinctively North American Killdeer Plover has been found in Britain, having somehow or other got across the Atlantic. We miss part of the meaning of evolution if we do not catch this note of insurgence and adventure, which some animal or other never ceases to sound, though many establish themselves in a security not easily disturbed, and though a small minority give up the struggle against the stream and are content to acquiesce, as parasites or rottenness eaters, in a drifting life of ease.

More important than very peculiar cases is the broad fact that over and over again in different groups of animals there have been attempts to master different kinds of haunts—such as the underground world, the trees, the freshwaters, and the air. There are burrowing amphibians, burrowing reptiles, burrowing birds, and burrowing mammals; there are tree-toads, tree-snakes, tree-lizards, tree-kangaroos, tree-sloths, tree-shrews, tree-mice, tree-porcupines, and so on; enough of a list to show, without mentioning birds, how many different kinds of animals have entered upon an arboreal apprenticeship—an apprenticeship often with far-reaching consequences. What the freeing of the hand from being an organ of terrestrial support has meant in the evolution of monkeys is a question that gives a spur to our imagination.

The Case of the Robber Crab

On some of the coral islands of the Indian and Pacific Oceans there lives a land-crab, Birgus, which has learned to breathe on land. It breathes dry air by means of curious blood-containing tufts in the upper part of its gill-cavity, and it has also rudimentary gills. It is often about a foot long, and it has very heavy great claws, especially on the left-hand side. With this great claw it hammers on the "eye-hole" of a coconut, from which it has torn off the fibrous husk. It hammers until a hole is made by which it can get at the pulp. Part of the shell is sometimes used as a protection for the soft abdomen—for the robber-crab, as it is called, is an offshoot from the hermit-crab stock. Every year this quaint explorer, which may go far up the hills and climb the coco-palms, has to go back to the sea to spawn. The young ones are hatched in the same state as in our common shore-crab. That is to say, they are free-swimming larvæ which pass through an open-water period before they settle down on the shore, and eventually creep up on to dry land. Just as open-water turtles lay their eggs on sandy shores, going back to their old terrestrial haunt, so the robber-crab, which has almost conquered the dry land, has to return to the seashore to breed. There is a peculiar interest in the association of the robber-crab with the coco-palm, for that tree is not a native of these coral islands, but has been introduced, perhaps from Mexico, by the Polynesian mariners before the discovery of America by Columbus. So the learning to deal with coconuts is a recent achievement, and we are face to face with a very good example of evolution going on.

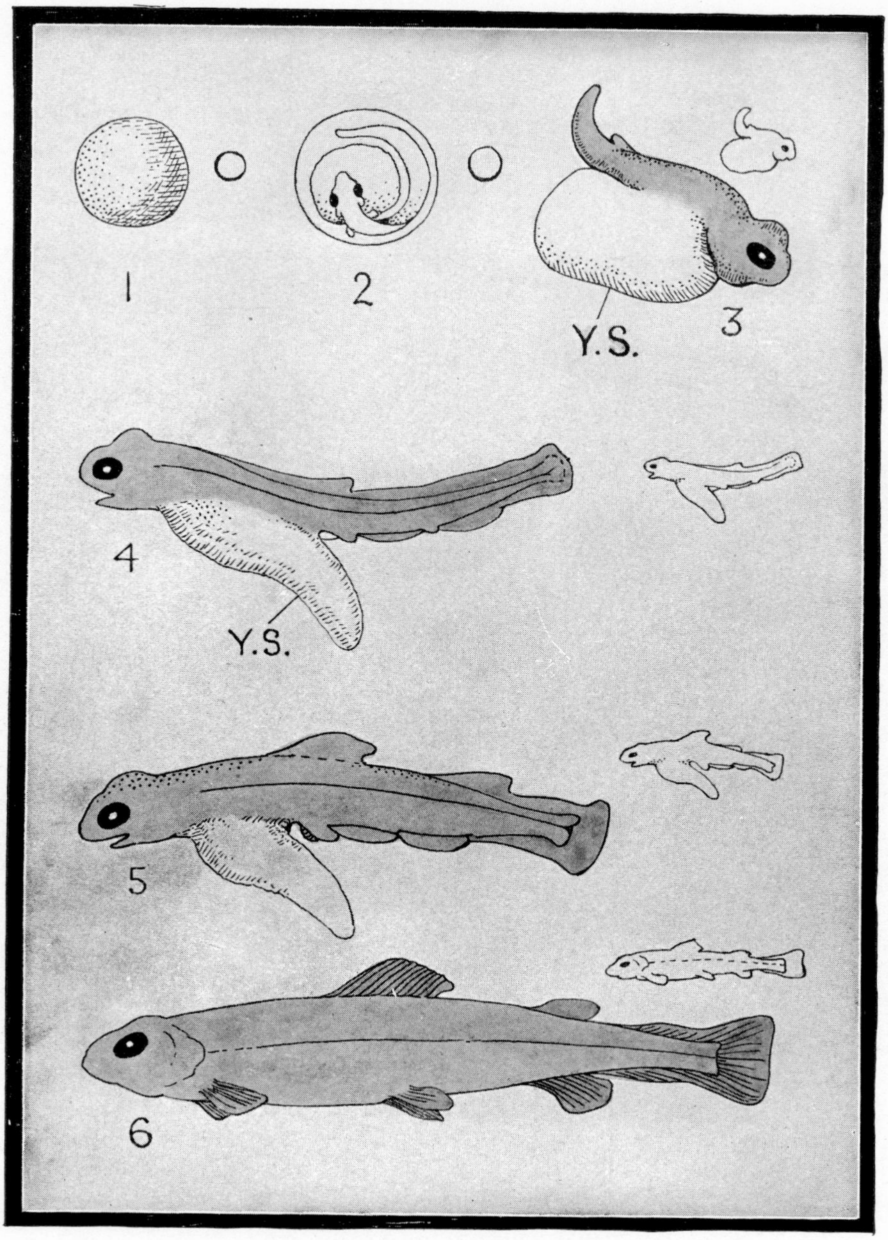

EARLY LIFE-HISTORY OF THE SALMON

1. The fertilised egg, shed in the gravelly bed of the river.

2. The embryo within the egg, just before hatching. The embryo has been constricted off from the yolk-laden portion of the egg.

3. The newly hatched salmon, or alevin, encumbered with its legacy of yolk (Y.S.).

4 and 5. The larval salmon, still being nourished from the yolk-sac (Y.S.), which is diminishing in size as the fish grows larger.

6. The salmon fry about six weeks old, with the yolk fully absorbed, so that the young fish has now to feed for itself. The fry become parr, which go to the sea as smolts, and return as grilse.

In all cases the small figures to the right indicate the natural size.

THE SALMON LEAPING AT THE FALL IS A MOST FASCINATING SPECTACLE

Again and again we see them jumping out of the seething foam beneath the fall, casting themselves into the curtain of the down-rushing water, only to be carried back by it into the depths whence they have risen. One here and another there makes its effort good, touches the upper lip of the cataract, gives a swift stroke of its tail, and rushes on towards those upper reaches which are the immemorial spawning beds of its race.

The Story of the Salmon

In late autumn or in winter the salmon spawn in the rivers. The female makes a shallow trough in the gravel by moving her tail from side to side, and therein lays many eggs. The male, who is in attendance, fertilises these with the milt, and then the female covers them deeply with gravel. The process is repeated over and over again for a week or more till all the eggs are shed. For three to four months the eggs develop, and eventually there emerge the larvæ or *alevins,* which lurk among the pebbles. They cannot swim much, for they are encumbered by a big legacy of yolk. In a few weeks, perhaps eight, the protruding bag of yolk has disappeared and the *fry,* about an inch long, begin to move about more actively and to fend for themselves. By the end of the year they have grown to be rather trout-like *parr,* about four inches long. In two years these are double that length. Usually in the second year, but it may be earlier or later, the parr become silvery *smolts,* which go out to sea, usually about the month of May. They feed on young herring and the like and grow large and strong. When they are about three and a half years old they come up the rivers as *grilse* and may spawn. Or they may pass through the whole grilse stage in the sea and come up the rivers with all the characters of the full-grown fish. In many cases the salmon spawn only once, and some (they are called *kelts* after spawning) are so much exhausted by starting a new generation that they die or fall a victim to otters and other enemies. In the case of the salmon of the North Pacific (in the genus *Oncorhynchus,* not *Salmo*) all the individuals die after spawning, none being able to return to the sea. It must be remembered that full-grown salmon do not as a rule feed in fresh water, though they may be unable to resist snapping at the angler's strange creations. A very interesting fact is that the salmon keeps as it were a diary of its movements, which vary a good deal in different rivers. This diary is written in the scales, and a careful reading of the concentric lines on the scales shows the age of the fish, and when it went out to sea, and whether it has spawned or not, and more besides.

Interpretation of the Salmon's Story

When an animal frequents two different haunts, in one of which it breeds, it is very often safe to say that the breeding-place represents the original home. The flounder is quite comfortable far up the rivers, but it has to go to the shore-waters to spawn, and there is no doubt that the flounder is a marine fish which has recently learned to colonise the fresh waters. Its relatives, like plaice and sole, are strictly marine. But it is impossible to make a dogma of the rule that the breeding-place corresponds to the original home. Thus some kinds of bass, which belong to the marine family of sea-perches, live in the sea or in estuaries, while two have become permanent residents in fresh water. Or, again, the members of the herring family are very distinctively marine, but the shad, which belong to this family, spawn in rivers and may spend their lives there.

So there are two different ways of interpreting the life-history of the salmon. Some authorities regard the salmon as a marine fish which is establishing itself in fresh water. But others read the story the other way and regard the salmon as a member of a fresh-water race, that has taken to the sea for feeding purposes. In regard to trout, we know that the ranks of those in rivers and lakes are continually being reinforced by migrants from the sea, and that some trout go down to the sea while others remain in the freshwater. We know also in regard to a related fish, the char, that while the great majority of kinds are now permanent residents in cold and deep, isolated northern lakes, there are Arctic forms which live in the sea but enter the rivers to spawn. These facts favour the view that the salmon was originally a marine fish. But there are arguments on both sides, and, for our present purpose, the important fact is that the salmon is conquering *two* haunts. Its evolution is going on.

The Romance of the Eel

Early in summer, at dates varying with the distance of the rivers from the open Atlantic, crowds of young eels or elvers come up-stream. Sometimes the procession or eel-fare includes thousands of individuals, each about the length of our first finger, and as thick as a stout knitting needle. They obey an inborn impulse to swim against the stream, seeking automatically to have both sides of their body equally stimulated by the current. So they go straight ahead. The obligation works only during the day, for when the sun goes down behind the hills the elvers snuggle under stones or beneath the bank and rest till dawn. In the course of time they reach the quiet upper reaches of the river or go up rivulets and drainpipes to the isolated ponds. Their impulse to go on must be very imperious, for they may wriggle up the wet moss by the side of a waterfall or even make a short excursion in a damp meadow.

In the quiet-flowing stretches of the river or in the ponds they feed and grow for years and years. They account for a good many young fishes. Eventually, after five or six years in the case of the males, six to eight years in the case of the females, the well-grown fishes, perhaps a foot and a half to two feet long, are seized by a novel restlessness. They are beginning to be mature. They put on a silvery jacket and become large of eye, and they return to the sea. In getting away from the pond it may be necessary to wriggle through the damp meadow-grass before reaching the river. They travel by night and rather excitedly. The Arctic Ocean is too cold for them and the North Sea too shallow. They must go far out to sea, to where the old margin of the once larger continent of Europe slopes down to the great abysses, from the Hebrides southwards. Eels seem to spawn in the deep dark water; but the just liberated eggs have not yet been found. The young fry rises to near the surface and becomes a knife-blade-like larva, transparent all but its eye. It lives for many months in this state, growing to be about three inches long, rising and sinking in the water, and swimming gently. These open-sea young eels are known as Leptocephali, a name given to them before their real nature was proved. They gradually become shorter, and the shape changes from knife-blade-like to cylindrical. During this change they fast, and the weight of their delicate body decreases. They turn into glass-eels, about 2½ inches long, like a knitting-needle in girth. They begin to move towards the distant shores and rivers, and they may be a year and a half old before they reach their destination and go up-stream as elvers. Those that ascend the rivers of the Eastern Baltic must have journeyed three thousand miles. It is certain that no eel ever matures or spawns in fresh water. It is practically certain that all the young eels ascending the rivers of North Europe have come in from the Atlantic, some of them perhaps from the Azores or further out still. It is interesting to inquire how the young eels circumvent the Falls of the Rhine and get into Lake Constance, or how their kindred on the other side of the Atlantic overcome the obstacle of Niagara; but it is more important to lay emphasis on the variety of habitats which this fish is trying—the deep waters, the open sea, the shore, the river, the pond, and even, it may be, a little taste of solid earth. It seems highly probable that the common eel is a deep-water marine fish which has learned to colonise the freshwaters. It has been adventurous and it has succeeded. The only shadow on the story of achievement is that there seems to be no return from the spawning. There is little doubt that death is the nemesis of their reproduction. In any case, no adult eel ever comes back from the deep sea. We are minded of Goethe's hard saying: "Death is Nature's expert advice to get plenty of life."

§ 4

Forming New Habits

There is a well-known mudfish of Australia, Neoceratodus by name, which has turned its swim-bladder into a lung and comes to the surface to spout. It expels vitiated air with considerable

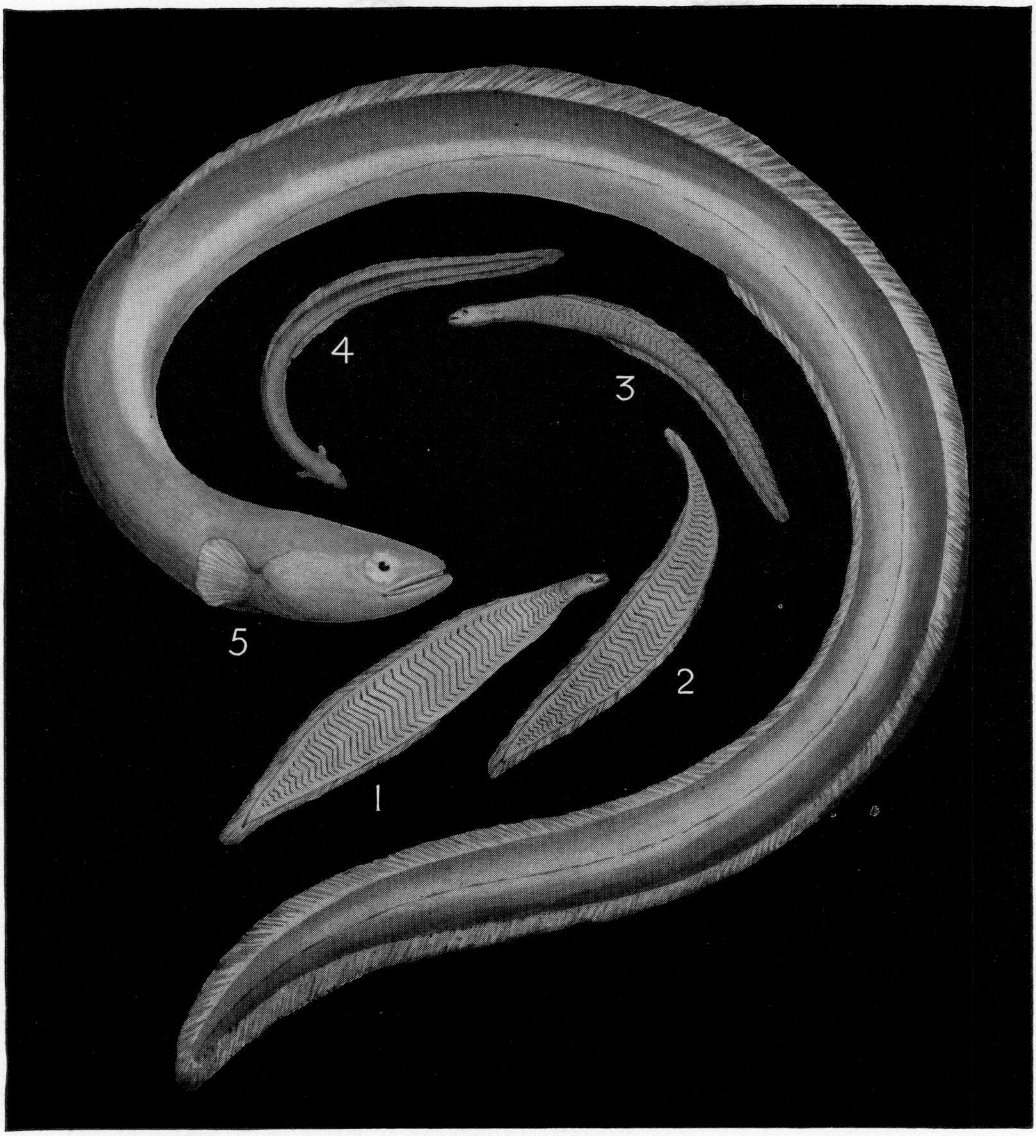

DIAGRAM OF THE LIFE HISTORY OF THE COMMON EEL (*Anguilla Vulgaris*)

1. The transparent open-sea knife-blade-like larva called a Leptocephalus.

2 and 3. The gradual change of shape from knife-blade-like to cylindrical. The body becomes shorter and loses weight.

4. The young elver, at least a year old, which makes its way from the open sea to the estuaries and rivers. It is 2/3 inches long and almost cylindrical.

5. The fully-formed eel.

Photo: Gambier Bolton.

CASSOWARY

Its bare head is capped with a helmet. Unlike the plumage of most birds its feathers are loose and hair-like, whilst its wings are merely represented by a few black quills. It is flightless and entirely dependent on its short powerful legs to carry it out of danger.

Photo: Gambier Bolton.

THE KIWI, ANOTHER FLIGHTLESS BIRD, OF REMARKABLE APPEARANCE, HABITS, AND STRUCTURE force and takes fresh gulps. At the same time, like an ordinary fish, it has gills which allow the usual interchange of gases between the blood and the water. Now this Australian mudfish or double-breather (Dipnoan), which may be a long way over a yard in length, is a direct and little-changed descendant of an ancient extinct fish, Ceratodus, which lived in Mesozoic times, as far back as the Jurassic, which probably means over five millions of years ago. The Queensland mudfish is an antiquity, and there has not been much change in its lineage for millions of years. We might take it as an illustration of the inertia of evolution. And yet, though its structure has changed but little, the fish probably illustrates evolution in process, for it is a fish that is learning to breathe dry air. It cannot leave the water; but it can live comfortably in pools which are foul with decomposing animal and vegetable matter. In partially dried-up and foul waterholes, full of dead fishes of various kinds, Neoceratodus has been found vigorous and lively. Unless we take the view, which is *possible,* that the swim-bladder of fishes was originally a lung, the mudfishes are learning to breathe dry air. They illustrate evolution agoing.

The herring-gull is by nature a fish-eater; but of recent years, in some parts of Britain, it has been becoming in the summer months more and more of a vegetarian, scooping out the turnips, devouring potatoes, settling on the sheaves in the harvest field and gorging itself with grain. Similar experiments, usually less striking, are known in many birds; but the most signal illustration is that of the kea or Nestor parrot of New Zealand, which has taken to lighting on the loins of the sheep, tearing away the fleece, cutting at the skin, and gouging out fat. Now the parrot belongs to a vegetarian or frugivorous stock, and this change of diet in the relatively short time since sheep-ranches were established in New Zealand is very striking. Here, since we know the dates, we may speak of evolution going on under our eyes. It must be remembered that variations in habit may give an animal a new opportunity to test variations in structure which arise mysteriously from within, as expressions of germinal changefulness rather than as imprints from without. For of the transmissibility of the latter there is little secure evidence.

Experiments in Locomotion

It is very interesting to think of the numerous types of locomotion which animals have discovered—pulling and punting, sculling and rowing, and of the changes that are rung on these four main methods. How striking is the case of the frilled lizard (Chlamydosaurus) of Australia, which at the present time is, as it were, experimenting in bipedal progression—always a rather eventful thing to do. It gets up on its hind-legs and runs totteringly for a few feet, just like a baby learning to walk.

How beautiful is the adventure which has led our dipper or water-ouzel—a bird allied to the wrens—to try walking and flying under water! How admirable is the volplaning of numerous parachutists—"flying fish," "flying frog," "flying dragon," "flying phalanger," "flying squirrel," and more besides, which take great leaps through the air. For are these not the splendid failures that might have succeeded in starting new modes of flight?

Most daring of all, perhaps, are the aerial journeys undertaken by many small spiders. On a breezy morning, especially in the autumn, they mount on gateposts and palings and herbage, and, standing with their head to the wind, pay out three or four long threads of silk. When the wind tugs at these threads, the spinners let go, and are borne, usually back downwards, on the wings of the wind from one parish to another. It is said that if the wind falls they can unfurl more sail, or furl if it rises. In any case, these wingless creatures make aerial journeys. When tens of thousands of the used threads sink to earth, there is a "shower of gossamer." On his *Beagle* voyage Darwin observed that vast numbers of small gossamer spiders were borne on to the ship when it was sixty miles distant from the land.

THE AUSTRALIAN FRILLED LIZARD, WHICH IS AT PRESENT TRYING TO BECOME A BIPED

When it gets up on its hind-legs and runs for a short distance it folds its big collar round its neck.

A CARPET OF GOSSAMER

The silken threads used by thousands of gossamer spiders in their migrations are here seen entangled in the grass, forming what is called a shower of gossamer. At the edge of the grass the gossamer forms a curtain, floating out and looking extraordinarily like waves breaking on a sea-shore.

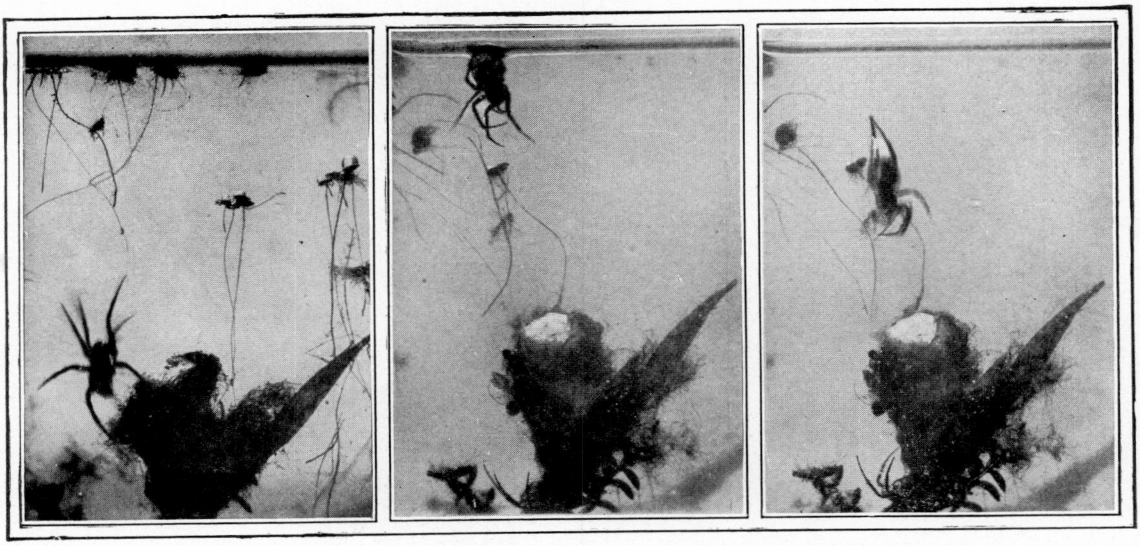

The spider is seen just leaving its diving-bell to ascend to the surface to capture air.

The spider jerks its body and legs out at the surface and then dives—

—carrying with it what looks like a silvery air-bubble—air entangled in the hair.

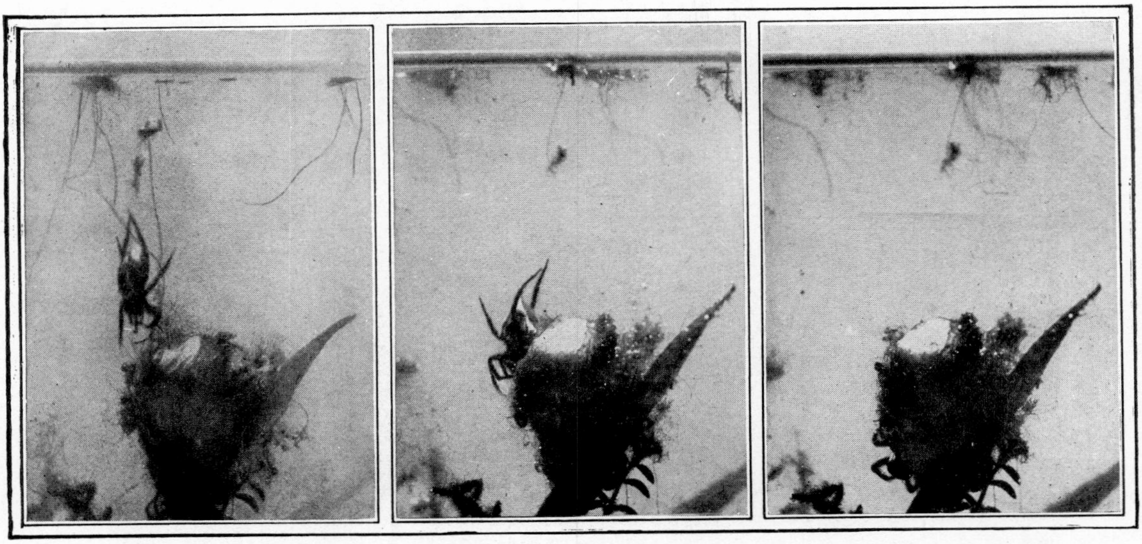

The spider reaches its air-dome. Note how the touch of its legs indents the inflated balloon.

Running down the side of the nest, the spider

—brushes off the air at the entrance, and the bubble ascends into the silken balloon.

Photos: J. J. Ward, F.E.S.

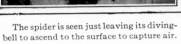

New Devices

It is impossible, we must admit, to fix dates, except in a few cases, relatively recent; but there is a smack of modernity in some striking devices which we can observe in operation to-day. Thus no one will dispute the statement that spiders are thoroughly terrestrial animals breathing dry air, but we have the fact of the water-spider conquering the under-water world. There are a few spiders about the sea-shore, and a few that can survive douching with freshwater, but the particular case of the true water-spider, *Argyroneta natans,* stands by itself because the creature, as regards the female at least, has *conquered* the sub-aquatic environment. A flattish web is woven, somehow, underneath the water, and pegged down by threads of silk. Along a special vertical line the mother spider ascends to the surface and descends again, having entangled air in the hairs of her body. She brushes off this air underneath her web, which is thereby buoyed up into a sort of dome. She does this over and over again, never getting wet all the time, until the domed web has become like a diving-bell, full of dry air. In this eloquent anticipation of man's rational device, this creature—far from being endowed with reason—lays her eggs and looks after her young. The general significance of the facts is that when competition is keen, a new area of exploitation is a promised land. Thus spiders have spread over all the earth except the polar areas. But here is a spider with some spirit of adventure, which has endeavoured, instead of trekking, to find a new corner near at home. It has tackled a problem surely difficult for a terrestrial animal, the problem of living in great part under water, and it has solved it in a manner at once effective and beautiful.

In Conclusion

We have given but a few representative illustrations of a great theme. When we consider the changefulness of living creatures, the transformations of cultivated plants and domesticated animals, the gradual alterations in the fauna of a country, the search after new haunts, the forming of new habits, and the discovery of many inventions, are we not convinced that Evolution is going on? And why should it stop?

VII

THE DAWN OF MIND

THE DAWN OF MIND

IN the story of evolution there is no chapter more interesting than the emergence of mind in the animal kingdom. But it is a difficult chapter to read, partly because "mind" cannot be seen or measured, only *inferred* from the outward behaviour of the creature, and partly because it is almost impossible to avoid reading ourselves into the much simpler animals.

§ 1

Two Extremes to be Avoided

The one extreme is that of uncritical generosity which credits every animal, like Brer Rabbit—who, by the way, was the hare—with human qualities. The other extreme is that of thinking of the animal as if it were an automatic machine, in the working of which there is no place or use for mind. Both these extremes are to be avoided.

When Professor Whitman took the eggs of the Passenger Pigeon (which became extinct not long ago with startling rapidity) and placed them a few inches to one side of the nest, the bird looked a little uneasy and put her beak under her body as if to feel for something that was not there. But she did not try to retrieve her eggs, close at hand as they were. In a short time she flew away altogether. This shows that the mind of the pigeon is in some respects very different from the mind of man. On the other hand, when a certain clever dog, carrying a basket of eggs, with the handle in his mouth, came to a stile which had to be negotiated, he laid the basket on the ground, pushed it gently through a low gap to the other side, and then took a running leap over. We dare not talk of this dog as an automatic machine.

A Caution in Regard to Instinct

In studying the behaviour of animals, which is the only way of getting at their mind, for it is only of our own mind that we have direct knowledge, it is essential to give prominence to the fact that there has been throughout the evolution of living creatures a strong tendency to enregister or engrain capacities of doing things effectively. Thus certain abilities come to be inborn; they are parts of the inheritance, which will express themselves whenever the appropriate trigger is pulled. The newly born child does not require to learn its breathing movements, as it afterwards requires to learn its walking movements. The ability to go through the breathing movements is inborn, engrained, enregistered.

In other words, there are hereditary pre-arrangements of nerve-cells and muscle-cells which come into activity almost as easily as the beating of the heart. In a minute or two the newborn pigling creeps close to its mother and sucks milk. It has not to learn how to do this any more than we have to learn to cough or sneeze. Thus animals have many useful ready-made, or almost ready-made, capacities of doing apparently clever things. In simple cases of these inborn pre-arrangements we speak of reflex actions; in more complicated cases, of instinctive behaviour. Now the caution is this, that while these inborn capacities usually work well in natural conditions, they sometimes work badly when the ordinary routine is disturbed. We see this when a pigeon continues sitting for many days on an empty nest, or when it fails to retrieve its eggs only two inches away. But it would be a mistake to call the pigeon, because of this, an unutterably stupid bird. We have only to think of the achievements of homing pigeons to know that this cannot be true. We must not judge animals in regard to those kinds of behaviour which have been handed over to instinct, and go badly agee when the normal routine is disturbed. In ninety-nine cases out of a hundred the enregistered instinctive capacities work well, and the advantage of

Photo: O. J. Wilkinson.

JACKDAW BALANCING ON A GATEPOST

The jackdaw is a big-brained, extremely alert, very educable, loquacious bird.

From Ingersoll's "The Wit of the Wild."

TWO OPOSSUMS FEIGNING DEATH

The Opossums are mainly arboreal marsupials, insectivorous and carnivorous, confined to the American Continent from the United States to Patagonia. Many have no pouch and carry their numerous young ones on their back, the tail of the young twined round that of the mother. The opossums are agile, clever creatures, and famous for "playing 'possum," lying inert just as if they were dead.

MALE OF THREE-SPINED STICKLEBACK, MAKING A NEST OF WATER-WEED, GLUED TOGETHER BY VISCID THREADS SECRETED FROM THE KIDNEYS AT THE BREEDING SEASON

A FEMALE STICKLEBACK ENTERS THE NEST WHICH THE MALE HAS MADE, LAYS THE EGGS INSIDE, AND THEN DEPARTS

In many cases two or three females use the same nest, the stickleback being polygamous. Above the nest the male, who mounts guard, is seen driving away an intruder.

their becoming stereotyped was to leave the animal more free for adventures at a higher level. Being "a slave of instinct" may give the animal a security that enables it to discover some new home or new food or new joy. Somewhat in the same way, a man of methodical habits, which he has himself established, may gain leisure to make some new departure of racial profit.

When we draw back our finger from something very hot, or shut our eye to avoid a blow from a rebounding branch, we do not will the action; and this is more or less the case, probably, when a young mammal sucks its mother for the first time. Some Mound-birds of Celebes lay their eggs in warm volcanic ash by the shore of the sea, others in a great mass of fermenting vegetation; it is inborn in the newly hatched bird to struggle out as quickly as it can from such a strange nest, else it will suffocate. If it stops struggling too soon, it perishes, for it seems that the trigger of the instinct cannot be pulled twice. Similarly, when the eggs of the turtle, that have been laid in the sand of the shore, hatch out, the young ones make *instinctively* for the sea. Some of the crocodiles bury their eggs two feet or so below the surface among sand and decaying vegetation—an awkward situation for a birthplace. When the young crocodile is ready to break out of the egg-shell, just as a chick does at the end of the three weeks of brooding, it utters *instinctively* a piping cry. On hearing this, the watchful mother digs away the heavy blankets, otherwise the young crocodile would be buried alive at birth. Now there is no warrant for believing that the young Mound-birds, young crocodiles, and young turtles have an intelligent appreciation of what they do when they are hatched. They act instinctively, "as to the manner born." But this is not to say that their activity is not backed by endeavour or even suffused with a certain amount of awareness. Of course, it is necessarily difficult for man, who is so much a creature of intelligence, to get even an inkling of the mental side of instinctive behaviour.

In many of the higher reaches of animal instinct, as in courtship or nest-building, in hunting or preparing the food, it looks as if the starting of the routine activity also "rang up" the higher centres of the brain and put the intelligence on the *qui vive,* ready to interpose when needed. So the twofold caution is this: (1) We must not depreciate the creature too much if, in unusual circumstances, it acts in an ineffective way along lines of behaviour which are normally handed over to instinct; and (2) we must leave open the possibility that even routine instinctive behaviour may be suffused with awareness and backed by endeavour.

§ 2

A Useful Law

But how are we to know when to credit the animal with intelligence and when with something less spontaneous? Above all, how are we to know when the effective action, like opening the mouth the very instant it is touched by food in the mother's beak, is just a physiological action like coughing or sneezing, and when there is behind it—a mind at work? The answer to this question is no doubt that given by Prof. Lloyd Morgan, who may be called the founder of comparative psychology, that we must describe the piece of behaviour very carefully, just as it occurred, without reading anything into it, and that we must not ascribe it to a higher faculty if it can be satisfactorily accounted for in terms of a lower one. In following this principle we may be sometimes niggardly, for the behaviour may have a mental subtlety that we have missed; but in nine cases out of ten our conclusions are likely to be sound. It is the critical, scientific way.

Bearing this law in mind, let us take a survey of the emergence of mind among backboned animals.

Senses of Fishes

Fishes cannot shut their eyes, having no true lids; but the eyes themselves are very well developed and the vision is acute, especially for moving objects. Except in gristly fishes, the external opening to the ear has been lost, so that sound-waves and coarser vibrations must influence the inner ear, which is well developed, through the surrounding flesh and bones. It seems that the main use of the ear in fishes is in connection with balancing, not with hearing. In many cases, however, the sense of hearing has been demonstrated; thus fishes will come to the side of a pond to be fed when a bell is rung or when a whistle is blown by someone not visible from the water. The fact that many fishes pay no attention at all to loud noises does not prove that they are deaf, for an animal may hear a sound and yet remain quite indifferent or irresponsive. This merely means that the sound has no vital interest for the animal. Some fishes, such as bullhead and dogfish, have a true sense of smell, detecting by their nostrils very dilute substances permeating the water from a distance. Others, such as members of the cod family, perceive their food in part at least by the sense of taste, which is susceptible to substances near at hand and present in considerable quantity. This sense of taste may be located on the fins as well as about the mouth. At this low level the senses of smell and taste do not seem to be very readily separated. The chief use of the sensitive line or lateral line seen on each side of a bony fish is to make the animal aware of slow vibrations and changes of pressure in the water. The skin responds to pressures, the ear to vibrations of high frequency; the lateral line is between the two in its function.

Interesting Ways of Fishes

The brain of the ordinary bony fish is at a very low level. Thus the cerebral hemispheres, destined to become more and more the seat of intelligence, are poorly developed. In gristly fishes, like skates and sharks, the brain is much more promising. But although the state of the brain does not lead one to expect very much from a bony fish like trout or eel, haddock or herring, illustrations are not wanting of what might be called pretty pieces of behaviour. Let us select a few cases.

The Stickleback's Nest

The three-spined and two-spined sticklebacks live equally well in fresh or salt water; the larger fifteen-spined stickleback is entirely marine. In all three species the male fish makes a nest, in fresh or brackish water in the first two cases, in shore-pools in the third case. The little species use the leaves and stems of water-plants; the larger species use seaweed and zoophyte. The leaves or fronds are entangled together and fastened by glue-like threads, secreted, strange to say, by the kidneys. It is just as if a temporary diseased condition had been regularised and turned to good purpose. Going through the nest several times, the male makes a little room in the middle. Partly by coercion and partly by coaxing he induces a female—first one and then another—to pass through the nest with two doors, depositing eggs during her short sojourn. The females go their way, and the male mounts guard over the nest. He drives off intruding fishes much bigger than himself. When the young are hatched, the male has for a time much to do, keeping his charges within bounds until they are able to move about with agility. It seems that sticklebacks are short-lived fishes, probably breeding only once; and it is reasonable to suppose that their success as a race depends to some extent on the paternal care. Now if we could believe that the nesting behaviour had appeared suddenly in its present form, we should be inclined to credit the fish with considerable mental ability. But we are less likely to be so generous if we reflect that the routine has been in all likelihood the outcome of a long racial process of slight improvements and critical testings. The secretion of the glue probably came about as a pathological variation; its utilisation was perhaps discovered by accident; the types that had wit enough to take advantage of this were most successful; the routine became enregistered hereditarily. The stickleback is not so clever as it looks.

Photo: Imperial War Museum.

HOMING PIGEON

A blue chequer hen, which during the War (in September of 1918) flew 22 miles in as many minutes, saving the crew of an aeroplane in difficulties.

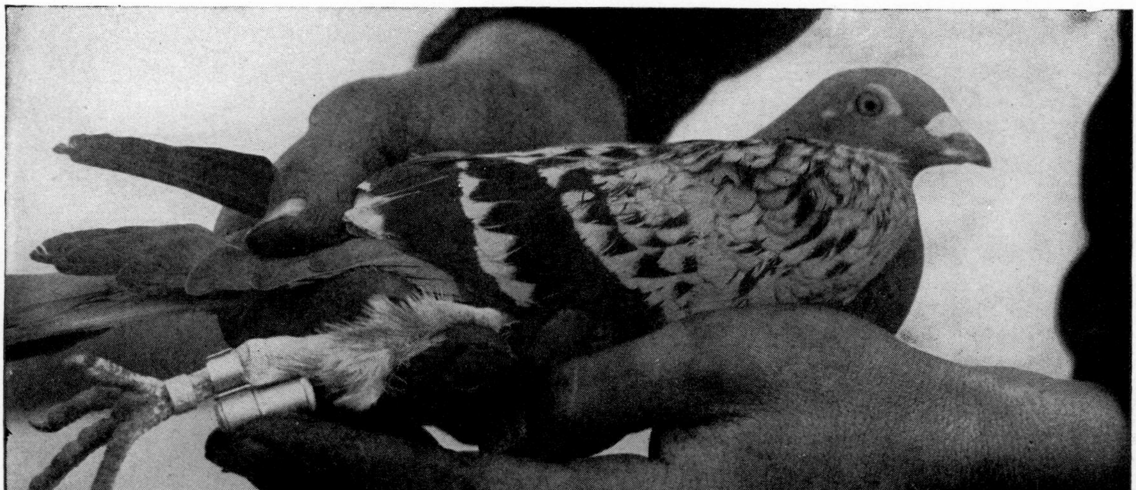

Photo: Imperial War Museum.

CARRIER PIGEON

Carrier pigeons were much used in the War to carry messages. The photograph shows how the message is fixed to the carrier pigeon's leg, in the form of light rings.

Photo: James's Press Agency.

YELLOW-CROWNED PENGUIN

Notice the flightless wings turned into flippers, which are often flapped very vigorously. The very strong feet are also noteworthy. Penguins are mostly confined to the Far South.

Photo: Cagcombe & Co.

PENGUINS ARE "A PECULIAR PEOPLE"

Their wings have been turned into flippers for swimming in the sea and tobogganing on snow. The penguins come back over hundreds of miles of trackless waste to their birthplace, where they breed. When they reach the Antarctic shore they walk with determination to a suitable site, often at the top of a steep cliff. Some species waddle 130 steps per minute, 6 inches per step, two-thirds of a mile per hour.

The Mind of a Minnow

To find solid ground on which to base an appreciation of the behaviour of fishes, it is necessary to experiment, and we may refer to Miss Gertrude White's interesting work on American minnows and sticklebacks. After the fishes had become quite at home in their artificial surroundings, their lessons began. Cloth packets, one of which contained meat and the other cotton, were suspended at opposite ends of the aquarium. The mud-minnows did not show that they perceived either packet, though they swam close by them; the sticklebacks were intrigued at once. Those that went towards the packet containing meat darted furiously upon it and pulled at it with great excitement. Those that went towards the cotton packet turned sharply away when they were within about two inches off. They then perceived what those at the other end were after and joined them—a common habit amongst fishes. Although the minnows were not interested in the tiny "bags of mystery," they were even more alert than the sticklebacks in perceiving moving objects in or on the water, and there is no doubt that both these shallow-water species discover their food largely by sense of sight.

The next set of lessons had to do with colour-associations. The fishes were fed on minced snail, chopped earthworm, fragments of liver, and the like, and the food was given to them from the end of forceps held above the surface of the water, so that the fishes could not be influenced by smell. They had to leap out of the water to take the food from the forceps. Discs of coloured cardboard were slipped over the end of the forceps, so that what the fishes saw was a morsel of food in the centre of a coloured disc. After a week or so of preliminary training, they were so well accustomed to the coloured discs that the presentation of one served as a signal for the fishes to dart to the surface and spring out of the water. When baits of paper were substituted for the food, the fishes continued to jump at the discs. When, however, a blue disc was persistently used for the paper bait and a red disc for the real food, or *vice versa,* some of the minnows learned to discriminate infallibly between shadow and substance, both when these were presented alternately and when they were presented simultaneously. This is not far from the dawn of mind.

In the course of a few lessons, both minnows and sticklebacks learned to associate particular colours with food, and other associations were also formed. A kind of larva that a minnow could make nothing of after repeated trials was subsequently ignored. The approach of the experimenter or anyone else soon began to serve as a food-signal. There can be no doubt that in the ordinary life of fishes there is a process of forming useful associations and suppressing useless responses. Given an inborn repertory of profitable movements that require no training, given the power of forming associations such as those we have illustrated, and given a considerable degree of sensory alertness along certain lines, fishes do not require much more. And in truth they have not got it. Moving with great freedom in three dimensions in a medium that supports them and is very uniform and constant, able in most cases to get plenty of food without fatiguing exertions and to dispense with it for considerable periods if it is scarce, multiplying usually in great abundance so that the huge infantile mortality hardly counts, rarely dying a natural death but usually coming with their strength unabated to a violent end, fishes hold their own in the struggle for existence without much in the way of mental endowment. Their brain has more to do with motion than with mentality, and they have remained at a low psychical level.

Yet just as we should greatly misjudge our own race if we confined our attention to everyday routine, so in our total, as distinguished from our average, estimate of fishes, we must remember the salmon surmounting the falls, the wary trout eluding the angler's skill, the common mud-skipper (Periophthalmus) of many tropical shores which climbs on the rocks and the roots of the mangrove-trees, or actively hunts small shore-animals. We must remember the adventurous life-history of the eel and the quaint ways in which some fishes, males especially, look after their family. The male sea-horse puts the eggs in his breast-pocket; the male Kurtus carries them on the top of his head; the cock-paidle or lumpsucker guards them and aerates them in a corner of a shore-pool.

§ 3

The Mind of Amphibians

Towards the end of the age of the Old Red Sandstone or Devonian, a great step in evolution was taken—the emergence of Amphibians. The earliest representatives had fish-like characters even more marked than those which may be discerned in the tadpoles of our frogs and toads, and there is no doubt that amphibians sprang from a fish stock. But they made great strides, associated in part with their attempts to get out of the water on to dry land. From fossil forms we cannot say much in regard to soft parts; but if we consider the living representatives of the class, we may credit amphibians with such important acquisitions as fingers and toes, a three-chambered heart, true ventral lungs, a drum to the ear, a mobile tongue, and vocal cords. When animals began to be able to grasp an object and when they began to be able to utter sufficient sounds, two new doors were opened. Apart from insects, whose instrumental music had probably begun before the end of the Devonian age, amphibians were the first animals to have a voice. The primary meaning of this voice was doubtless, as it is to-day in our frogs, a sex-call; but it was the beginning of what was destined to play a very important part in the evolution of the mind. In the course of ages the significance of the voice broadened out; it became a parental call; it became an infant's cry. Broadening still, it became a very useful means of recognition among kindred, especially in the dark and in the intricacies of the forest. Ages passed, and the voice rose on another turn of the evolutionary spiral to be expressive of particular emotions beyond the immediate circle of sex—emotions of joy and of fear, of jealousy and of contentment. Finally, we judge, the animal—perhaps the bird was first—began to give utterance to particular "words," indicative not merely of emotions, but of particular things with an emotional halo, such as "food," "enemy," "home." Long afterwards, words became *in man* the medium of reasoned discourse. Sentences were made and judgments expressed. But was not the beginning in the croaking of Amphibia?

Senses of Amphibians

Frogs have good eyes, and the toad's eyes are "jewels." There is evidence of precise vision in the neat way in which a frog catches a fly, flicking out its tongue, which is fixed in front and loose behind. There is also experimental proof that a frog discriminates between red and blue, or between red and white, and an interesting point is that while our skin is sensitive to heat rays but not to light, the skin of the frog answers back to light rays as well. Professor Yerkes experimented with a frog which had to go through a simple labyrinth if it wished to reach a tank of water. At the first alternative between two paths, a red card was placed on the wrong side and a white one on the other. When the frog had learned to take the correct path, marked by the white card, Prof. Yerkes changed the cards. The confusion of the frog showed how thoroughly it had learned its lesson.

We know very little in regard to sense of smell or taste in amphibians; but the sense of hearing is well developed, more developed than might be inferred from the indifference that frogs show to almost all sounds except the croaking of their kindred and splashes in the water.

The toad looks almost sagacious when it is climbing up a bank, and some of the tree-frogs are very alert; but there is very little that we dare say about the amphibian mind. We have mentioned that frogs may learn the secret of a simple maze, and toads

Photo: W. S. Berridge.

HARPY-EAGLE

"Clean and dainty and proud as a Spanish Don."

It is an arboreal and cliff-loving bird, feeding chiefly on mammals, very fierce and strong. The under parts are mostly white, with a greyish zone on the chest. The upper parts are blackish-grey. The harpy occurs from Mexico to Paraguay and Bolivia.

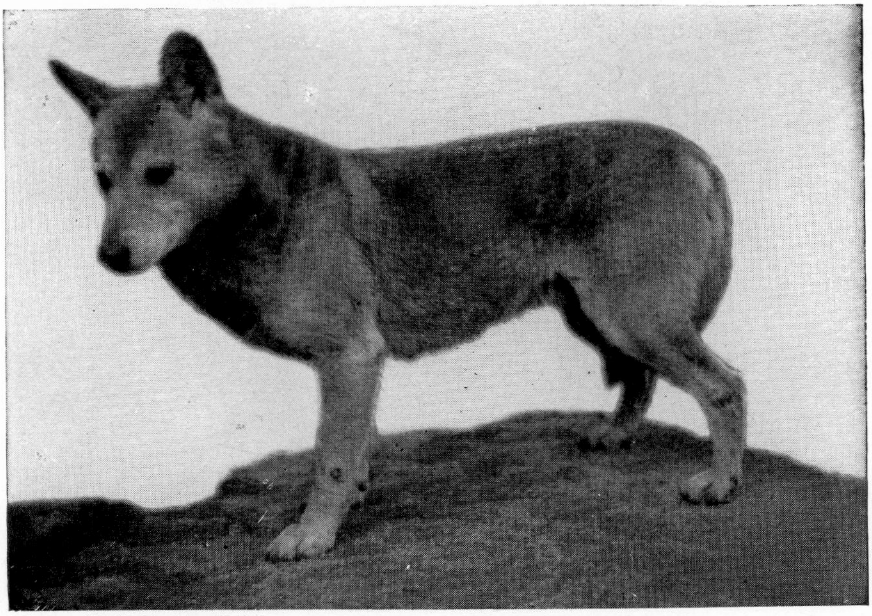

Photo: W. S. Berridge, F.Z.S.

THE DINGO OR WILD DOG OF AUSTRALIA, PERHAPS AN INDIGENOUS WILD SPECIES, PERHAPS A DOMESTICATED DOG THAT HAS GONE WILD OR FERAL

It does much harm in destroying sheep. It is famous for its persistent "death-feigning," for an individual has been known to allow part of its skin to be removed, in the belief that it was dead, before betraying its vitality.

WOODPECKER, HAMMERING AT A COTTON-REEL, ATTACHED TO A TREE

Notice how the stiff tail-feathers braced against the stem help the bird to cling on with its toes. The original hole, in which this woodpecker inserted nuts for the purposes of cracking the shell and extracting the kernel, is seen towards the top of the tree. But the taker of the photograph tied on a hollowed-out cotton-reel as a receptacle for a nut, and it was promptly discovered and used by the bird.

sometimes make for a particular spawning-pond from a considerable distance. But an examination of their brains, occupying a relatively small part of the broad, flat skull, warns us not to expect much intelligence. On the other hand, when we take frogs along a line that is very vital to them, namely, the discrimination of palatable and unpalatable insects, we find, by experiment, that they are quick to learn and that they remember their lessons for many days. Frogs sometimes deposit their eggs in very unsuitable pools of water; but perhaps that is not quite so stupid as it looks. The egg-laying is a matter that has been, as it were, handed over to instinctive registration.

Experiments in Parental Care

It must be put to the credit of amphibians that they have made many experiments in methods of parental care, as if they were feeling their way to new devices. A common frog lays her clumps of eggs in the cradle of the water, sometimes far over a thousand together; the toad winds two long strings round and between water-weeds; and in both cases that is all. There is no parental care, and the prolific multiplication covers the enormous infantile mortality. This is the spawning solution of the problem of securing the continuance of the race. But there is another solution, that of parental care associated with an economical reduction of the number of eggs. Thus the male of the Nurse-Frog (Alytes), not uncommon on the Continent, fixes a string of twenty to fifty eggs to the upper part of his hind-legs, and retires to his hole, only coming out at night to get some food and to keep up the moisture about the eggs. In three weeks, when the tadpoles are ready to come out, he plunges into the pond and is freed from his living burden and his family cares. In the case of the thoroughly aquatic Surinam Toad (Pipa), the male helps to press the eggs, perhaps a hundred in number, on to the back of the female, where each sinks into a pocket of skin with a little lid. By and by fully formed young toads jump out of the pockets.

In the South American tree-frogs called Nototrema there is a pouch on the back of the female in which the eggs develop, and it is interesting to find that in some species what come out are ordinary tadpoles, while in other species the young emerge as miniatures of their parents. Strangest of all, perhaps, is the case of Darwin's Frog (Rhinoderma of Chili), where the young, about ten to fifteen in number, develop in the male's croaking-sacs, which become in consequence enormously distended. Eventually the strange spectacle is seen of miniature frogs jumping out of their father's mouth. Needless to say we are not citing these methods of parental care as examples of intelligence; but perhaps they correct the impression of amphibians as a rather humdrum race. Whatever be the mental aspect of the facts, there has certainly been some kind of experimenting, and the increase of parental care, so marked in many amphibians, with associated reduction of the number of offspring is a finger-post on the path of progress.

§ 4

The Reptilian Mind

We speak of the wisdom of the serpent; but it is not very easy to justify the phrase. Among all the multitude of reptiles—snakes, lizards, turtles, and crocodiles, a motley crowd—we cannot see much more than occasional traces of intelligence. The inner life remains a tiny rill.

No doubt many reptiles are very effective; but it is an instinctive rather than an intelligent efficiency. The well-known "soft-shell" tortoise of the United States swims with powerful strokes and runs so quickly that it can hardly be overtaken. It hunts vigorously for crayfish and insect larvæ in the rivers. It buries itself in the mud when cold weather comes. It may lie on a floating log ready to slip into the water at a moment's notice; it may bask on a sunny bank or in the warm shallows. Great wariness is shown in choosing times and places for egg-laying. The mother tramps the earth down upon the buried eggs. All is effective. Similar statements might be made in regard to scores of other reptiles; but what we see is almost wholly of the nature of instinctive routine, and we get little glimpse of more than efficiency and endeavour.

In a few cases there is proof of reptiles finding their way back to their homes from a considerable distance, and recognition of persons is indubitable. Gilbert White remarks of his tortoise: "Whenever the good old lady came in sight who had waited on it for more than thirty years, it always hobbled with awkward alacrity towards its benefactress, while to strangers it was altogether inattentive." Of definite learning there are a few records. Thus Professor Yerkes studied a sluggish turtle of retiring disposition, taking advantage of its strong desire to efface itself. On the path of the darkened nest of damp grass he interposed a simple maze in the form of a partitioned box. After wandering about constantly for thirty-five minutes the turtle found its way through the maze by chance. Two hours afterwards it reached the nest in fifteen minutes; and after another interval of two hours it only required five minutes. After the third trial, the routes became more direct, there was less aimless wandering. The time of the twentieth trial was forty-five seconds; that of the thirtieth, forty seconds. In the thirtieth case, the path followed was quite direct, and so it was on the fiftieth trip, which only required thirty-five seconds. Of course, the whole thing did not amount to very much; but there was a definite learning, *a learning from experience,* which has played an important part in the evolution of animal behaviour.

Comparing reptiles with amphibians, we may recognise an increased masterliness of behaviour and a hint of greater plasticity. The records of observers who have made pets of reptiles suggest that the life of feeling or emotion is growing stronger, and so do stories, if they can be accepted, which suggest the beginning of conjugal affection.

The error must be guarded against of interpreting in terms

of intelligence what is merely the outcome of long-continued structure adaptation. When the limbless lizard called the Slow-worm is suddenly seized by the tail, it escapes by surrendering the appendage, which breaks across a preformed weak plane. But this is a reflex action, not a reflective one. It is comparable to our sudden withdrawal of our finger from a very hot cinder. The Egg-eating African snake Dasypeltis gets the egg of a bird into its gullet unbroken, and cuts the shell against downward-projecting sharp points of the vertebræ. None of the precious contents is lost and the broken "empties" are returned. It is admirable, indeed unsurpassable; but it is not intelligent.

§ 5

Mind in Birds

Sight and hearing are highly developed in birds, and the senses, besides pulling the triggers of inborn efficiencies, supply the raw materials for intelligence. There is some truth, though not the whole truth, in the old philosophical dictum, that there is nothing in the intellect which was not previously in the senses. Many people have admired the certainty and alacrity with which gulls pick up a fragment of biscuit from the white wake of a steamer, and the incident is characteristic. In their power of rapidly altering the focus of the eye, birds are unsurpassed.

To the sense of sight in birds, the sense of hearing comes a good second. A twig breaks under our feet, and out sounds the danger-call of the bird we were trying to watch. Many young birds, like partridges, respond when two or three hours old to the anxious warning note of the parents, and squat motionless on the ground, though other sounds, such as the excited clucking of a foster-mother hen, leave them indifferent. They do not know what they are doing when they squat; they are obeying the living hand of the past which is within them. Their behaviour is instinctive. But the present point is the discriminating quality of the sense of hearing; and that is corroborated by the singing of birds.

THE BEAVER

The beaver will gnaw through trees a foot in diameter; to save itself more trouble than is necessary, it will stop when it has gnawed the trunk till there is only a narrow core left, having the wit to know that the autumn gales will do the rest.

Photo: F. R. Hinkins & Son.

THE THRUSH AT ITS ANVIL

The song-thrush takes the snail's shell in its bill, and knocks it against a stone until it breaks, making the palatable flesh available. Many broken shells are often found around the anvil.

It is emotional art, expressing feelings in the medium of sound. On the part of the females, who are supposed to listen, it betokens a cultivated ear.

As to the other senses, touch is not highly developed except about the bill, where it reaches a climax in birds like the woodcock, which probe for unseen earthworms in the soft soil. Taste seems to be poorly developed, for most birds bolt their food, but there is sometimes an emphatic rejection of unpalatable things, like toads and caterpillars. Of smell in birds little is known, but it has been proved to be present in certain cases, e.g. in some nocturnal birds of prey. It seems certain that it is by sight, not by smell, that the eagles gather to the carcass; but perhaps there is more smell in birds than they are usually credited with. One would like to experiment with the oil from the preen gland of birds to see whether the scent of this does not help in the recognition of kin by kin at night or amid the darkness of the forest. There may be other senses in birds, such as a sense of temperature and a sense of balance; but no success has attended the attempts made to demonstrate a magnetic sense, which has been impatiently postulated by students of bird migration in order to "explain" how the birds find their way. The big fact is that in birds there are two widely open gateways of knowledge, the sense of sight and the sense of hearing.

Instinctive Aptitudes

Many a young water-bird, such as a coot, swims right away when it is tumbled into water for the first time. So chicks peck without any learning or teaching, very young ducklings catch small moths that flit by, and young plovers lie low when the danger-signal sounds. But birds seem strangely limited as regards many of these instinctive capacities—limited when compared with the "little-brained" ants and bees, which have from the first such a rich repertory of ready-made cleverness. The limitation in birds is of great interest, for it means that intelligence is coming to its own and is going to take up the reins at many corners of the daily round. Professor Lloyd Morgan observed that his chickens incubated in the laboratory had no instinctive awareness of the significance of their mother's cluck when she was brought outside the door. Although thirsty and willing to drink from a moistened finger-tip, they did not instinctively recognize water, even when they walked through a saucerful. Only when they happened to peck their toes as they stood in the water did they appreciate water as the stuff they wanted, and raise their bills up to the sky. Once or twice they actually stuffed their crops with "worms" of red worsted!

Instinctive aptitudes, then, the young birds have, but these are more limited than in ants, bees, and wasps; and the reason is to be found in the fact that the brain is now evolving on the tack of what Sir Ray Lankester has called "educability." Young birds *learn* with prodigious rapidity; the emancipation of the mind from the tyranny of hereditary obligations has begun. Young birds make mistakes, like the red worsted mistake, but they do not make the same mistakes often. They are able to profit by experience in a very rapid way. We do not mean that creatures of the little-brain type, like ants, bees, and wasps, are unable to profit by experience or are without intelligence. There are no such hard-and-fast lines. We mean that in the ordinary life of insects the enregistered instinctive capacities are on the whole sufficient for the occasion, and that intelligent educability is very slightly developed. Nor do we mean that birds are quite emancipated from the tyranny of engrained instinctive obligations, and can always "ring up" intelligence in a way that is impossible for the stereotyped bee. The sight of a pigeon brooding on an empty nest, while her two eggs lie disregarded only a couple of inches away, is enough to show that along certain lines birds may find it impossible to get free from the trammels of instinct. The peculiar interest of birds is that they have many instincts and yet a notable power of learning intelligently.

Intelligence co-operating with Instinct

Professor Lloyd Morgan was foster-parent to two moorhens which grew up in isolation from their kindred. They swam instinctively, but they would not dive, neither in a large bath nor in a current. But it happened one day when one of these moorhens was swimming in a pool on a Yorkshire stream, that a puppy came barking down the bank and made an awkward feint towards the young bird. In a moment the moorhen dived, disappeared from view, and soon partially reappeared, his head just peeping above the water beneath the overhanging bank. This was the first time the bird had dived, and the performance was absolutely true to type.

There can be little doubt as to the meaning of this observation. The moorhen has an hereditary or instinctive capacity for swimming and diving, but the latter is not so easily called into activity as the former. The particular moorhen in question had enjoyed about two months of swimming experience, which probably counted for something, but in the course of that experience nothing had pulled the trigger of the diving capacity. On an eventful day the young moorhen saw and heard the dog; it was emotionally excited; it probably did to some extent intelligently appreciate a novel and meaningful situation. Intelligence co-operated with instinct, and the bird dived appropriately.

Birds have inborn predispositions to certain effective ways of pecking, scratching, swimming, diving, flying, crouching, lying low, nest-building, and so on; but they are marked off from the much more purely instinctive ants and bees by the extent to which individual "nurture" seems to mingle with the inherited "nature." The two together result in the fine product which we call the bird's behaviour. After Lloyd Morgan's chicks had tried a few conspicuous and unpalatable caterpillars, they had no use for any more. They learned in their early days with prodigious rapidity, illustrating the deep difference between the "big-brain" type, relatively poor in its endowment of instinctive capacities, but eminently "educable," and the "little-brain" type, say, of ants and bees, richly endowed with instinctive capacities, but very far from being quick or glad to learn. We owe it to Sir Ray Lankester to have made it clear that these two types of brain are, as it were, on different tacks of evolution, and should not be directly pitted against one another. The "little-brain" type makes for a climax in the ant, where instinctive behaviour reaches a high degree of perfection; the "big-brain" type reaches its climax in horse and dog, in elephant and monkey. The particular interest that attaches to the behaviour of birds is in the combination of a good deal of instinct with a great deal of intelligent learning. This is well illustrated when birds make a nest out of new materials or in some quite novel situation. It is clearly seen when birds turn to some new kind of food, like the Kea parrot, which attacks the sheep in New Zealand.

Some young woodpeckers are quite clever in opening fir cones to get at the seeds, and this might be hastily referred to a well-defined hereditary capacity. But the facts are that the parents bring their young ones first the seeds themselves, then partly opened cones, and then intact ones. There is an educative process, and so it is in scores of cases.

Using their Wits

When the Greek eagle lifts the Greek tortoise in its talons, and lets it fall from a height so that the strong carapace is broken and the flesh exposed, it is making intelligent use of an expedient. Whether it discovered the expedient by experimenting, as is possible, or by chance, as is more likely, it uses it intelligently. In the same way herring-gulls lift sea-urchins and clams in their bills, and let them fall on the rocks so that the shells are broken. In the same way rooks deal with freshwater mussels.

The Thrush's Anvil

A very instructive case is the behaviour of the song-thrush when it takes a wood-snail in its beak and hammers it against a stone, its so-called anvil. To a young thrush, which she had brought up by hand, Miss Frances Pitt offered some wood-snails, but it took no interest in them until one put out its head and began to move about. The bird then pecked at the snail's horns, but was evidently puzzled when the creature retreated within the shelter of the shell. This happened over and over again, the thrush's inquisitive interest increasing day by day. It pecked at the shell and even picked it up by the lip, but no real progress was made till the sixth day, when the thrush seized the snail and beat it on the ground as it would a big worm. On the same day it picked up a shell and knocked it repeatedly against a stone, trying first one snail and then another. After fifteen minutes' hard work, the thrush managed to break one, and after that it was all easy. A certain predisposition to beat things on the ground was doubtless present, but the experiment showed that the use of an anvil could be arrived at by an untutored bird. After prolonged trying it found out how to deal with a difficult situation. It may be said that in more natural conditions this might be picked up by imitation, but while this is quite possible, it is useful to notice that experiments with animals lead us to doubt whether imitation counts for nearly so much as used to be believed.

§ 6

The Mind of the Mammal

When we watch a collie at a sheep-driving competition, or an elephant helping the forester, or a horse shunting waggons at a railway siding, we are apt to be too generous to the mammal mind. For in the cases we have just mentioned, part of man's mind has, so to speak, got into the animal's. On the other hand, when we study rabbits and guinea-pigs, we are apt to be too stingy, for these rodents are under the average of mammals, and those that live in domestication illustrate the stupefying effect of a too sheltered life. The same applies to domesticated sheep contrasted with wild sheep, or even with their own lambs. If we are to form a sound judgment on the intelligence of mammals we must not attend too much to those that have profited by man's training, nor to those whose mental life has been dulled by domestication.

Instinctive Aptitudes

What is to be said of the behaviour of beavers who gnaw the base of a tree with their chisel-edged teeth till only a narrow core is left—to snap in the first gale, bringing the useful branches down to the ground? What is to be said of the harvest-mouse constructing its nest, or of the squirrel making cache after cache of nuts? These and many similar pieces of behaviour are fundamentally instinctive, due to inborn predispositions of nerve-cells and muscle-cells. But in mammals they seem to be often attended by a certain amount of intelligent attention, saving the creature from the tyranny of routine so marked in the ways of ants and bees.

Sheer Dexterity

Besides instinctive aptitudes, which are exhibited in almost equal perfection by all the members of the same species, there are acquired dexterities which depend on individual opportunities. They are also marked by being outside and beyond ordinary routine—not that any rigorous boundary line can be drawn. We read that at Mathura on the Jumna doles of food are provided by the piety of pilgrims for the sacred river-tortoises, which are so crowded when there is food going that their smooth carapaces form a more or less continuous raft across the river. On that unsteady slippery bridge the Langur monkeys (*Semnopithecus entellus*) venture out and in spite of vicious snaps secure a share of the booty. This picture of the monkeys securing a footing on the moving mass of turtle-backs is almost a diagram of sheer dexterity. It illustrates the spirit of adventure, the will to experiment, which is, we believe, the main motive-force in new departures in behaviour.

Photo: Lafayette

ALSATIAN WOLF-DOG

An animal of acute senses and great intelligence. It was of great service in the war. (The dog shown, Arno von Indetal, is a trained police dog and did service abroad during the war.)

Photo: W. S. Berridge.

THE POLAR BEAR OF THE FAR NORTH

An animal of extraordinary strength, able with a stroke of its paw to lift a big seal right out of the water and send it crashing along the ice. The food consists chiefly of seals. The sexes wander separately. A hole is often dug as a winter retreat, but there is no hibernation. A polar bear in captivity has been seen making a current with its paw in the water of its pool in order to secure floating buns without trouble—an instance of sheer intelligence.

From the Smithsonian Report, 1914

AN ALLIGATOR "YAWNING" IN EXPECTATION OF FOOD

Note the large number of sharp conical teeth fixed in sockets along the jaws.

Power of Association

A bull-terrier called Jasper, studied by Prof. J. B. Watson, showed great power of associating certain words with certain actions. From a position invisible to the dog the owner would give certain commands, such as "Go into the next room and bring me a paper lying on the floor." Jasper did this at once, and a score of similar things.

Lord Avebury's dog Van was accustomed to go to a box containing a small number of printed cards and select the card TEA or OUT, as the occasion suggested. It had established an association between certain black marks on a white background and the gratification of certain desires. It is probable that some of the extraordinary things horses and dogs have been known to do in the way of stamping a certain number of times in supposed indication of an answer to an arithmetical question (in the case of horses), or of the name of an object drawn (in the case of dogs), are dependent on clever associations established by the teacher between minute signs and a number of stampings. What is certain is that mammals have in varying degrees a strong power of establishing associations. There is often some delicacy in the association established. Everyone knows of cases where a dog, a cat, or a horse will remain quite uninterested, to all appearance, in its owner's movements until some little detail, such as taking a key from its peg, pulls the trigger. Now the importance of this in the wild life of the fox or the hare, the otter or the squirrel, is obviously that the young animals learn to associate certain sounds in their environment with definite possibilities. They have to learn an alphabet of woodcraft, the letters of which are chiefly sounds and scents.

The Dancing Mouse as a Pupil

The dancing or waltzing mouse is a Japanese variety with many peculiarities, such as having only one of the three semicircular canals of the ear well developed. It has a strong tendency to waltz round and round in circles without sufficient cause and to trip sideways towards its dormitory instead of proceeding in the orthodox head-on fashion. But this freak is a very educable creature, as Professor Yerkes has shown. In a careful way he confronted his mouse-pupil with alternative pathways marked by different degrees of illumination, or by different colours. If the mouse chose compartment A, it found a clear passage direct to its nest; if it chose compartment B, it was punished by a mild electric shock and it had to take a roundabout road home. Needless to say, the A compartment was sometimes to the right hand, sometimes to the left, else mere position would have been a guide. The experiments showed that the dancing mice learn to discriminate the right path from the wrong, and similar results have been got from other mammals, such as rats and squirrels. There is no proof of learning by ideas, but there is proof of learning by experience. And the same must be true in wild life.

Many mammals, such as cats and rats, learn how to manipulate puzzle-boxes and how to get at the treasure at the heart of a Hampton Court maze. Some of the puzzle-boxes, with a reward of food inside, are quite difficult, for the various bolts and bars have to be dealt with in a particular order, and yet many mammals master the problem. What is plain is that they gradually eliminate useless movements, that they make fewer and fewer mistakes, that they eventually succeed, and that they register the solution within themselves so that it remains with them for a time. It looks a little like the behaviour of a man who learns a game of skill without thinking. It is a learning by experience, not by ideas or reflection. Thus it is very difficult to suppose that a rat or a cat could form any idea or even picture of the Hampton Court maze—which they nevertheless master.

Learning Tricks

Given sufficient inducement many of the cleverer mammals will learn to do very sensible things, and no one is wise enough to say that they never understand what they are doing. Yet it is certain that trained animals often exhibit pieces of behaviour which are not nearly so clever as they look. The elephant at the Belle Vue Gardens in Manchester used to collect pennies from benevolent visitors. When it got a penny in its trunk it put it in the slot of an automatic machine which delivered up a biscuit. When a visitor gave the elephant a halfpenny it used to throw it back with disgust. At first sight this seemed almost wise, and there was no doubt some intelligent appreciation of the situation. But it was largely a matter of habituation, the outcome of careful and prolonged training. The elephant was laboriously taught to put the penny in the slot and to discriminate between the useful pennies and the useless halfpennies. It was not nearly so clever as it looked.

Using their Wits

In the beautiful Zoological Park in Edinburgh the Polar Bear was wont to sit on a rocky peninsula of a water-filled quarry. The visitors threw in buns, some of which floated on the surface. It was often easy for the Polar Bear to collect half a dozen by plunging into the pool. But it had discovered a more interesting way. At the edge of the peninsula it scooped the water gently with its huge paw and made a current which brought the buns ashore. This was a simple piece of behaviour, but it has the smack of intelligence—of putting two and two together in a novel way. It suggests the power of making what is called a "perceptual inference."

On the occasion of a great flood in a meadow it was observed that a number of mares brought their foals to the top of a knoll, and stood round about them protecting them against the rising water. A dog has been known to show what was at any rate a plastic appreciation of a varying situation in swimming across a tidal river. It changed its starting-point, they say, according to the flow or ebb of the tide. Arctic foxes and some other wild mammals show great cleverness in dealing with traps, and the manipulative intelligence of elephants is worthy of all our admiration.

§ 7

Why is there not more Intelligence?

When we allow for dexterity and power of association, when we recognise a certain amount of instinctive capacity and a capacity for profiting by experience in an intelligent way, we must admit a certain degree of disappointment when we take a survey of the behaviour of mammals, especially of those with very fine brains, from which we should naturally expect great things. Why is there not more frequent exhibition of intelligence in the stricter sense?

The answer is that most mammals have become in the course of time very well adapted to the ordinary conditions of their life, and tend to leave well alone. They have got their repertory of efficient answers to the ordinary questions of everyday life, and why should they experiment? In the course of the struggle for existence what has been established is efficiency in normal circumstances, and therefore even the higher animals tend to be no cleverer than is necessary. So while many mammals are extraordinarily efficient, they tend to be a little dull. Their mental equipment is adequate for the everyday conditions of their life, but it is not on sufficiently generous lines to admit of, let us say, an interest in Nature or adventurous experiment. Mammals always tend to "play for safety."

We hasten, however, to insert here some very interesting saving clauses.

Experimentation in Play

A glimpse of what mammals are capable of, were it necessary, may be obtained by watching those that are playful, such as lambs and kids, foals and calves, young foxes and others. For these young creatures let themselves go irresponsibly, they are still unstereotyped, they test what they and their fellows can do. The experimental character of much of animal play is very marked.

It is now recognised by biologists that play among animals is the young form of work, and that the playing period, often so conspicuous, is vitally important as an apprenticeship to the serious business of life and as an opportunity for learning the alphabet of Nature. But the playing period is much more; it is one of the few opportunities animals have of making experiments without too serious responsibilities. Play is Nature's device for allowing elbow-room for new departures (behaviour-variations) which may form part of the raw materials of progress. Play, we repeat, gives us a glimpse of the possibilities of the mammal mind.

Other Glimpses of Intelligence

A squirrel is just as clever as it needs to be and no more; and of some vanishing mammals, like the beaver, not even this can be said. Humdrum non-plastic efficiency is apt to mean stagnation. Now we have just seen that in the play of young mammals there is an indication of unexhausted possibilities, and we get the same impression when we think of three other facts. (*a*) In those mammals, like dog and horse, which have entered into active co-operative relations with man, we see that the mind of the mammal is capable of much more than the average would lead us to think. When man's sheltering is too complete and the domesticated creature is passive in his grip, the intelligence deteriorates. (*b*) When we study mammals, like the otter, which live a versatile life in a very complex and difficult environment, we get an inspiriting picture of the play of wits. (*c*) Thirdly, when we pass to monkeys, where the fore-limb has become a free hand, where the brain shows a relatively great improvement, where "words" are much used, we cannot fail to recognise the emergence of something new—a restless inquisitiveness, a desire to investigate the world, an unsatisfied tendency to experiment. We are approaching the Dawn of Reason.

THE MIND OF MONKEYS

§ 8

There is a long gamut between the bushy-tailed, almost squirrel-like marmosets and the big-brained chimpanzee. There is great variety of attainment at different levels in the Simian tribe.

Keen Senses

To begin at the beginning, it is certain that monkeys have a first-class sensory equipment, especially as regards sight, hearing, and touch. The axes of the two eyes are directed forwards as in man, and a large section of the field of vision is common to both eyes. In other words, monkeys have a more complete stereoscopic vision than the rest of the mammals enjoy. They look more and smell less. They can distinguish different colours, apart from different degrees of brightness in the coloured objects. They are quick to discriminate differences in the shapes of things, e.g. boxes similar in size but different in shape, for if the prize is always put in a box of the same shape they soon learn (by association) to select the profitable one. They learn to discriminate cards with short words or with signs printed on them, coming down when the "Yes" card is shown, remaining on their perch when the card says "No." Bred to a forest life where alertness is a life-or-death quality, they are quick to respond to a sudden movement or to pick out some new feature in their surroundings. And what is true of vision holds also for hearing.

Power of Manipulation

Another quality which separates monkeys very markedly from ordinary mammals is their manipulative expertness, the co-

Photo: W. P. Dando

BABY ORANG

Notice the small ears and the suggestion of good temper. The mother orang will throw prickly fruits and pieces of branches at those who intrude on her maternal care.

Photo: Gambier Bolton.

ORANG-UTAN

A large and heavy ape, frequenting forests in Sumatra and Borneo, living mainly in trees, where a temporary nest is made. The expression is melancholy, the belly very protuberant, the colour yellow-brown, the movements are cautious and slow.

1. CHIMPANZEE
2. BABY ORANG-UTAN
3. ORANG-UTAN
4. BABY CHIMPANZEES

Photos: James's Press Agency.

In his famous book on *The Expression of the Emotions in Man and Animals* (1872) Charles Darwin showed that many forms of facial expression familiar in man have their counterparts in apes and other mammals. He also showed how important the movements of expression are as means of communication between mother and offspring, mate and mate, kith and kin.

The anthropoid apes show notable differences of temperament as the photographs show. The chimpanzee is lively, cheerful, and educable. The orang is also mild of temper, but often and naturally appears melancholy in captivity. This is not suggested, however, by our photograph of the adult. Both chimpanzee and orang are markedly contrasted with the fierce and gloomy gorilla.

ordination of hand and eye. This great gift follows from the fact that among monkeys the fore-leg has been emancipated. It has ceased to be indispensable as an organ of support; it has become a climbing, grasping, lifting, handling organ. The fore-limb has become a free hand, and everyone who knows monkeys at all is aware of the zest with which they use their tool. They enjoy pulling things to pieces—a kind of dissection—or screwing the handle off a brush and screwing it on again.

Activity for Activity's Sake

Professor Thorndike hits the nail on the head when he lays stress on the intensity of activity in monkeys—activity both of body and mind. They are pent-up reservoirs of energy, which almost any influence will tap. Watch a cat or a dog, Professor Thorndike says; it does comparatively few things and is content for long periods to do nothing. It will be splendidly active in response to some stimulus such as food or a friend or a fight, but if nothing appeals to its special make-up, which is very utilitarian in its interests, it will do nothing. "Watch a monkey and you cannot enumerate the things he does, cannot discover the stimuli to which he reacts, cannot conceive the *raison d'etre* of his pursuits. Everything appeals to him. He likes to be active for the sake of activity."

This applies to mental activity as well, and the quality is one of extraordinary interest, for it shows the experimenting mood at a higher turn of the spiral than in any other creature, save man. It points forward to the scientific spirit. We cannot, indeed, believe in the sudden beginning of any quality, and we recall the experimenting of playing mammals, such as kids and kittens, or of inquisitive adults like Kipling's mongoose, Riki-Tiki-Tavi, which made it his business in life to find out about things. But in monkeys the habit of restless experimenting rises to a higher pitch. They appear to be curious about the world. The psychologist whom we have quoted tells of a monkey which happened to hit a projecting wire so as to make it vibrate. He went on repeating the performance hundreds of times during the next few days. Of course, he got nothing out of it, save fun, but it was grist to his mental mill. "The fact of mental life is to monkeys it own reward." The monkey's brain is "tender all over, functioning throughout, set off in action by anything and everything."

Sheer Quickness

Correlated with the quality of restless inquisitiveness and delight in activity for its own sake there is the quality of quickness. We mean not merely the locomotor agility that marks most monkeys, but quickness of perception and plan. It is the sort of quality that life among the branches will engender, where it is so often a case of neck or nothing. It is the quality which we describe as being on the spot, though the phrase has slipped from its original moorings. Speaking of his Bonnet Monkey, an Indian macaque, second cousin to the kind that lives on the Rock of Gibraltar, Professor S. J. Holmes writes: "For keenness of perception, rapidity of action, facility in forming good practical judgments about ways and means of escaping pursuit and of attaining various other ends, Lizzie had few rivals in the animal world. . . . Her perceptions and decisions were so much more rapid than my own that she would frequently transfer her attention, decide upon a line of action, and carry it into effect before I was aware of what she was about. Until I came to guard against her nimble and unexpected manœuvres, she succeeded in getting possession of many apples and peanuts which I had not intended to give her except upon the successful performance of some task."

Quick to Learn

Quite fundamental to any understanding of animal behaviour is the distinction so clearly drawn by Sir Ray Lankester between the "little-brain" type, rich in inborn or instinctive capacities, but relatively slow to learn, and the "big-brain" type, with a relatively poor endowment of specialised instincts, but with great educability. The "little-brain" type finds its climax in ants and bees; the "big-brain" type in horses and dogs, elephants and monkeys. And of all animals monkeys are the quickest to learn, if we use the word "learn" to mean the formation of useful associations between this and that, between a given sense-presentation and a particular piece of behaviour.

The Case of Sally

Some of us remember Sally, the chimpanzee at the "Zoo" with which Dr. Romanes used to experiment. She was taught to give her teacher the number of straws he asked for, and she soon learned to do so up to five. If she handed a number not asked for, her offer was refused; if she gave the proper number, she got a piece of fruit. If she was asked for five straws, she picked them up individually and placed them in her mouth, and when she had gathered five she presented them together in her hand. Attempts to teach her to give six to ten straws were not very successful. For Sally "above six" meant "many," and besides, her limits of patience were probably less than her range of computation. This was hinted at by the highly interesting circumstance that when dealing with numbers above five she very frequently doubled over a straw so as to make it present two ends and thus appear as two straws. The doubling of the straw looked like an intelligent device to save time, and it was persistently resorted to in spite of the fact that her teacher always refused to accept a doubled straw as equivalent to two straws. Here we get a glimpse of something beyond the mere association of a sound—"Five"—and that number of straws.

The Case of Lizzie

The front of the cage in which Professor Holmes kept Lizzie was made of vertical bars which allowed her to reach out with her arm. On a board with an upright nail as handle there was placed an apple—out of Lizzie's reach. She reached immediately for the nail, pulled the board in and got the apple. "There was no employment of the method of trial and error; there was direct appropriate action following the perception of her relation to board, nail, and apple." Of course her ancestors may have been adepts at drawing a fruit-laden branch within their reach, but the simple experiment was very instructive. All the more instructive because in many other cases the experiments indicate a gradual sifting out of useless movements and an eventful retention of the one that pays. When Lizzie was given a vaseline bottle containing a peanut and closed with a cork, she at once pulled the cork out with her teeth, obeying the instinct to bite at new objects, but she never learned to turn the bottle upside down and let the nut drop out. She often got the nut, and after some education she got it more quickly than she did at first, but there was no indication that she ever perceived the fit and proper way of getting what she wanted. "In the course of her intent efforts her mind seemed so absorbed with the object of desire that it was never focussed on the means of attaining that object. There was no deliberation, and no discrimination between the important and the unimportant elements in her behaviour. The gradually increasing facility of her performances depended on the apparently unconscious elimination of useless movements." This may be called learning, but it is learning at a very low level; it is far from learning by ideas; it is hardly even learning by experiment; it is not more than learning by experience, it is not more than fumbling at learning!

Trial and Error

A higher note is struck in the behaviour of some more highly endowed monkeys. In many experiments, chiefly in the way of getting into boxes difficult to open, there is evidence (1) of attentive persistent experiment (2) of the rapid elimination of ineffective movements, and (3) of remembering the solution when it was discovered. Kinnaman taught two macaques the Hampton Court Maze, a feat which probably means a memory of movements, and we get an interesting glimpse in his observation that they began to smack their lips audibly when they reached the latter part of their course, and began to feel, dare one say, "We are right this time."

In getting into "puzzle-boxes" and into "combination-boxes" (where the barriers must be overcome in a definite order), monkeys learn by the trial and error method much more quickly than cats and dogs do, and a very suggestive fact emphasized by Professor Thorndike is "a process of sudden acquisition by a rapid, often apparently instantaneous abandonment of the unsuccessful movements and selection of the appropriate one, which rivals in suddenness the selections made by human beings in similar performances." A higher note still was sounded by one of Thorndike's monkeys which opened a puzzle-box at once, eight months after his previous experience with it. For here was some sort of registration of a solution.

Imitation

Two chimpanzees in the Dublin Zoo were often to be seen washing the two shelves of their cupboard and "wringing" the wet cloth in the approved fashion. It was like a caricature of a washerwoman, and someone said, "What mimics they are!" Now we do not know whether that was or was not the case with the chimpanzees, but the majority of the experiments that have been made do not lead us to attach to imitation so much importance as is usually given to it by the popular interpreter. There are instances where a monkey that had given up a puzzle in despair returned to it when it had seen its neighbour succeed, but most of the experiments suggested that the creature has to find out for itself. Even with such a simple problem as drawing food near with a stick, it often seems of little use to show the monkey how it is done. Placing a bit of food outside his monkey's cage, Professor Holmes "poked it about with the stick so as to give her a suggestion of how the stick might be employed to move the food within reach, but although the act was repeated many times Lizzie never showed the least inclination to use the stick to her advantage." Perhaps the idea of a "tool" is beyond the Bonnet Monkey, yet here again we must be cautious, for Professor L. T. Hobhouse had a monkey of the same macaque genus which learned in the course of time to use a crooked stick with great effect.

The Case of Peter

Perhaps the cleverest monkey as yet studied was a performing chimpanzee called Peter, which has been generally described by Dr. Lightner Witmer. Peter could skate and cycle, thread needles and untie knots, smoke a cigarette and string beads, screw in nails and unlock locks. But what Peter was thinking about all the time it was hard to guess, and there is very little evidence to suggest that his rapid power of putting two and two together ever rose above a sort of concrete mental experimenting, which Dr. Romanes used to call perceptual inference. Without supposing that there are hard-and-fast boundary lines, we cannot avoid the general conclusion that, while monkeys are often intelligent, they seldom, if ever, show even hints of reason, i.e. of working or playing with general ideas. That remains Man's prerogative.

The Bustle of the Mind

In mammals like otters, foxes, stoats, hares, and elephants, what a complex of tides and currents there must be in the brain-mind! We may think of a stream with currents at different levels. Lowest there are the *basal appetites* of hunger and sex, often with eddies rising to the surface. Then there are the *primary emotions,* such as fear of hereditary enemies and maternal affection for offspring. Above these are *instinctive aptitudes,* inborn powers of doing clever things without having to learn

Photo: W. P. Dando.

CHIMPANZEE

An African ape, at home in the equatorial forests, a lively and playful creature, eminently educable.

Photo: W. S. Berridge.

YOUNG CHEETAHS, OR HUNTING LEOPARDS

Trained to hunt from time immemorial and quite easily tamed. Cheetahs occur in India, Persia, Turkestan, and Africa.

Photo: C. Reid.

COMMON OTTER

One of the most resourceful of animals and the "most playsomest crittur on God's earth." It neither stores nor hibernates, but survives in virtue of its wits and because of the careful education of the young. The otter is a roving animal, often with more than one resting-place; it has been known to travel fifteen miles in a night.

how. But in mammals these are often expressed along with, or as it were through, the controlled life of *intelligent activity*, where there is more clear-cut perceptual influence.

Higher still are the records or memories of individual experience and the registration of individual habits, while on the surface is the instreaming multitude of messages from the outside world, like raindrops and hailstones on the stream, some of them penetrating deeply, being, as we say, full of meaning. The mind of the higher animal is in some respects like a child's mind, in having little in the way of clear-cut ideas, in showing no reason in the strict sense, and in its extraordinary educability, but it differs from the child's mind entirely in the sure effectiveness of a certain repertory of responses. It is efficient to a degree.

"Until at last arose the Man."

Man's brain is more complicated than that of the higher apes—gorilla, orang, and chimpanzee—and it is relatively larger. But the improvements in structure do not seem in themselves sufficient to account for man's great advance in intelligence. The rill of inner life has become a swift stream, sometimes a rushing torrent. Besides perceptual inference or *Intelligence*—a sort of picture-logic, which some animals likewise have—there is conceptual inference—or *Reason*—an internal experimenting with general ideas. Even the cleverest animals, it would seem, do not get much beyond playing with "particulars"; man plays an internal game of chess with "universals." Intelligent behaviour may go a long way with mental images; rational conduct demands general ideas. It may be, however, that "percepts" and "concepts" differ rather in degree than in kind, and that the passage from one to the other meant a higher power of forming associations. A clever dog has probably a generalised percept of man, as distinguished from a memory-image of the particular men it has known, but man alone has the concept Man, or Mankind, or Humanity. Experimenting with concepts or general ideas is what we call Reason.

Here, of course, we get into deep waters, and perhaps it is wisest not to attempt too much. So we shall content ourselves here with pointing out that Man's advance in intelligence and from intelligence to reason is closely wrapped up with his power of speech. What animals began—a small vocabulary—he has carried to high perfection. But what is distinctive is not the vocabulary so much as the habit of making sentences, of expressing judgments in a way which admitted of communication between mind and mind. The multiplication of words meant much, the use of words as symbols of general ideas meant even more, for it meant the possibility of playing the internal game of thinking; but perhaps the most important advance of all was the means of comparing notes with neighbours, of corroborating individual experience by social intercourse. With words, also, it became easier to enregister outside himself the gains of the past. It is not without significance that the Greek Logos, which may be translated "the word," may also be translated Mind.

§ 9

Looking Backwards

When we take a survey of animal behaviour we see a long inclined plane. The outer world provokes simple creatures to answer back; simple creatures act experimentally on their surroundings. From the beginning this twofold process has been going on, receiving stimuli from the environment and acting upon the environment, and according to the efficiency of the reactions and actions living creatures have been sifted for millions of years. One main line of advance has been opening new gateways of knowledge—the senses, which are far more than five in number. The other main line of advance has been in most general terms, experimenting or testing, probing and proving, trying one key after another till a door is unlocked. There is progress in multiplying the gateways of knowledge and making them more discriminating, and there is progress in making the modes of experimenting more wide-awake, more controlled, and more resolute. But behind both of these is the characteristically vital power of enregistering within the organism the lessons of the past. In the life of the individual these enregistrations are illustrated by memories and habituations and habits; in the life of the race they are illustrated by reflex actions and instinctive capacities.

Body and Mind

We must not shirk the very difficult question of the relation between the bodily and the mental side of behaviour.

(*a*) Some great thinkers have taught that the mind is a reality by itself which plays upon the instrument of the brain and body. As the instrument gets worn and dusty the playing is not so good as it once was, but the player is still himself. This theory of the essential independence of the mind is a very beautiful one, but those who like it when applied to themselves are not always so fond of it when it is applied to other intelligent creatures like rooks and elephants. It may be, however, that there is a gradual emancipation of the mind which has gone furthest in Man and is still progressing.

(*b*) Some other thinkers have taught that the inner life of thought and feeling is only, as it were, an echo of the really important activity—that of the body and brain. Ideas are just foam-bells on the hurrying streams and circling eddies of matter and energy that make up our physiological life. To most of us this theory is impossible, because we are quite sure that ideas and feelings and purposes, which cannot be translated into matter and motion, are the clearest realities in our experience, and that they count for good and ill all through our life. They are more than the tickings of the clock; they make the wheels go round.

(*c*) There are others who think that the most scientific position is simply to recognise both the bodily and the mental activities as equally important, and so closely interwoven that they cannot be separated. Perhaps they are just the outer and the inner aspects of one reality—the life of the creature. Perhaps they are like the concave and convex curves of a dome, like the two sides of a shield. Perhaps the life of the organism is always a unity, at one time appearing more conspicuously as Mind-body, at another time as Body-mind. The most important fact is that neither aspect can be left out. By no jugglery with words can we get Mind out of Matter and Motion. And since we are in ourselves quite sure of our Mind, we are probably safe in saying that in the beginning was Mind. This is in accordance with Aristotle's saying that there is nothing in the end which was not also in kind present in the beginning—whatever we mean by beginning.

In conclusion

What has led to the truly wonderful result which we admire in a creature like a dog or an otter, a horse or a hare? In general, we may say, just two main processes—(1) testing all things, and (2) holding fast that which is good. New departures occur and these are tested for what they are worth. Idiosyncrasies crop up and they are sifted. New cards come mysteriously from within into the creature's hand, and they are played—for better or for worse. So by new variations and their sifting, by experimenting and enregistering the results, the mind has gradually evolved and will continue to evolve.

VIII

FOUNDATIONS OF THE UNIVERSE

THE WORLD OF ATOMS

MOST people have heard of the oriental race which puzzled over the foundations of the universe, and decided that it must be supported on the back of a giant elephant. But the elephant? They put it on the back of a monstrous tortoise, and there they let the matter end. If every animal in nature had been called upon, they would have been no nearer a foundation. Most ancient peoples, indeed, made no effort to find a foundation. The universe was a very compact little structure, mainly composed of the earth and the great canopy over the earth which they called the sky. They left it, as a whole, floating in nothing. And in this the ancients were wiser than they knew. Things do not fall down unless they are pulled down by that mysterious force which we call gravitation. The earth, it is true, is pulled by the sun, and would fall into it; but the earth escapes this fiery fate by circulating at great speed round the sun. The stars pull each other; but it has already been explained that they meet this by travelling rapidly in gigantic orbits. Yet we do, in a new sense of the word, need foundations of the universe. Our mind craves for some explanation of the matter out of which the universe is made. For this explanation we turn to modern Physics and Chemistry. Both these sciences study, under different aspects, matter and energy; and between them they have put together a conception of the fundamental nature of things which marks an epoch in the history of human thought.

§ 1

The Bricks of the Cosmos

More than two thousand years ago the first men of science, the Greeks of the cities of Asia Minor, speculated on the nature of matter. You can grind a piece of stone into dust. You can divide a spoonful of water into as many drops as you like. Apparently you can go on dividing as long as you have got apparatus fine enough for the work. But there must be a limit, these Greeks said, and so they supposed that all matter was ultimately composed of minute particles which were indivisible. That is the meaning of the Greek word "atom."

Like so many other ideas of these brilliant early Greek thinkers, the atom was a sound conception. We know to-day that matter is composed of atoms. But science was then so young that the way in which the Greeks applied the idea was not very profound. A liquid or a gas, they said, consisted of round, smooth atoms, which would not cling together. Then there were atoms with rough surfaces, "hooky" surfaces, and these stuck together and formed solids. The atoms of iron or marble, for instance, were so very hooky that, once they got together, a strong man could not tear them apart. The Greeks thought that the explanation of the universe was that an infinite number of these atoms had been moving and mixing in an infinite space during an infinite time, and had at last hit by chance on the particular combination which is our universe.

This was too simple and superficial. The idea of atoms was cast aside, only to be advanced again in various ways. It was the famous Manchester chemist, John Dalton, who restored it in the early years of the nineteenth century. He first definitely formulated the atomic theory as a scientific hypothesis. The whole physical and chemical science of that century was now based upon the atom, and it is quite a mistake to suppose that recent discoveries have discredited "atomism." An atom is the smallest particle

Photo: Elliott & Fry.

SIR ERNEST RUTHERFORD

One of our most eminent physicists who has succeeded Sir J. J. Thomson as Cavendish Professor of Physics at the University of Cambridge. The modern theory of the structure of the atom is largely due to him.

Photo: Rischgitz Collection.

J. CLERK-MAXWELL

One of the greatest scientific men who have ever lived. He revolutionised physics with his electro-magnetic theory of light, and practically all modern researches have had their origin, direct or indirect, in his work. Together with Faraday he constitutes one of the main scientific glories of the nineteenth century.

Photo: Ernest H. Mills.

SIR WILLIAM CROOKES

Sir William Crookes experimented on the electric discharge in vacuum tubes and described the phenomena as a "fourth state of matter." He was actually observing the flight of electrons, but he did not fully appreciate the nature of his experiments.

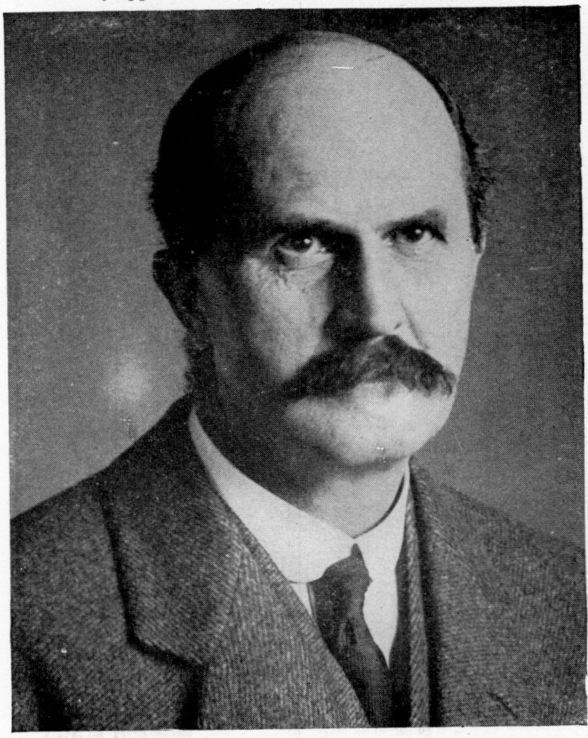

Photo: Photo Press

PROFESSOR SIR W. H. BRAGG

One of the most distinguished physicists of the present day.

of a chemical element. No one has ever seen an atom. Even the wonderful new microscope which has just been invented cannot possibly show us particles of matter which are a million times smaller than the breadth of a hair; for that is the size of atoms. We can weigh them and measure them, though they are invisible, and we know that all matter is composed of them. It is a new discovery that atoms are not indivisible. They consist themselves of still smaller particles, as we shall see. But the atoms exist all the same, and we may still say that they are the bricks of which the material universe is built.

But if we had some magical glass by means of which we could see into the structure of material things, we should not see the atoms put evenly together as bricks are in a wall. As a rule, two or more atoms first come together to form a larger particle, which we call a "molecule." Single atoms do not, as a rule, exist apart from other atoms; if a molecule is broken up, the individual atoms seek to unite with other atoms of another kind or amongst themselves. For example, three atoms of oxygen form what we call ozone; two atoms of hydrogen uniting with one atom of oxygen form water. It is molecules that form the mass of matter; a molecule, as it has been expressed, is a little building of which atoms are the bricks.

In this way we get a useful first view of the material things we handle. In a liquid the molecules of the liquid cling together loosely. They remain together as a body, but they roll over and away from each other. There is "cohesion" between them, but it is less powerful than in a solid. Put some water in a kettle over the lighted gas, and presently the tiny molecules of water will rush through the spout in a cloud of steam and scatter over the kitchen. The heat has broken their bond of association and turned the water into something like a gas; though we know that the particles will come together again, as they cool, and form once more drops of water.

In a gas the molecules have full individual liberty. They

are in a state of violent movement, and they form no union with each other. If we want to force them to enter into the loose sort of association which molecules have in a liquid, we have to slow down their individual movements by applying severe cold. That is how a modern man of science liquefies gases. No power that we have will liquefy air at its ordinary temperature. In *very* severe cold, on the other hand, the air will spontaneously become liquid. Some day, when the fires of the sun have sunk very low, the temperature of the earth will be less than—200° C.: that is to say, more than two hundred degrees Centigrade below freezing-point. It will sink to the temperature of the moon. Our atmosphere will then be an ocean of liquid air, 35 feet deep, lying upon the solidly frozen masses of our water-oceans.

In a solid the molecules cling firmly to each other. We need a force equal to twenty-five tons to tear asunder the molecules in a bar of iron an inch thick. Yet the structure is not "solid" in the popular sense of the word. If you put a piece of solid gold in a little pool of mercury, the gold will take in the mercury *between* its molecules, as if it were porous like a sponge. The hardest solid is more like a lattice-work than what we usually mean by "solid"; though the molecules are not fixed, like the bars of a lattice-work, but are in violent motion; they vibrate about equilibrium positions. If we could see right into the heart of a bit of the hardest steel, we should see billions of separate molecules, at some distance from each other, all moving rapidly to and fro.

This molecular movement can, in a measure, be made visible. It was noticed by a microscopist named Brown that, in a solution containing very fine suspended particles, the particles were in constant movement. Under a powerful microscope these particles are seen to be violently agitated; they are each independently darting hither and thither somewhat like a lot of billiard balls on a billiard table, colliding and bounding about in all directions. Thousands of times a second these encounters occur, and this lively commotion is always going on, this incessant colliding of one molecule with another is the normal condition of affairs; not one of them is at rest. The reason for this has been worked out, and it is now known that these particles move about because they are being incessantly bombarded by the molecules of the liquid. The molecules cannot, of course, be seen, but the fact of their incessant movement is revealed to the eye by the behaviour of the visible suspended particles. This incessant movement in the world of molecules is called the Brownian movement, and is a striking proof of the reality of molecular motions.

§ 2

The Wonder-World of Atoms

The exploration of this wonder-world of atoms and molecules by the physicists and chemists of to-day is one of the most impressive triumphs of modern science. Quite apart from radium and electrons and other sensational discoveries of recent years, the study of ordinary matter is hardly inferior, either in interest or audacity, to the work of the astronomer. And there is the same foundation in both cases—marvellous apparatus, and trains of mathematical reasoning that would have astonished Euclid or Archimedes. Extraordinary, therefore, as are some of the facts and figures we are now going to give in connection with the minuteness of atoms and molecules, let us bear in mind that we owe them to the most solid and severe processes of human thought.

Yet the principle can in most cases be made so clear that the reader will not be asked to take much on trust. It is, for instance, a matter of common knowledge that gold is soft enough to be beaten into gold leaf. It is a matter of common sense, one hopes, that if you beat a measured cube of gold into a leaf six inches square, the mathematician can tell the thickness of that leaf without measuring it. As a matter of fact, a single grain of gold has been beaten into a leaf seventy-five inches square. Now the mathematician can easily find that when a single grain of gold is beaten out to that size, the leaf must be $\frac{1}{367,000}$ of an inch thick, or about a thousand times thinner than the paper on which these words are printed; yet the leaf must be several molecules thick.

The finest gold leaf is, in fact, too thick for our purpose, and we turn with a new interest to that toy of our boyhood the soap-bubble. If you carefully examine one of these delicate films of soapy water, you notice certain dark spots or patches on them. These are their thinnest parts, and by two quite independent methods—one using electricity and the other light—we have found that at these spots the bubble is less than the three-millionth of an inch thick! But the molecules in the film cling together so firmly that they must be at least twenty or thirty deep in the thinnest part. A molecule, therefore, must be far less than the three-millionth of an inch thick.

We found next that a film of oil on the surface of water may be even thinner than a soap-bubble. Professor Perrin, the great French authority on atoms, got films of oil down to the fifty-millionth of an inch in thickness! He poured a measured drop of oil upon water. Then he found the exact limits of the area of the oil-sheet by blowing upon the water a fine powder which spread to the edge of the film and clearly outlined it. The rest is safe and simple calculation, as in the case of the beaten grain of gold. Now this film of oil must have been at least two molecules deep, so a single molecule of oil is considerably less than a hundred-millionth of an inch in diameter.

Innumerable methods have been tried, and the result is always the same. A single grain of indigo, for instance, will colour a ton of water. This obviously means that the grain contains billions of molecules which spread through the water. A grain of musk will scent a room—pour molecules into every part of it—for several years, yet not lose one-millionth of its mass in a year. There are a hundred ways of showing the minuteness of the ultimate particles of matter, and some of these enable us to give definite figures. On a careful comparison of the best methods we can say that the average molecule of matter is less

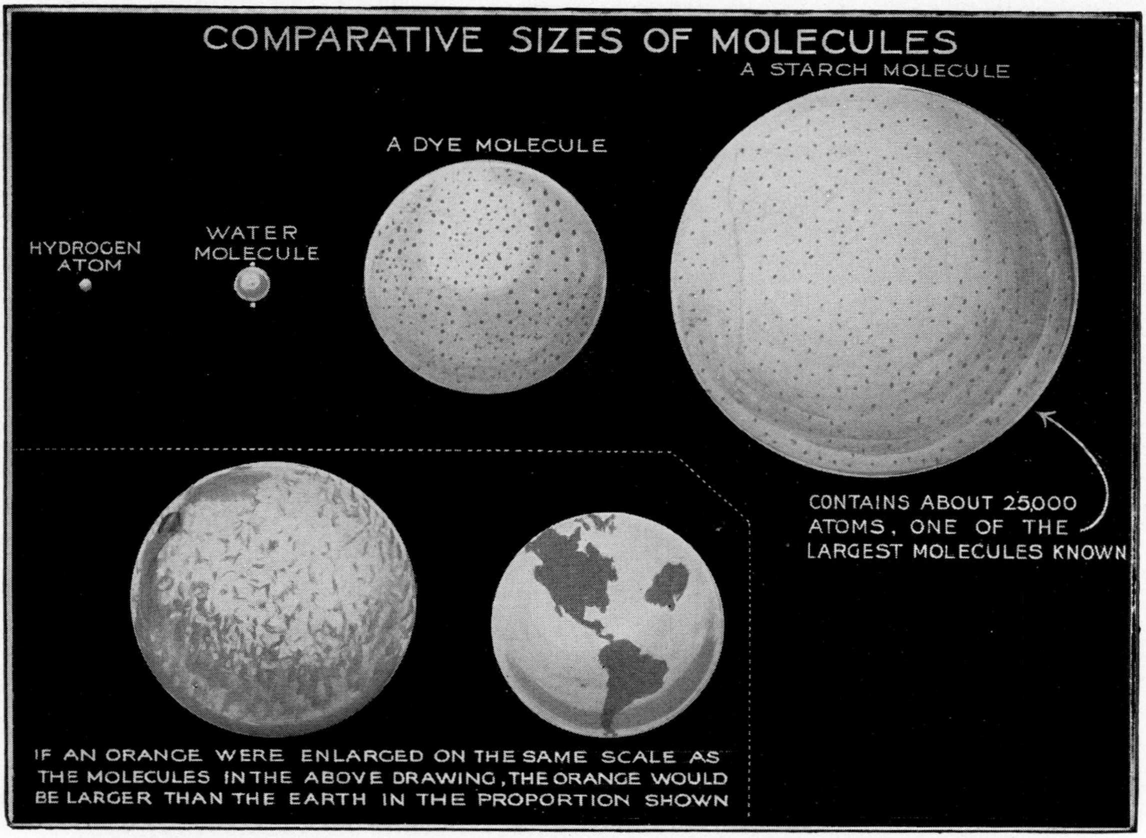
COMPARATIVE SIZES OF MOLECULES
A STARCH MOLECULE
A DYE MOLECULE
HYDROGEN ATOM
WATER MOLECULE
CONTAINS ABOUT 25,000 ATOMS, ONE OF THE LARGEST MOLECULES KNOWN
IF AN ORANGE WERE ENLARGED ON THE SAME SCALE AS THE MOLECULES IN THE ABOVE DRAWING, THE ORANGE WOULD BE LARGER THAN THE EARTH IN THE PROPORTION SHOWN

An atom is the smallest particle of a chemical element. Two or more atoms come together to form a molecule: thus molecules form the mass of matter. A molecule of water is made up of two atoms of hydrogen and one atom of oxygen. Molecules of different substances, therefore, are of different sizes according to the number and kind of the particular atoms of which they are composed. A starch molecule contains no less than 25,000 atoms.

Molecules, of course, are invisible. The above diagram illustrates the *comparative* sizes of molecules.

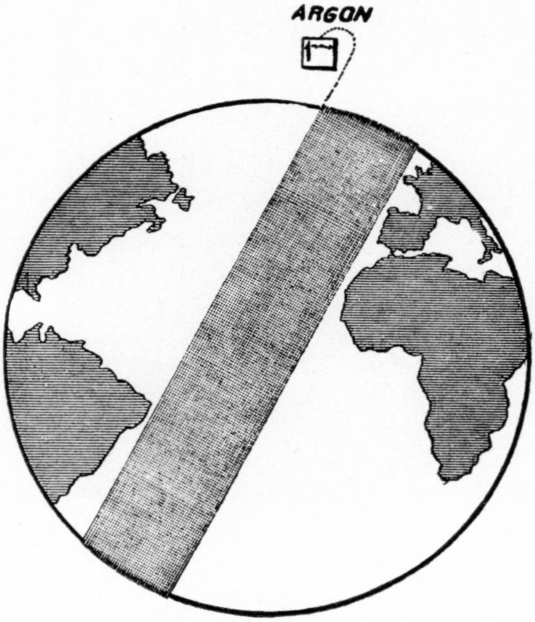
ARGON

INCONCEIVABLE NUMBERS AND INCONCEIVABLY SMALL PARTICLES

The molecules, which are inconceivably small, are, on the other hand, so numerous that if one was able to place, end to end, all those contained in, for example, a cubic centimetre of gas (less than a fifteenth of a cubic inch), one would obtain a line capable of passing two hundred times round the earth.

WHAT IS A MILLION?

In dealing with the infinitely small, it is difficult to apprehend the vast figures with which scientists confront us. A million is one thousand thousand. We may realise what this implies if we consider that a clock, beating seconds, takes approximately 278 hours (i.e. one week four days fourteen hours) to tick one million times. A billion is one million million. To tick a billion the clock would tick for over 31,735 years.

(In France and America a thousand millions is called a billion.)

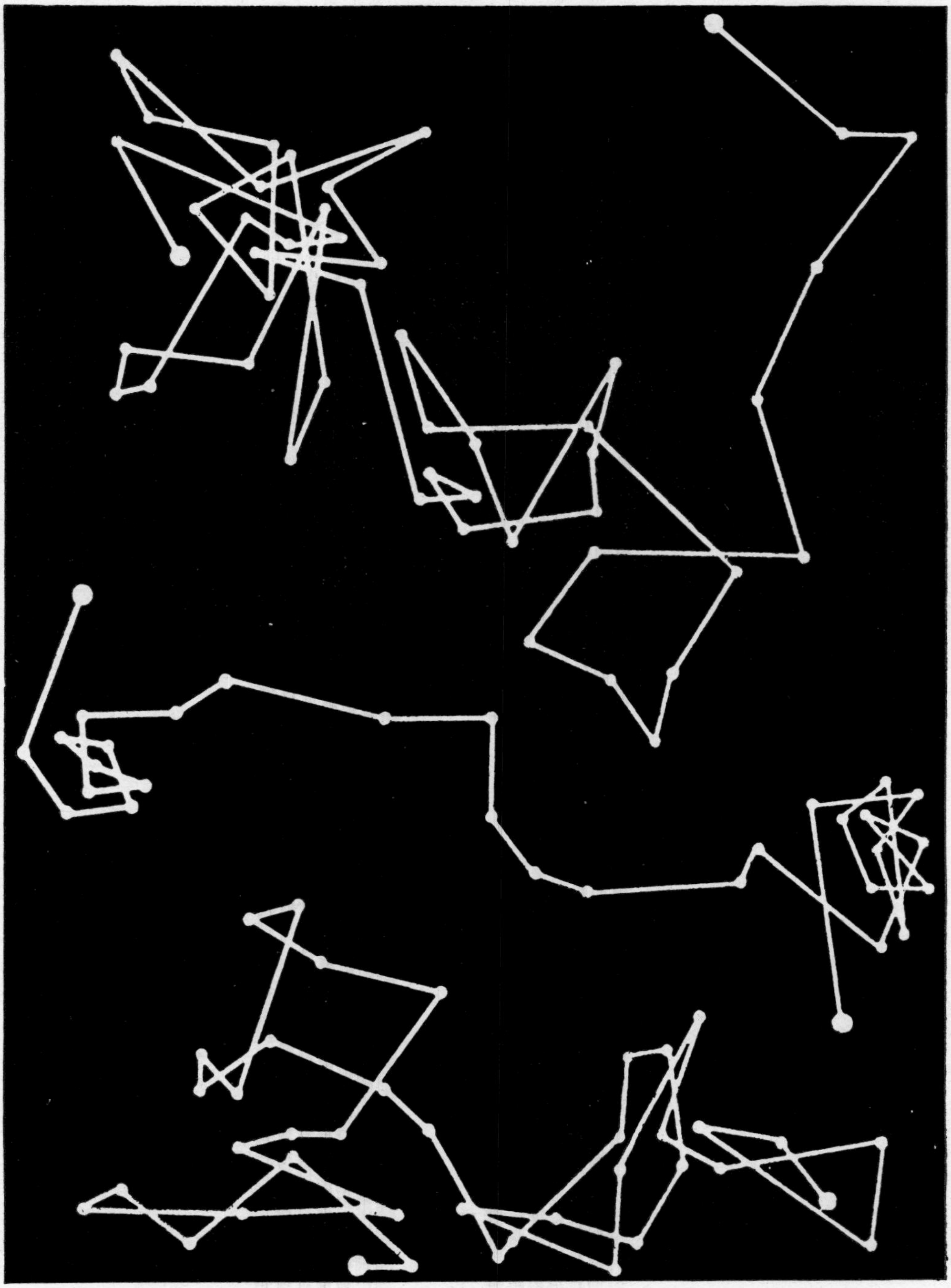

THE BROWNIAN MOVEMENT

A diagram, constructed from actual observations, showing the erratic paths pursued by very fine particles suspended in a liquid, when bombarded by the molecules of the liquid. This movement is called the Brownian movement, and it furnishes a striking illustration of the truth of the theory that the molecules of a body are in a state of continual motion.

than the $\frac{1}{125,000,000}$ of an inch in diameter. In a single cubic centimetre of air—a globule about the size of a small marble—there are thirty million trillion molecules. And since the molecule is, as we saw, a group or cluster of atoms, the atom itself is smaller. Atoms, for reasons which we shall see later, differ very greatly from each other in size and weight. It is enough to say that some of them are so small that it would take 400,000,000 of them, in a line, to cover an inch of space; and that it takes at least a quintillion atoms of gold to weigh a single gramme. Five million atoms of helium could be placed in a line across the diameter of a full stop.

The Energy of Atoms

And this is only the beginning of the wonders that were done with "ordinary matter," quite apart from radium and its revelations, to which we will come presently. Most people have heard of "atomic energy," and the extraordinary things that might be accomplished if we could harness this energy and turn it to human use. A deeper and more wonderful source of this energy has been discovered in the last twenty years, but it is well to realise that the atoms themselves have stupendous energy. The atoms of matter are vibrating or gyrating with extraordinary vigour. The piece of cold iron you hold in your hand, the bit of brick you pick up, or the penny you take from your pocket is a colossal reservoir of energy, since it consists of trillions of moving atoms. To realise the total energy, of course, we should have to witness a transformation such as we do in atoms of radio-active elements, about which we shall have something to say presently.

If we put a grain of indigo in a glass of water, or a grain of musk in a perfectly still room, we soon realise that molecules travel. Similarly, the fact that gases spread until they fill every "empty" available space shows definitely that they consist of small particles travelling at great speed. The physicist brings his refined methods to bear on these things, and he measures the energy and velocity of these infinitely minute molecules. He tells us that molecules of oxygen, at the temperature of melting ice, travel at the rate of about 500 yards a second—more than a quarter of a mile a second. Molecules of hydrogen travel at four times that speed, or three times the speed with which a bullet leaves a rifle. Each molecule of the air, which seems so still in the house on a summer's day, is really travelling faster than a rifle bullet does at the beginning of its journey. It collides with another molecule every twenty-thousandth of an inch of its journey. It is turned from its course 5,000,000,000 times in every second by collisions. If we could stop the molecules of hydrogen gas, and utilise their energy, as we utilise the energy of steam or the energy of the water at Niagara, we should find enough in every gramme of gas (about two-thousandths of a pound) to raise a third of a ton to a height of forty inches.

I have used for comparison the speed of a rifle bullet, and in an earlier generation people would have thought it impossible even to estimate this. It is, of course, easy. We put two screens in the path of the bullet, one near the rifle and the other some distance away. We connect them electrically and use a fine time-recording machine, and the bullet itself registers the time it takes to travel from the first to the second screen.

Now this is very simple and superficial work in comparison with the system of exact and minute measurements which the physicist and chemist use. In one of his interesting works Mr. Charles R. Gibson gives a photograph of two exactly equal pieces of paper in the opposite pans of a fine balance. A single word has been written in pencil on one of these papers, and that little scraping of lead has been enough to bring down the scale! The spectroscope will detect a quantity of matter four million times smaller even than this; and the electroscope is a million times still more sensitive than the spectroscope. We have a heat-measuring instrument, the bolometer, which makes the best thermometer seem Early Victorian. It records the millionth of a degree of

Reproduced from "The Forces of Nature" (Messrs. Macmillan).

A SOAP BUBBLE

The iridescent colours sometimes seen on a soap bubble, as in the illustration, may also be seen in very fine sections of crystals, in glass blown into extremely fine bulbs, on the wings of dragon-flies and the surface of oily water. The different colours correspond to different thicknesses of the surface. Part of the light which strikes these thin coatings is reflected from the upper surface, but another part of the light penetrates the transparent coating and is reflected from the lower surface. It is the mixture of these two reflected rays, their "interference" as it is called, which produces the colours observed. The "black spots" on a soap bubble are the places where the soapy film is thinnest. At the black spots the thickness of the bubble is about the three-millionth part of an inch. If the whole bubble were as thin as this it would be completely invisible.

temperature. It is such instruments, multiplied by the score, which enable us to do the fine work recorded in these pages.

§ 3

THE DISCOVERY OF X-RAYS AND RADIUM

The Discovery of Sir Wm. Crookes

But these wonders of the atom are only a prelude to the more romantic and far-reaching discoveries of the new physics—the wonders of the electron. Another and the most important phase of our exploration of the material universe opened with the discovery of radium in 1898.

In the discovery of radio-active elements, a new property of matter was discovered. What followed on the discovery of radium and of the X-rays we shall see.

As Sir Ernest Rutherford, one of our greatest authorities, recently said, the new physics has dissipated the last doubt about the reality of atoms and molecules. The closer examination of matter which we have been able to make shows positively that it is composed of atoms. But we must not take the word now in its original Greek meaning (an "indivisible" thing). The atoms are not indivisible. They can be broken up. They are composed of still smaller particles.

The discovery that the atom was composed of smaller particles was the welcome realisation of a dream that had haunted the imagination of the nineteenth century. Chemists said that there were about eighty different kinds of atoms—different kinds of matter—but no one was satisfied with the multiplicity. Science is always aiming at simplicity and unity. It may be that science has now taken a long step in the direction of explaining the fundamental unity of all the matter. The chemist was unable to break up these "elements" into something simpler, so he called their atoms "indivisible" in that sense. But one man of science after another expressed the hope that we would yet discover some fundamental matter of which the various atoms were composed—*one primordial substance from which all the varying forms of matter have been evolved or built up.* Prout suggested this at the very beginning of the century, when atoms were rediscovered by Dalton. Father Secchi, the famous Jesuit astronomer said that all the atoms were probably evolved from ether; and this was a very favoured speculation. Sir William Crookes talked of "prothyl" as the fundamental substance. Others thought hydrogen was the stuff out of which all the other atoms were composed.

The work which finally resulted in the discovery of radium began with some beautiful experiments of Professor (later Sir William) Crookes in the eighties.

It had been noticed in 1869 that a strange colouring was caused when an electric charge was sent through a vacuum tube—the walls of the glass tube began to glow with a greenish phosphorescence. A vacuum tube is one from which nearly all the air has been pumped, although we can never completely empty the tube. Crookes used such ingenious methods that he reduced the gas in his tubes until it was twenty million times thinner than the atmosphere. He then sent an electric discharge through, and got very remarkable results. The negative pole of the electric current (the "cathode") *gave off rays which faintly lit the molecules of the thin gas in the tube,* and caused a pretty fluorescence on the glass walls of the tube. What were these Rays? Crookes at first thought they corresponded to a "new or fourth state of matter." Hitherto we had only been familiar with matter in the three conditions of solid, liquid, and gaseous.

Now Crookes really had the great secret under his eyes. But about twenty years elapsed before the true nature of these rays was finally and independently established by various experiments. The experiments proved "that the rays consisted of a stream of negatively charged particles travelling with enormous velocities from 10,000 to 100,000 miles a second. In addition, it was found

From "Scientific Ideas of To-day."

DETECTING A SMALL QUANTITY OF MATTER

In the left-hand photograph the two pieces of paper exactly balance. The balance used is very sensitive, and when the single word "atoms" has been written with a lead pencil upon one of the papers the additional weight is sufficient to depress one of the pans as shown in the second photograph. The spectroscope will detect less than one-millionth of the matter contained in the word pencilled above.

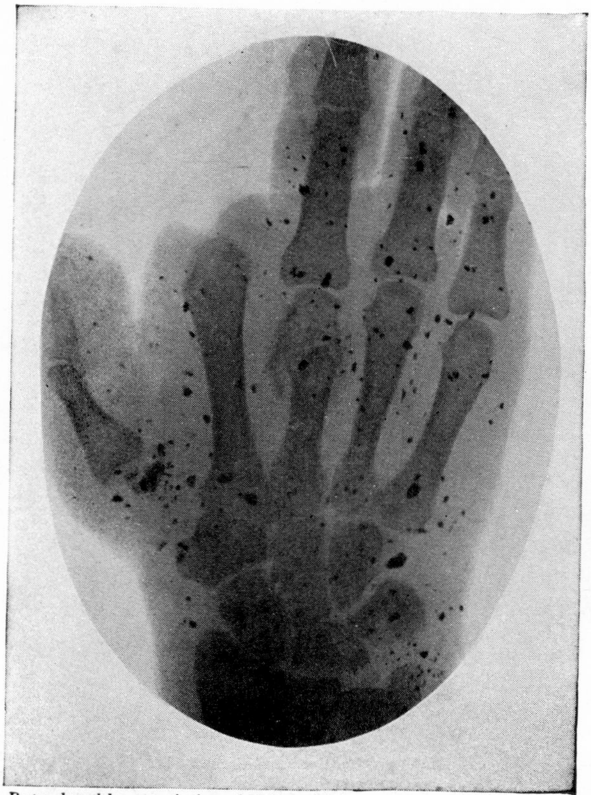

Reproduced by permission of X-Rays Ltd.

THIS X-RAY PHOTOGRAPH IS THAT OF A HAND OF A SOLDIER WOUNDED IN THE GREAT WAR

Note the pieces of shrapnel which are revealed.

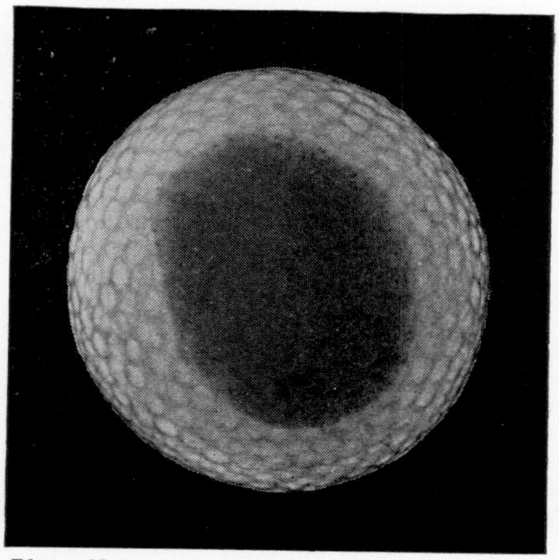

Photo: National Physical Laboratory.

AN X-RAY PHOTOGRAPH OF A GOLF BALL, REVEALING AN IMPERFECT CORE

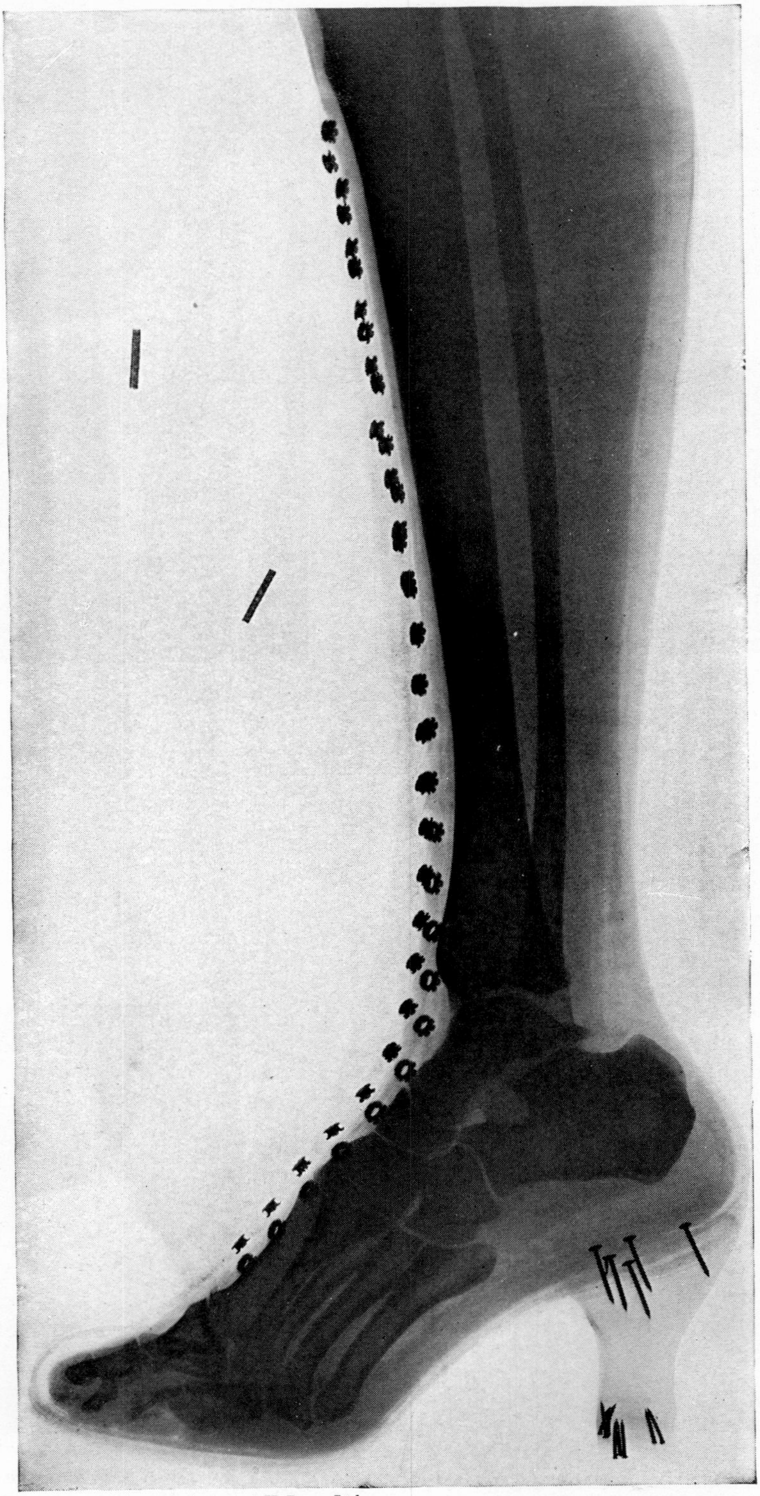

Reproduced by permission of X-Rays Ltd.

A WONDERFUL X-RAY PHOTOGRAPH

Note the fine details revealed, down to the metal tags of the bootlace and the nails in the heel of the boot.

that the mass of each particle was exceedingly small, about $\frac{1}{1800}$ of the mass of a hydrogen atom, the lightest atom known to science." *These particles or electrons, as they are now called, were being liberated from the atom.* The atoms of matter were breaking down in Crookes tubes. At that time, however, it was premature to think of such a thing, and Crookes preferred to say that the particles of the gas were electrified and hurled against the walls of the tube. He said that it was ordinary matter in a new state—"radiant matter." Another distinguished man of science, Lenard, found that, when he fitted a little plate of aluminum in the glass wall of the tube, the mysterious rays passed through this as if it were a window. They must be waves in the ether, he said.

§ 4

The Discovery of X-rays

So the story went on from year to year. We shall see in a moment to what it led. Meanwhile the next great step was when, in 1895, Röntgen discovered the X-rays, which are now known to everybody. He was following up the work of Lenard, and he one day covered a "Crookes tube" with some black stuff. To his astonishment a prepared chemical screen which was near the tube began to glow. *The rays had gone through the black stuff; and on further experiment he found that they would go through stone, living flesh, and all sorts of "opaque" substances.* In a short time the world was astonished to learn that we could photograph the skeleton in a living man's body, locate a penny in the interior of a child that had swallowed one, or take an impression of a coin through a slab of stone.

And what are these X-rays? They are not a form of matter; they are not material particles. X-rays were found to be a new variety of *light* with a remarkable power of penetration. We have seen what the spectroscope reveals about the varying nature of light wave-lengths. Light-waves are set up by vibrations in ether,[1] and, as we shall see, these ether disturbances are all of the same kind; they only differ as regards wave-lengths. The X-rays which Rontgen discovered, then, are light, but a variety of light previously unknown to us; they are ether waves of very short length. X-rays have proved of great value in many directions, as all the world knows, but that we need not discuss at this point. Let us see what followed Rontgen's discovery.

While the world wondered at these marvels, the men of science were eagerly following up the new clue to the mystery of matter which was exercising the mind of Crookes and other investigators. In 1896 Becquerel brought us to the threshold of the great discovery.

Certain substances are phosphorescent—they become luminous after they have been exposed to sunlight for some time, and Becquerel was trying to find if any of these substances give rise to X-rays. One day he chose a salt of the metal uranium. He was going to see if, after exposing it to sunlight, he could photograph a cross with it through an opaque substance. He wrapped it up and laid it aside, to wait for the sun, but he found the uranium salt did not wait for the sun. Some strong radiation from it went through the opaque covering and made an impression of the cross upon the plate underneath. Light or darkness was immaterial. The mysterious rays streamed night and day from the salt. This was something new. Here was a substance which appeared to be producing X-rays; the rays emitted by uranium would penetrate the same opaque substances as the X-rays discovered by Röntgen.

Discovery of Radium

Now, at the same time as many other investigators, Professor Curie and his Polish wife took up the search. They decided to

[1] We refer throughout to the "ether" because, although modern theories dispense largely with this conception, the theories of physics are so inextricably interwoven with it that it is necessary, in an elementary exposition, to assume its existence. The modern view will be explained later in the article on Einstein's Theory.

find out whether the emission came from the uranium itself or *from something associated with it,* and for this purpose they made a chemical analysis of great quantities of minerals. They found a certain kind of pitchblende which was very active, and they analysed tons of it, concentrating always on the radiant element in it. After a time, as they successively worked out the non-radiant matter, the stuff began to glow. In the end they extracted from eight tons of pitchblende about half a teaspoonful of something *that was a million times more radiant than uranium.* There was only one name for it—Radium.

That was the starting-point of the new development of physics and chemistry. From every laboratory in the world came a cry for radium salts (as pure radium was too precious), and hundreds of brilliant workers fastened on the new element. The inquiry was broadened, and, as year followed year, one substance after another was found to possess the power of emitting rays, that is, to be radio-active. We know to-day that nearly every form of matter can be stimulated to radio-activity; which, as we shall see, means that *its atoms break up into smaller and wonderfully energetic particles which we call "electrons."* This discovery of electrons has brought about a complete change in our ideas in many directions.

So, instead of atoms being indivisible, they are actually dividing themselves, spontaneously, and giving off throughout the universe tiny fragments of their substance. We shall explain presently what was later discovered about the electron; meanwhile we can say that every glowing metal is pouring out a stream of these electrons. Every arc-lamp is discharging them. Every clap of thunder means a shower of them. Every star is flooding space with them. We are witnessing the spontaneous breaking up of atoms, atoms which had been thought to be indivisible. The sun not only pours out streams of electrons from its own atoms, but the ultra-violet light which it sends to the earth is one of the most powerful agencies for releasing electrons from the surface-atoms of matter on the earth. It is fortunate for us that our atmosphere absorbs most of this ultra-violet or invisible light of the sun—a kind of light which will be explained presently. It has been suggested that, if we received the full flood of it from the sun, our metals would disintegrate under its influence and this "steel civilisation" of ours would be impossible!

But we are here anticipating, we are going beyond radium to the wonderful discoveries which were made by the chemists and physicists of the world who concentrated upon it. The work of Professor and Mme. Curie was merely the final clue to guide the great search. How it was followed up, how we penetrated into the very heart of the minute atom and discovered new and portentous mines of energy, and how we were able to understand, not only matter, but electricity and light, will be told in the next chapter.

THE DISCOVERY OF THE ELECTRON AND HOW IT EFFECTED A REVOLUTION IN IDEAS

What the discovery of radium implied was only gradually realised. Radium captivated the imagination of the world; it was a boon to medicine, but to the man of science it was at first a most puzzling and most attractive phenomenon. It was felt that some great secret of nature was dimly unveiled in its wonderful manifestations, and there now concentrated upon it as gifted a body of men—conspicuous amongst them Sir J. J. Thomson, Sir Ernest Rutherford, Sir W. Ramsay, and Professor Soddy—as any age could boast, with an apparatus of research as far beyond that of any other age as the *Aquitania* is beyond a Roman galley. Within five years the secret was fairly mastered. Not only were all kinds of matter reduced to a common basis, but the forces of the universe were brought into a unity and understood as they had never been understood before.

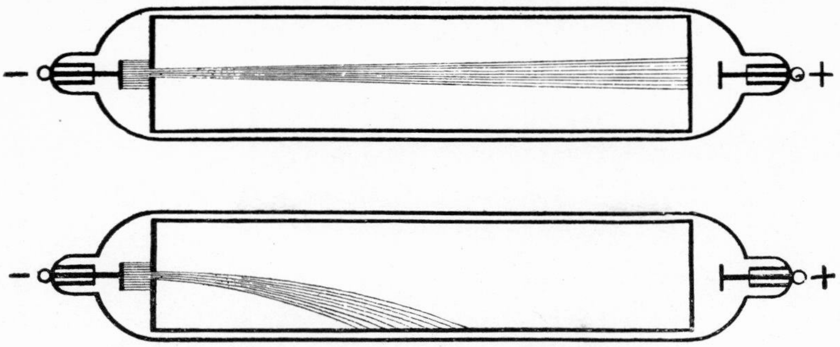

ELECTRIC DISCHARGE IN A VACUUM TUBE

The two ends, marked + and —, of a tube from which nearly all air has been exhausted are connected to electric terminals, thus producing an electric discharge in the vacuum tube. This discharge travels straight along the tube, as in the upper diagram. When a magnetic field is applied, however, the rays are deflected, as shown in the lower diagram. The similarity of the behaviour of the electric discharge with the radium rays (see diagram of deflection of radium rays, *post*) shows that the two phenomena may be identified. It was by this means that the characteristics of electrons were first discovered.

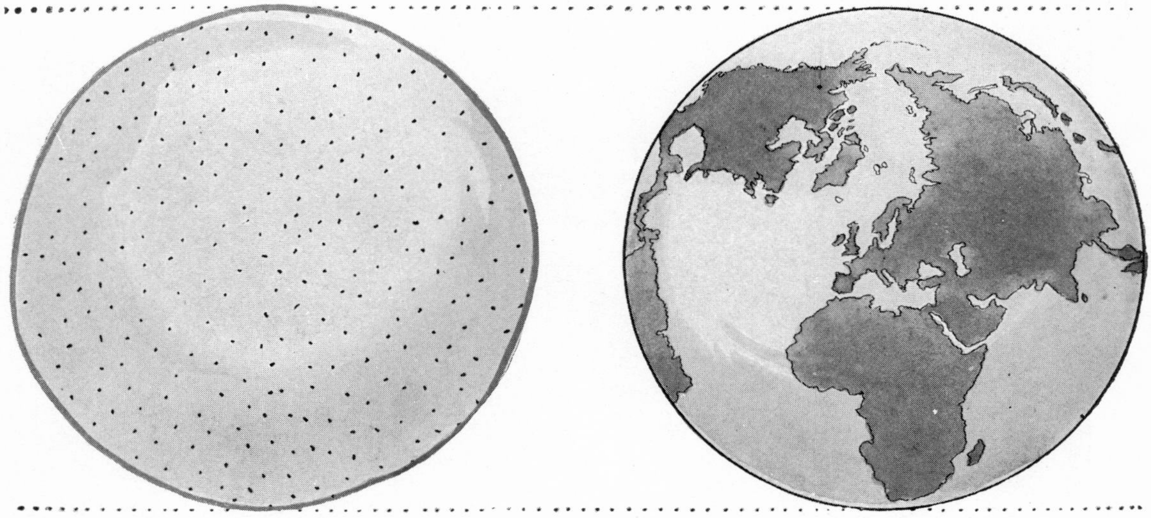

THE RELATIVE SIZES OF ATOMS AND ELECTRONS

An atom is far too small to be seen. In a bubble of hydrogen gas no larger than the letter "O" there are billions of atoms, whilst an electron is more than a thousand times smaller than the smallest atom. How their size is ascertained is described in the text. In this diagram a bubble of gas is magnified to the size of the world. Adopting this scale, *each atom* in the bubble would then be as large as a tennis ball.

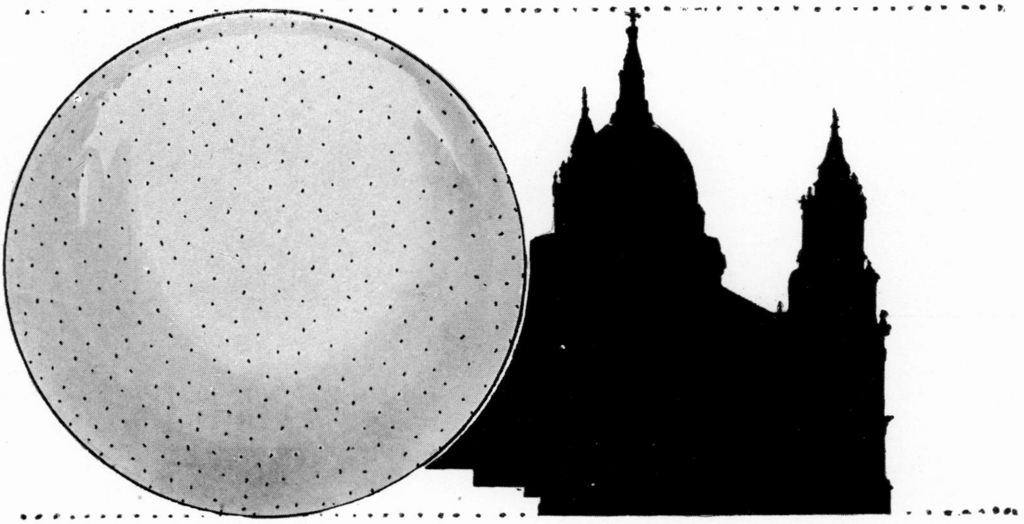

IF AN ATOM WERE MAGNIFIED TO THE SIZE OF ST. PAUL'S CATHEDRAL, EACH ELECTRON IN THE ATOM (AS REPRESENTED BY THE CATHEDRAL) WOULD THEN BE ABOUT THE SIZE OF A SMALL BULLET

ELECTRONS STREAMING FROM THE SUN TO THE EARTH

There are strong reasons for supposing that sun-spots are huge electronic cyclones. The sun is constantly pouring out vast streams of electrons into space. Many of these streams encounter the earth, giving rise to various electrical phenomena.

§ 5

The Discovery of the Electron

Physicists did not take long to discover that the radiation from radium was very like the radiation in a "Crookes tube." It was quickly recognised, moreover, that both in the tube and in radium (and other metals) the atoms of matter were somehow breaking down.

However, the first step was to recognise that there were three distinct and different rays that were given off by such metals as radium and uranium. Sir Ernest Rutherford christened them, after the first three letters of the Greek alphabet, the Alpha, the Beta, and Gamma rays. We are concerned chiefly with the second group and purpose here to deal with that group only.[1]

The "Beta rays," as they were at first called, have proved to be one of the most interesting discoveries that science ever made. They proved what Crookes had surmised about the radiations he discovered in his vacuum tube. But it was *not* a fourth state of matter that had been found, but a new *property* of matter, a property common to all atoms of matter. The Beta rays were later christened Electrons. They are particles of disembodied electricity, here spontaneously liberated from the atoms of matter: only when the electron was isolated from the atom was it recognised for the first time as a separate entity. Electrons, therefore, are a constituent of the atoms of matter, and we have discovered that they can be released from the atom by a variety of agencies. Electrons are to be found everywhere, forming part of every atom.

"An electron," Sir William Bragg says, "can only maintain a separate existence if it is travelling at an immense rate, from one three-hundredth of the velocity of light upwards, that is to

[1] The "Alpha rays" were presently recognised as atoms of helium gas, shot out at the rate of 12,000 miles a second.

The "Gamma rays" are *waves*, like the X-rays, not material particles. They appear to be a type of X-rays. They possess the remarkable power of penetrating opaque substances; they will pass through a foot of solid iron, for example.

say, at least 600 *miles a second, or thereabouts.* Otherwise the electron sticks to the first atom it meets." These amazing particles may travel with the enormous velocity of from 10,000 to more than 100,000 miles a second. It was first learned that they are of an electrical nature, because they are bent out of their normal path if a magnet is brought near them. And this fact led to a further discovery: to one of those sensational estimates which the general public is apt to believe to be founded on the most abstruse speculations. The physicist set up a little chemical screen for the "Beta rays" to hit, and he so arranged his tube that only a narrow sheaf of the rays poured on to the screen. He then drew this sheaf of rays out of its course with a magnet, and he accurately measured the shift of the luminous spot on the screen where the rays impinged on it. But when he knows the exact intensity of his magnetic field—which he can control as he likes—and the amount of deviation it causes, and the mass of the moving particles, he can tell the speed of the moving particles which he thus diverts. These particles were being hurled out of the atoms of radium, or from the negative pole in a vacuum tube, at a speed which, in good conditions, reached nearly the velocity of light, i.e. nearly 186,000 miles a second.

Their speed has, of course, been confirmed by numbers of experiments; and another series of experiments enabled physicists to determine the size of the particles. Only one of these need be described, to give the reader an idea how men of science arrived at their more startling results.

Fog, as most people know, is thick in our great cities because the water-vapour gathers on the particles of dust and smoke that are in the atmosphere. This fact was used as the basis of some beautiful experiments. Artificial fogs were created in little glass tubes, by introducing dust, in various proportions, for supersaturated vapour to gather on. In the end it was possible to cause tiny drops of rain, each with a particle of dust at its core, to fall upon a silver mirror and be counted. It was a method of counting the quite invisible particles of dust in the tube; and the method was now successfully applied to the new rays. Yet another method was to direct a slender stream of the particles upon a chemical screen. The screen glowed under the cannonade of particles, and a powerful lens resolved the glow into distinct sparks, which could be counted.

In short, a series of the most remarkable and beautiful experiments, checked in all the great laboratories of the world, settled the nature of these so-called rays. They were streams of particles more than a thousand times smaller than the smallest known atom. The mass of each particle is, according to the latest and finest measurements $\frac{1}{1845}$ of that of an atom of hydrogen. The physicist has not been able to find any character except electricity in them, and the name "electrons" has been generally adopted.

The Key to many Mysteries

The Electron is an atom, of disembodied electricity; it occupies an exceedingly small volume, and its "mass" is entirely electrical. These electrons are the key to half the mysteries of matter. Electrons in rapid motion, as we shall see, explain what we mean by an "electric current," not so long ago regarded as one of the most mysterious manifestations in nature.

"What a wonder, then, have we here!" says Professor R. K. Duncan. "An innocent-looking little pinch of salt and yet possessed of special properties utterly beyond even the fanciful imaginings of men of past time; for nowhere do we find in the records of thought even the hint of the possibility of things which we now regard as established fact. This pinch of salt projects from its surface bodies [i.e. electrons] possessing the inconceivable velocity of over 100,000 miles a second, a velocity sufficient to carry them, if unimpeded, five times around the earth in a second, and possessing with this velocity, masses a thousand times smaller than the smallest atom known to science. Furthermore, they are charged with negative electricity; they pass straight through bodies considered opaque with a sublime indifference to the properties of the body, with the exception of its mere density; they cause bodies which they strike to shine out in the dark; they affect a photographic plate; they render the air a conductor of electricity; they cause clouds in moist air; they cause chemical action and have a peculiar physiological action. Who, to-day, shall predict the ultimate service to humanity of the beta-rays from radium!"

§ 6

THE ELECTRON THEORY, OR THE NEW VIEW OF MATTER

The Structure of the Atom

There is general agreement amongst all chemists, physicists, and mathematicians upon the conclusions which we have so far given. We know that the atoms of matter are constantly—either spontaneously or under stimulation—giving off electrons, or breaking up into electrons; and they therefore contain electrons. Thus we have now complete proof of the independent existence of atoms and also of electrons.

When, however, the man of science tries to tell us *how* electrons compose atoms, he passes from facts to speculation, and very difficult speculation. Take the letter "o" as it is printed on this page. In a little bubble of hydrogen gas no larger than that letter there are *trillions* of atoms; and they are not packed together, but are circulating as freely as dancers in a ball-room. We are asking the physicist to take one of these minute atoms and tell us how the still smaller electrons are arranged in it. Naturally he can only make mental pictures, guesses or hypotheses, which he tries to fit to the facts, and discards when they will *not* fit.

At present, after nearly twenty years of critical discussion, there are two chief theories of the structure of the atom. At first

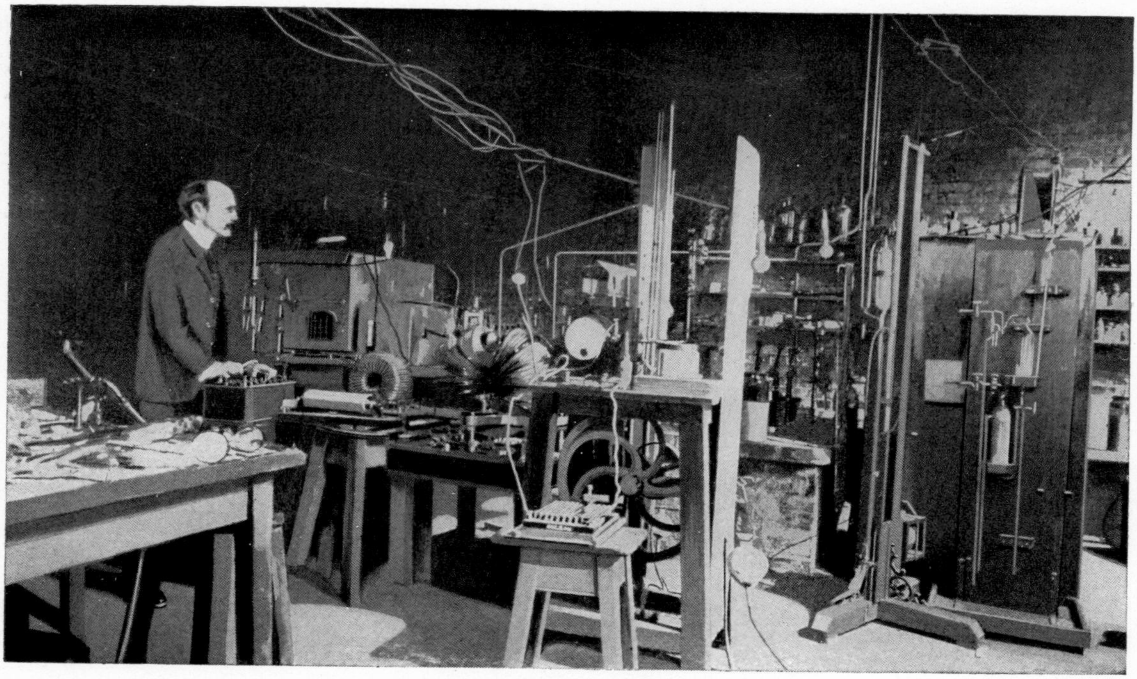

PROFESSOR SIR J. J. THOMSON

Experimental discoverer of the electronic constitution of matter, in the Cavendish Physical Laboratory, Cambridge. A great investigator, noted for the imaginative range of his hypotheses and his fertility in experimental devices.

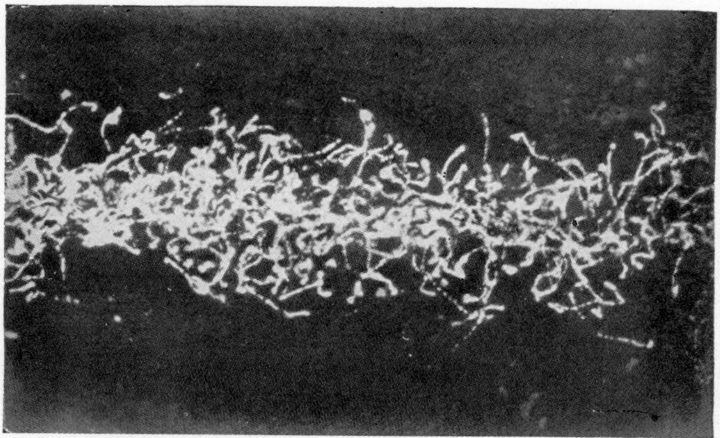

From the Smithsonian Report, 1915.

ELECTRONS PRODUCED BY PASSAGE OF X-RAYS THROUGH AIR

A photograph clearly showing that electrons are definite entities. As electrons leave atoms they may traverse matter or pass through the air in a straight path The illustration shows the tortuous path of electrons resulting from collision with atoms.

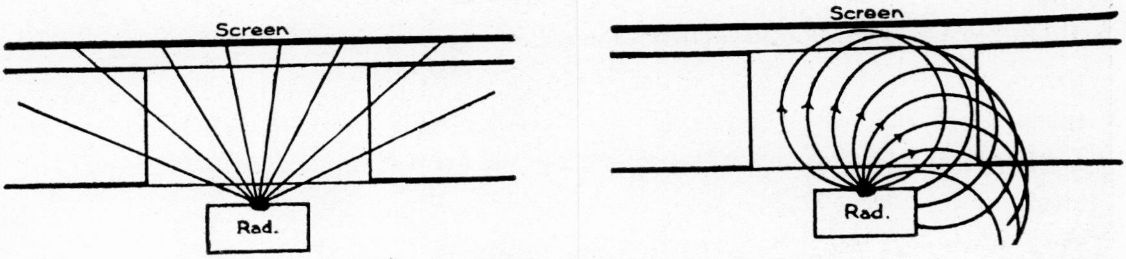

MAGNETJC DEFLECTION OF RADIUM RAYS

The radium rays are made to strike a screen, producing visible spots of light. When a magnetic field is applied the rays are seen to be deflected, as in the diagram. This can only happen if the rays carry an electric charge, and it was by experiments of this kind that we obtained our knowledge respecting the electric charges carried by radium rays.

Reproduced by permission of "Scientific American."

PROFESSOR R. A. MILLIKAN'S APPARATUS FOR COUNTING ELECTRONS

Sir J. J. Thomson imagined the electrons circulating in shells (like the layers of an onion) round the nucleus of the atom. This did not suit, and Sir E. Rutherford and others worked out a theory that the electrons circulated round a nucleus rather like the planets of our solar system revolving round the central sun. Is there a nucleus, then, round which the electrons revolve? The electron, as we saw, is a disembodied atom of electricity; we should say, of "negative" electricity. Let us picture these electrons all moving round in orbits with great velocity. Now it is suggested that there is a nucleus of "positive" electricity attracting or pulling the revolving electrons to it, and so forming an equilibrium, otherwise the electrons would fly off in all directions. This nucleus has been recently named the proton. We have thus two electricities in the atom: the positive = the nucleus; the negative = the electron. Of recent years Dr. Langmuir has put out a theory that the electrons do not *revolve round* the nucleus, but remain in a state of violent agitation of some sort at fixed distances from the nucleus.

But we will confine ourselves here to the facts, and leave the contending theories to scientific men. It is now pretty generally accepted that an atom of matter consists of a number of electrons, or charges of negative electricity, held together by a charge of positive electricity. It is not disputed that these electrons are in a state of violent motion or strain, and that therefore a vast energy is locked up in the atoms of matter. To that we will return later. Here, rather, we will notice another remarkable discovery which helps us to understand the nature of matter.

A brilliant young man of science who was killed in the war, Mr. Moseley, some years ago showed that, when the atoms of different substances are arranged in order of their weight, *they are also arranged in the order of increasing complexity of structure.* That is to say, the heavier the atom, the more electrons it contains. There is a gradual building up of atoms containing more and more electrons from the lightest atom to the heaviest.

Here it is enough to say that as he took element after element, from the lightest (hydrogen) to the heaviest (uranium) he found a strangely regular relation between them. If hydrogen were represented by the figure one, helium by two, lithium three, and so on up to uranium, then uranium should have the figure ninety-two. This makes it probable that there are in nature ninety-two elements—we have found eighty-seven—and that the number Mr. Moseley found is the number of electrons in the atom of each element; that is to say, the number is arranged in order of the atomic numbers of the various elements.

§ 7

The New View of Matter

Up to the point we have reached, then, we see what the new view of Matter is. Every atom of matter, of whatever kind throughout the whole universe, is built up of electrons in conjunction with a nucleus. From the smallest atom of all—the atom of hydrogen—which consists of one electron, rotating round a positively charged nucleus, to a heavy complicated atom, such as the atom of gold, constituted of many electrons and a complex nucleus, *we have only to do with positive and negative units of electricity*. The electron and its nucleus are particles of electricity. All Matter, therefore, is nothing but a manifestation of electricity. The atoms of matter, as we saw, combine and form molecules. Atoms and molecules are the bricks out of which nature has built up everything; ourselves, the earth, the stars, the whole universe.

But more than bricks are required to build a house. There are other fundamental existences, such as the various forms of energy, which give rise to several complex problems. And we have also to remember, that there are more than eighty distinct elements, each with its own definite type of atom. We shall deal with energy later. Meanwhile it remains to be said that, although we have discovered a great deal about the electron and the constitution of matter, and that while the physicists of our own day seem to see a possibility of explaining positive and negative electricity, the nature of them both is unknown. There exists the theory that the particles of positive and negative electricity, which make up the atoms of matter, are points or centres of disturbances of some kind in a universal ether, and that all the various forms of energy are, in some fundamental way, aspects of the same primary entity which constitutes matter itself.

But the discovery of the property of radio-activity has raised many other interesting questions, besides that which we have just dealt with. In radio-active elements, such as uranium for example, the element is breaking down; in what we call radio-activity we have a manifestation of the spontaneous change of elements. What is really taking place is a transmutation of one element into another, from a heavier to a lighter. The element uranium spontaneously becomes radium, and radium passes through a number of other stages until it, in turn, becomes lead. Each descending element is of lighter atomic weight than its predecessor. The changing process, of course, is a very slow one. It may be that all matter is radio-active, or can be made so. This raises the question whether all the matter in the universe may not undergo disintegration.

There is, however, another side of the question, which the discovery of radio-activity has brought to light, and which has effected a revolution in our views. We have seen that in radio-active substances the elements are breaking down. Is there a process of building up at work? If the more complicated atoms are breaking down into simpler forms, may there not be a converse process—a building up from simpler elements to more complicated elements? It is probably the case that both processes are at work.

There are some eighty-odd chemical elements on the earth to-day: are they all the outcome of an inorganic evolution, element giving rise to element, going back and back to some primeval stuff from which they were all originally derived infinitely long ago? Is there an evolution in the inorganic world which may be going on, parallel to that of the evolution of living things; or is organic evolution a continuation of inorganic evolution? We have seen what evidence there is of this inorganic evolution in the case of the stars. We cannot go deeply into the matter here, nor has the time come for any direct statement that can be based on the findings of modern investigation. Taking it altogether the evidence is steadily accumulating, and there are authorities who maintain that already the evidence of inorganic evolution is convincing enough. The heavier atoms would appear to behave as though they were evolved from the lighter. The more complex forms, it is supposed, have *evolved* from the simpler forms. Moseley's discovery, to which reference has been made, points to the conclusion that the elements are built up one from another.

§ 8

Other New Views

We may here refer to another new conception to which the discovery of radio-activity has given rise. Lord Kelvin, who estimated the age of the earth at twenty million years, reached this estimate by considering the earth as a body which is gradually cooling down, "losing its primitive heat, like a loaf taken from the oven, at a rate which could be calculated, and that the heat radiated by the sun was due to contraction." Uranium and radio-activity were not known to Kelvin, and their discovery has upset both his arguments. Radio-active substances, which are perpetually giving out heat, introduce an entirely new factor. We cannot now assume that the earth is necessarily cooling down; it may even, for all we know, be getting hotter. At the 1921 meeting of the British Association, Professor Rayleigh stated that further knowledge had extended the probable period during which there had been life on this globe to about one thousand

MAKING THE INVISIBLE VISIBLE

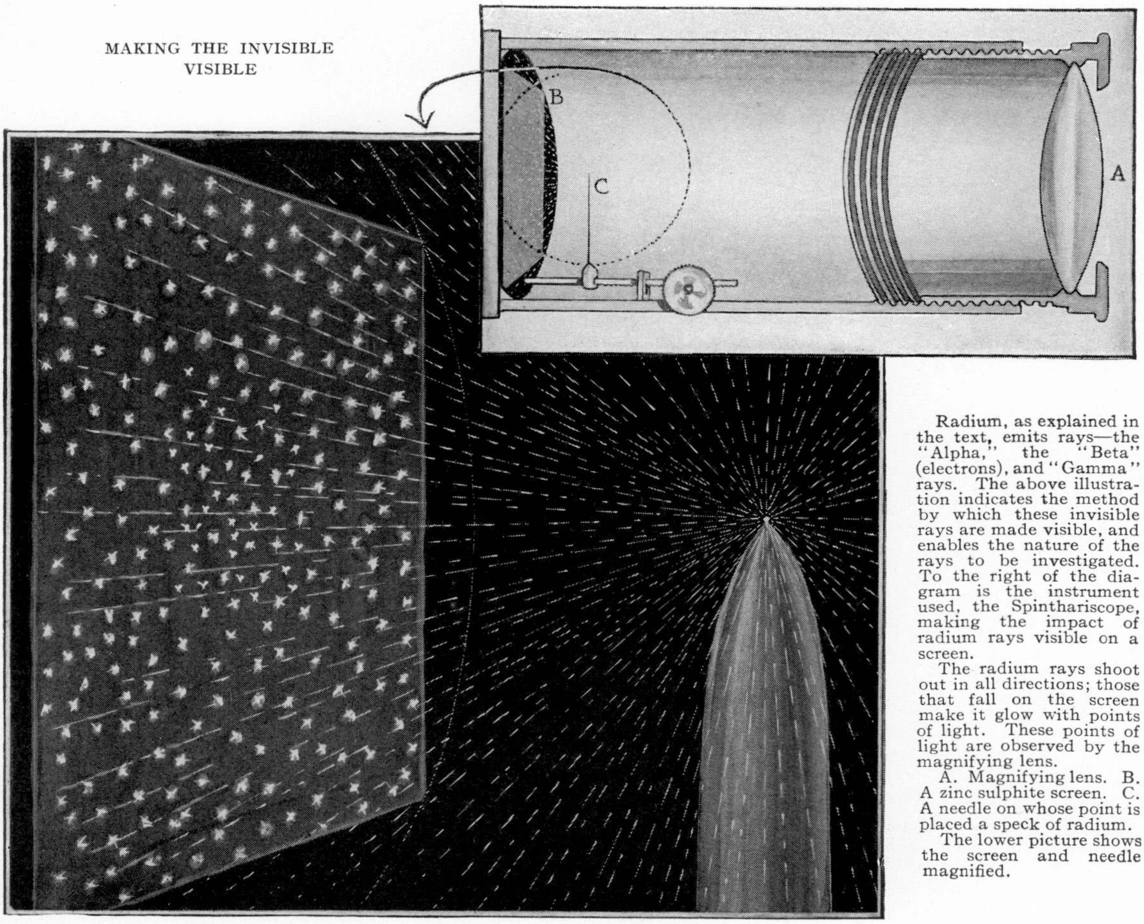

Radium, as explained in the text, emits rays—the "Alpha," the "Beta" (electrons), and "Gamma" rays. The above illustration indicates the method by which these invisible rays are made visible, and enables the nature of the rays to be investigated. To the right of the diagram is the instrument used, the Spinthariscope, making the impact of radium rays visible on a screen.

The radium rays shoot out in all directions; those that fall on the screen make it glow with points of light. These points of light are observed by the magnifying lens.

A. Magnifying lens. B. A zinc sulphite screen. C. A needle on whose point is placed a speck of radium.

The lower picture shows the screen and needle magnified.

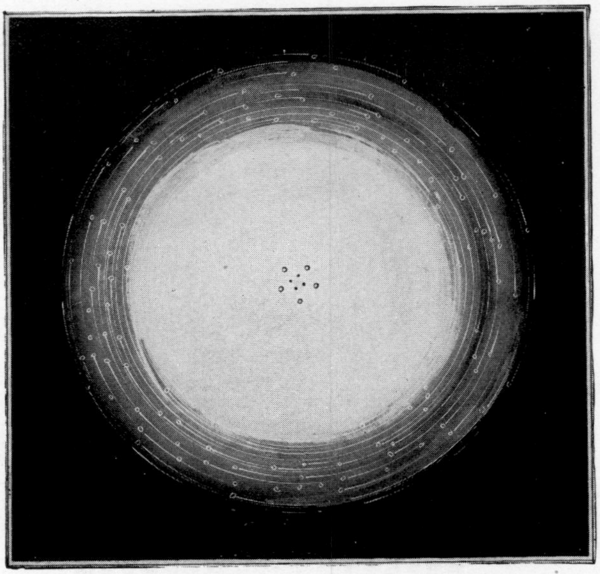

THE THEORY OF ELECTRONS

An atom of matter is composed of electrons. We picture an atom as a sort of miniature solar system, the electrons (particles of negative electricity rotating round a central nucleus of positive electricity, as described in the text. In the above pictorial representation of an atom the whirling electrons are indicated in the outer ring. Electrons move with incredible speed as they pass from one atom to another.

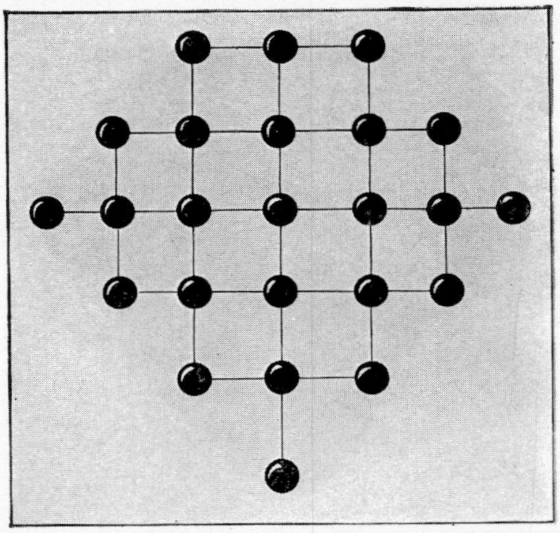

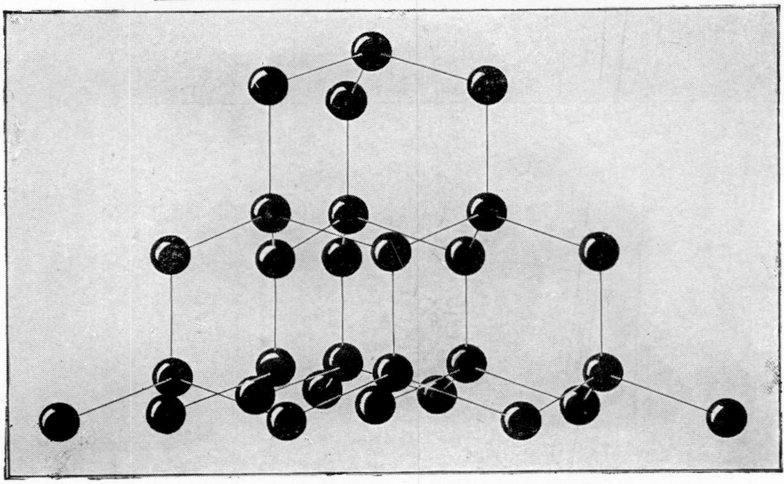

ARRANGEMENTS OF ATOMS IN A DIAMOND

The above is a model (seen from two points of view) of the arrangement of the atoms in a diamond. The arrangement is found by studying the X-ray spectra of the diamond.

million years, and the total age of the earth to some small multiple of that. The earth, he considers, is not cooling, but "contains an internal source of heat from the disintegration of uranium in the outer crust." On the whole the estimate obtained would seem to be in agreement with the geological estimates. The question, of course, cannot, in the present state of our knowledge, be settled within fixed limits that meet with general agreement.

As we have said, there are other fundamental existences which give rise to more complex problems. The three great fundamental entities in the physical universe are matter, ether, and energy; so far as we know, outside these there is nothing. We have dealt with matter, there remain ether and energy. We shall see that just as no particle of matter, however small, may be created or destroyed, and just as there is no such thing as empty space—ether pervades everything—so there is no such thing as *rest.* Every particle that goes to make up our solid earth is in a state of perpetual unremitting vibration; energy "is the universal commodity on which all life depends." Separate and distinct as these three fundamental entities—matter, ether, and energy—may appear, it may be that, after all, they are only different and mysterious phases of an essential "oneness" of the universe.

§ 9

The Future

Let us, in concluding this chapter, give just one illustration of the way in which all this new knowledge may prove to be as valuable practically as it is wonderful intellectually. We saw that electrons are shot out of atoms at a speed that may approach 160,000 miles a second. Sir Oliver Lodge has written recently that a seventieth of a grain of radium discharges, at a speed a thousand times that of a rifle bullet, thirty million electrons a second. Professor Le Bon has calculated that it would take 1,340,000 barrels of powder to give a bullet the speed of one of these electrons. He shows that the smallest French copper coin—smaller than a farthing—contains an energy equal to eighty million horse-power. A few pounds of matter contain more energy than we could extract from millions of tons of coal. Even in the atoms of hydrogen at a temperature which we could produce in an electric furnace the electrons spin round at a rate of nearly a hundred trillion revolutions a second!

Every man asks at once: "Will science ever tap this energy?" If it does, no more smoke, no mining, no transit, no bulky fuel. The energy of an atom is of course only liberated when an atom passes from one state to another. The stored up energy is fortunately fast bound by the electrons being held together as has been described. If it were not so "the earth would explode and become a gaseous nebula"! It is believed that some day we shall be able to release, harness, and utilise atomic energy. "I am of opinion," says Sir William Bragg, "that atom energy will supply our future need. A thousand years may pass before we can harness the atom, or to-morrow might see us with the reins in our hands. That is the peculiarity of Physics—research and 'accidental' discovery go hand in hand." Half a brick contains as much energy as a small coal-field. The difficulties are tremendous, but, as Sir Oliver Lodge reminds us, there was just as much scepticism at one time about the utilisation of steam or electricity. "Is it to be supposed," he asks, "that there can be no fresh invention, that all the discoveries have been made?" More than one man of science encourages us to hope. Here are some remarkable words written by Professor Soddy, one of the highest authorities on radio-active matter, in our chief scientific weekly (*Nature,* November 6, 1919):

> The prospects of the successful accomplishment of artificial transmutation brighten almost daily. The ancients seem to have had something more than an inkling that the accomplishment of transmutation would confer upon men powers hitherto the prerogative of the gods. But now we know definitely that the material aspect of transmutation

would be of small importance in comparison with the control over the inexhaustible stores of internal atomic energy to which its successful accomplishment would inevitably lead. It has become a problem, no longer redolent of the evil associations of the age of alchemy, but one big with the promise of a veritable physical renaissance of the whole world.

If that "promise" is ever realised, the economic and social face of the world will be transformed.

Before passing on to the consideration of ether, light, and energy, let us see what new light the discovery of the electron has thrown on the nature and manipulation of electricity.

WHAT IS ELECTRICITY?

The Nature of Electricity

There is at least one manifestation in nature, and so late as twenty years ago it seemed to be one of the most mysterious manifestations of all, which has been in great measure explained by the new discoveries. Already, at the beginning of this century, we spoke of our "age of electricity," yet there were few things in nature about which we knew less. The "electric current" rang our bells, drove our trains, lit our rooms, but none knew what the current was. There was a vague idea that it was a sort of fluid that flowed along copper wires as water flows in a pipe. We now suppose that it is *a rapid movement of electrons from atom to atom* in the wire or wherever the current is.

Let us try to grasp the principle of the new view of electricity and see how it applies to all the varied electrical phenomena in the world about us. As we saw, the nucleus of an atom of matter consists of positive electricity which holds together a number of electrons, or charges of negative electricity.[1] This

[1] The words "positive" and "negative" electricity belong to the days when it was regarded as a fluid. A body overcharged with the fluid was called positive; an undercharged body was called negative. A positively-electrified body is now one whose atoms have lost some of their outlying electrons, so that the positive charge of electricity predominates. The negatively-electrified body is one with more than the normal number of electrons.

certainly tells us to some extent what electricity is, and how it is related to matter, but it leaves us with the usual difficulty about fundamental realities. But we now know that electricity, like matter, is atomic in structure; a charge of electricity is made up of a number of small units or charges of a definite, constant amount. It has been suggested that the two kinds of electricity, i.e. positive and negative, are right-handed and left-handed vortices or whirlpools in ether, or rings in ether, but there are very serious difficulties, and we leave this to the future.

§ 10

What an Electric Current is

The discovery of these two kinds of electricity has, however, enabled us to understand very fairly what goes on in electrical phenomena. The outlying electrons, as we saw, may pass from atom to atom, and this, on a large scale, is the meaning of the electric current. In other words, we believe an electric current to be a flow of electrons. Let us take, to begin with, a simple electrical "cell," in which a feeble current is generated: such a cell as there is in every house to serve its electric bells.

In the original form this simple sort of "battery" consisted of a plate of zinc and a plate of copper immersed in a chemical. Long before anything was known about electrons it was known that, if you put zinc and copper together, you produce a mild current of electricity. We know now what this means. Zinc is a metal the atoms of which are particularly disposed to part with some of their outlying electrons. Why, we do not know; but the fact is the basis of these small batteries. Electrons from the atoms of zinc pass to the atoms of copper, and their passage is a "current." Each atom gives up an electron to its neighbour. It was further found long ago that if the zinc and copper were immersed in certain chemicals, which slowly dissolve the zinc, and the two metals were connected by a copper wire, the current was stronger. In modern language, there is a brisker flow of

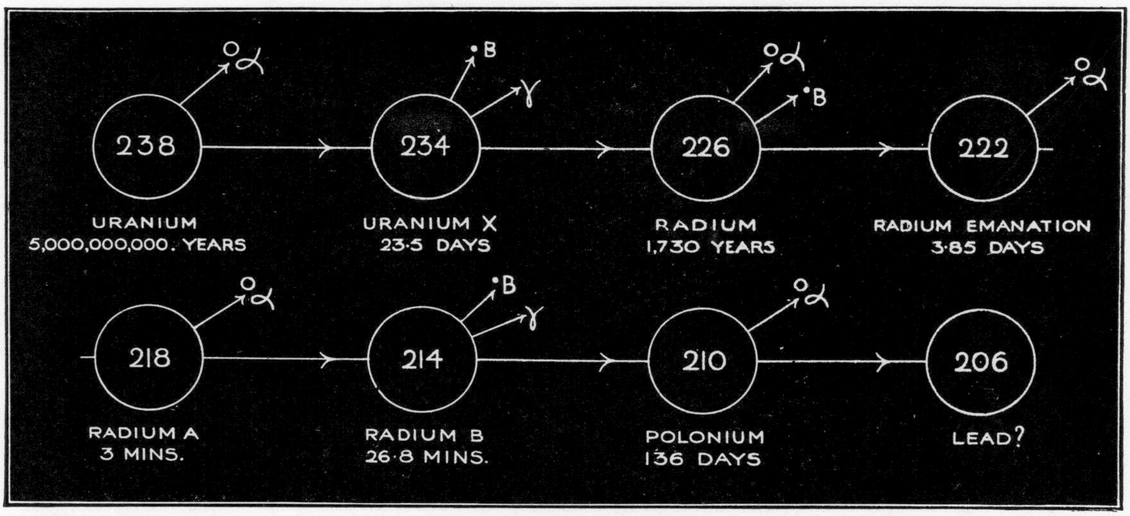

DISINTEGRATION OF ATOMS

An atom of Uranium, by ejecting an Alpha particle, becomes Uranium X. This substance, by ejecting Beta and Gamma rays, becomes Radium. Radium passes through a number of further changes, as shown in the diagram, and finally becomes lead. Some radio active substances disintegrate much faster than others. Thus Uranium changes very slowly, taking 5,000,000,000 years to reach the same stage of disintegration that Radium A reaches in 3 minutes. As the disintegration proceeds, the substances become of lighter and lighter atomic weights. Thus Uranium has an atomic weight of 238, whereas lead has an atomic weight of only 206. The breaking down of atoms is fully explained in the text.

Reproduced by permission from "The Interpretation of Radium" (John Murray).

SILK TASSEL ELECTRIFIED

The separate threads of the tassel, being each electrified with the same kind of electricity, repel one another, and thus the tassel branches out as in the photograph.

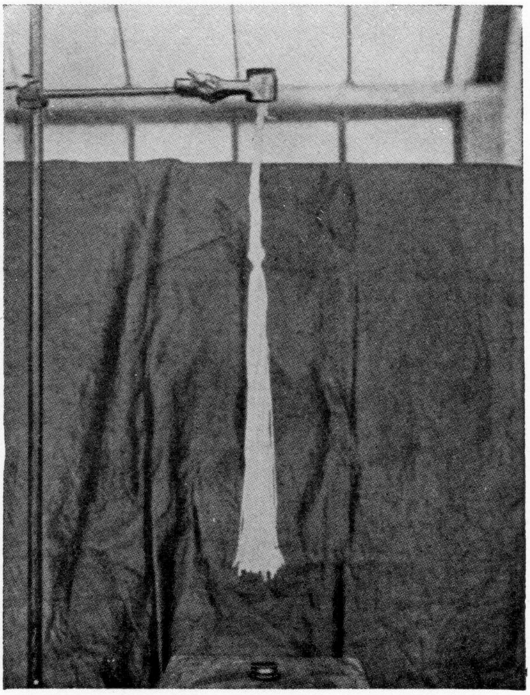

SILK TASSEL DISCHARGED BY THE RAYS FROM RADIUM

When the radium rays, carrying an opposite electric charge to that on the tassel, strikes the threads, the threads are neutralised, and hence fall together again.

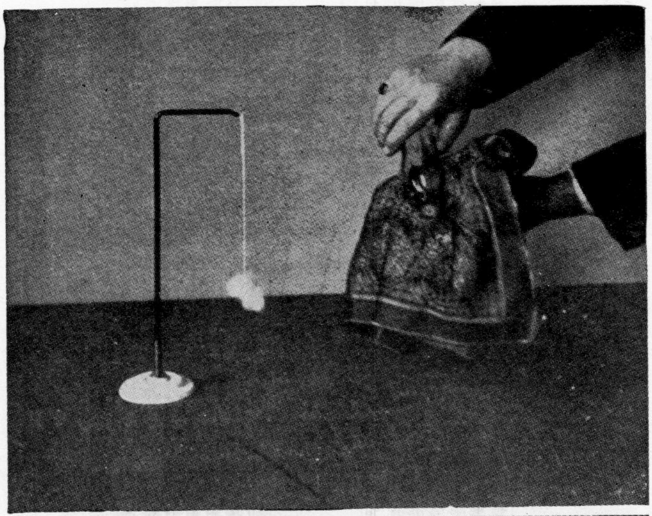

A HUGE ELECTRIC SPARK

This is an actual photograph of an electric spark. It is leaping a distance of about 10 feet, and is the discharge of a million volts. It is a graphic illustration of the tremendous energy of electrons.

From "Scientific Ideas of To-day."

ELECTRICAL ATTRACTION BETWEEN COMMON OBJECTS

Take an ordinary flower-vase well dried and energetically rub it with a silk handkerchief. The vase which thus becomes electrified will attract any light body, such as a feather, as shown in the above illustration.

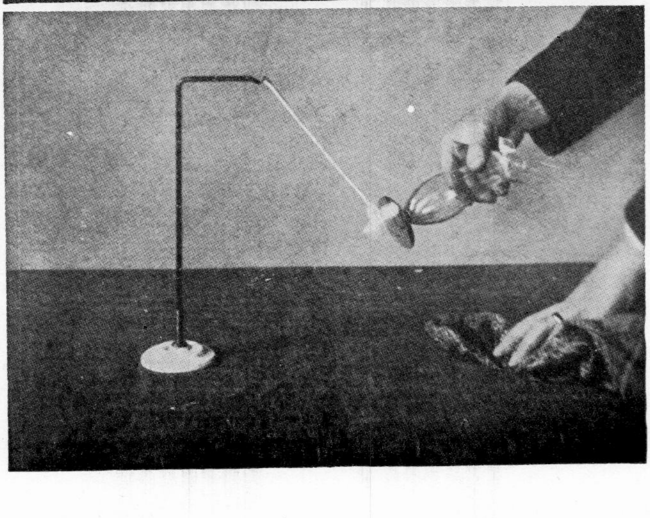

electrons. The reason is that the atoms of zinc which are stolen by the chemical leave their detachable electrons behind them, and the zinc has therefore more electrons to pass on to the copper.

Such cells are now made of zinc and carbon, immersed in sal-ammoniac, but the principle is the same. The flow of electricity is a flow of electrons; though we ought to repeat that they do not flow in a body, as molecules of water do. You may have seen boys place a row of bricks, each standing on one end, in such order that the first, if it is pushed, will knock over the second, the second the third, and so on to the last. There is a flow of *movement* all along the line, but each brick moves only a short distance. So an electron merely passes to the next atom, which sends on an electron to a third atom, and so on. In this case, however, the movement from atom to atom is so rapid that the ripple of movement, if we may call it so, may pass along at an enormous speed. We have seen how swiftly electrons travel.

But how is this turned into power enough even to ring a bell? The actual mechanical apparatus by which the energy of the electron current is turned into sound, or heat, or light will be described in a technical section later in this work. We are concerned here only with the principle, which is clear. While zinc is very apt to part with electrons, copper is just as obliging in facilitating their passage onward. Electrons will travel in this way in most metals, but copper is one of the best "conductors." So we lengthen the copper wire between the zinc and the carbon until it goes as far as the front door and the bell, which are included in the circuit. When you press the button at the door, two wires are brought together, and the current of electrons rushes round the circuit; and at the bell its energy is diverted into the mechanical apparatus which rings the bell.

Copper is a good conductor—six times as good as iron—and is therefore so common in electrical industries. Some other substances are just as stubborn as copper is yielding, and we call them "insulators," because they resist the current instead of letting it flow. Their atoms do not easily part with electrons. Glass, vulcanite, and porcelain are very good insulators for this reason.

What the Dynamo does

But even several cells together do not produce the currents needed in modern industry, and the flow is produced in a different manner. As the invisible electrons pass along a wire they produce what we call a magnetic field around the wire, they produce a disturbance in the surrounding ether. To be exact, it is through the ether surrounding the wire that the energy originated by the electrons is transmitted. To set electrons moving on a large scale we use a "dynamo." By means of the dynamo it is possible to transform mechanical energy into electrical energy. The modern dynamo, as Professor Soddy puts it, may be looked upon as an electron pump. We cannot go into the subject deeply here, we would only say that a large coil of copper wire is caused to turn round rapidly between the poles of a powerful magnet. That is the essential construction of the "dynamo," which is used for generating strong currents. We shall see in a moment how magnetism differs from electricity, and will say here only that round the poles of a large magnet there is a field of intense disturbance which will start a flow of electrons in any copper that is introduced into it. On account of the speed given to the coil of wire its atoms enter suddenly this magnetic field, and they give off crowds of electrons in a flash.

It is found that a similar disturbance is caused, though the flow is in the *opposite* direction, when the coil of wire leaves the magnetic field. And as the coil is revolving very rapidly we get a powerful current of electricity that runs in alternate directions —an "alternating" current. Electricians have apparatus for converting it into a continuous current where this is necessary.

A current, therefore, means a steady flow of the electrons from atom to atom. Sometimes, however, a number of electrons rush violently and explosively from one body to another, as in the electric spark or the occasional flash from an electric tram or train. The grandest and most spectacular display of this phenomenon is the thunder-storm. As we saw earlier, a portentous furnace like the sun is constantly pouring floods of electrons from its atoms into space. The earth intercepts great numbers of these electrons. In the upper regions of the air the stream of solar electrons has the effect of separating positively-electrified atoms from negatively-electrified ones, and the water-vapour, which is constantly rising from the surface of the sea, gathers more freely round the positively-electrified atoms, and brings them down, as rain, to the earth. Thus the upper air loses a proportion of positive electricity, or becomes "negatively electrified." In the thunderstorm we get both kinds of clouds—some with large excesses of electrons, and some deficient in electrons—and the tension grows until at last it is relieved by a sudden and violent discharge of electrons from one cloud to another or to the earth—an electric spark on a prodigious scale.

§ 11

Magnetism

We have seen that an electric current is really a flow of electrons. Now an electric current exhibits a magnetic effect. The surrounding space is endowed with energy which we call electromagnetic energy. A piece of magnetised iron attracting other pieces of iron to it is the popular idea of a magnet. If we arrange a wire to pass vertically through a piece of cardboard and then sprinkle iron filings on the cardboard we shall find that, on passing an electric current through the wire, the iron filings arrange themselves in circles round it. The magnetic force, due to the electric current, seems to exist in circles round the wire, an ether disturbance being set up. Even a single electron, when in movement, creates a magnetic "field," as it is called, round its path. There is no movement of electrons without this attendant field of energy, and their motion is not stopped until that field of energy disappears from the ether. The modern theory of magnetism supposes that all magnetism is produced in this way. All magnetism is supposed to arise from the small whirling motions of the electrons contained in the ultimate atoms of matter. We cannot here go into the details of the theory nor explain why, for instance, iron behaves so differently from other substances, but it is sufficient to say that here, also, the electron theory provides the key. This theory is not yet definitely *proved,* but it furnishes a sufficient theoretical basis for future research. The earth itself is a gigantic magnet, a fact which makes the compass possible, and it is well known that the earth's magnetism is affected by those great outbreaks on the sun called sun-spots. Now it has been recently shown that a sun-spot is a vast whirlpool of electrons and that it exerts a strong magnetic action. There is doubtless a connection between these outbreaks of electronic activity and the consequent changes in the earth's magnetism. The precise mechanism of the connection, however, is still a matter that is being investigated.

ETHER AND WAVES

Ether and Waves

The whole material universe is supposed to be embedded in a vast medium called the ether. It is true that the notion of the ether has been abandoned by some modern physicists, but, whether or not it is ultimately dispensed with, the conception of the ether has entered so deeply into the scientific mind that the science of physics cannot be understood unless we know something about the properties attributed to the ether. The ether was invented to explain the phenomena of light, and to account for the flow of energy across empty space. Light takes time to travel. We see the sun at any moment by the light that left it 8 minutes before. It has taken that 8 minutes for the light from the

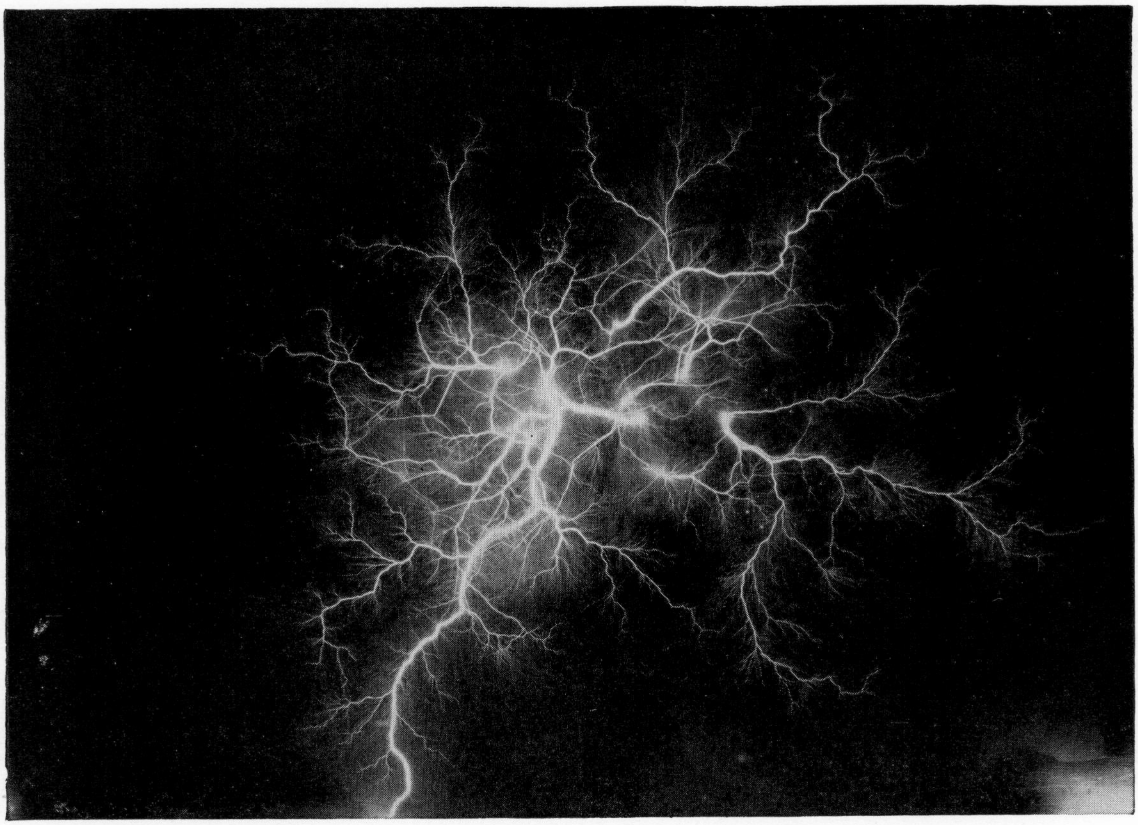

Photo: Leadbeater.

AN ELECTRIC SPARK

An electric spark consists of a rush of electrons across the space between the two terminals. A state of tension is established in the ether by the electric charges, and when this tension passes a certain limit the discharge takes place.

From "Scientific Ideas of To-day."

AN ETHER DISTURBANCE AROUND AN ELECTRON CURRENT

In the left-hand photograph an electric current is passing through the coil, thus producing a magnetic field and transforming the poker into a magnet. The poker is then able to support a pair of scissors. As soon as the electric current is broken off, as in the second photograph, the ether disturbance ceases. The poker loses its magnetism, and the scissors fall.

sun to travel that 93,000,000 miles odd which separates it from our earth. Besides the fact that light takes time to travel, it can be shown that light travels in the form of waves. We know that sound travels in waves; sound consists of waves in the air, or water or wood or whatever medium we hear it through. If an electric bell be put in a glass jar and the air be pumped out of the jar, the sound of the bell becomes feebler and feebler until, when enough air has been taken out, we do not hear the bell at all. Sound cannot travel in a vacuum. We continue to *see* the bell, however, so that evidently light can travel in a vacuum. The invisible medium through which the waves of light travel is the ether, and this ether permeates all space *and all matter.* Between us and the stars stretch vast regions empty of all matter. But we see the stars; their light reaches us, even though it may take centuries to do so. We conceive, then, that it is the universal ether which conveys that light. All the energy which has reached the earth from the sun and which, stored for ages in our coal-fields, is now used to propel our trains and steamships, to heat and light our cities, to perform all the multifarious tasks of modern life, was conveyed by the ether. Without that universal carrier of energy we should have nothing but a stagnant, lifeless world.

We have said that light consists of waves. The ether may be considered as resembling, in some respects, a jelly. It can transmit vibrations. The waves of light are really excessively small ripples, measuring from crest to crest. The distance from crest to crest of the ripples in a pond is sometimes no more than an inch or two. This distance is enormously great compared to the longest of the wave-lengths that constitute light. We say the longest, for the waves of light differ in length; the colour depends upon the length of the light. Red light has the longest waves and violet the shortest. The longest waves, the waves of deep-red light, are seven two hundred and fifty thousandths of an inch in length ($\frac{7}{250,000}$ inch). This is nearly twice the length of deep-violet light-waves, which are $\frac{1}{67,000}$ inch. But light-waves, the waves that affect the eye, are not the only waves carried by the ether. Waves too short to affect the eye can affect the photographic plate, and we can discover in this way the existence of waves only half the length of the deep-violet waves. Still shorter waves can be discovered, until we come to those excessively minute rays, the X-rays.

Below the Limits of Visibility

But we can extend our investigations in the other direction; we find that the ether carries many waves longer than light-waves. Special photographic emulsions can reveal the existence of waves five times longer than violet-light waves. Extending below the limits of visibility are waves we detect as heat-waves. Radiant heat, like the heat from a fire, is also a form of wave-motion in the ether, but the waves our senses recognise as heat are longer than light-waves. There are longer waves still, but our senses do not recognise them. But we can detect them by our instruments. These are the waves used in wireless telegraphy, and their length may be, in some cases, measured in miles. These waves are the so-called electro-magnetic waves. Light, radiant heat, and electro-magnetic waves are all of the same nature; they differ only as regards their wave-lengths.

LIGHT—VISIBLE AND INVISIBLE

If Light, then, consists of waves transmitted through the ether, what gives rise to the waves? Whatever sets up such wonderfully rapid series of waves must be something with an enormous vibration. We come back to the electron: all atoms of matter, as we have seen, are made up of electrons revolving in a regular orbit round a nucleus. These electrons may be affected by out-side influences, they may be agitated and their speed or vibration increased.

Electrons and Light

The particles even of a piece of cold iron are in a state of vibration. No nerves of ours are able to feel and register the waves they emit, but your cold poker is really radiating, or sending out a series of wave-movements, on every side. After what we saw about the nature of matter, this will surprise none. Put your poker in the fire for a time. The particles of the glowing coal, which are violently agitated, communicate some of their energy to the particles of iron in the poker. They move to and fro more rapidly, and the waves which they create are now able to affect your nerves and cause a sensation of heat. Put the poker again in the fire, until its temperature rises to 500° C. It begins to glow with a dull red. Its particles are now moving very violently, and the waves they send out are so short and rapid that they can be picked up by the eye—we have *visible* light. They would still not affect a photographic plate. Heat the iron further, and the crowds of electrons now send out waves of various lengths which blend into white light. What is happening is the agitated electrons flying round in their orbits at a speed of trillions of times a second. Make the iron "blue hot," and it pours out, in addition to light, the *invisible* waves which alter the film on the photographic plate. And beyond these there is a long range of still shorter waves, culminating in the X-rays, which will pass between the atoms of flesh or stone.

Nearly two hundred and fifty years ago it was proved that light travelled at least 600,000 times faster than sound. Jupiter, as we saw, has moons, which circle round it. They pass behind the body of the planet, and reappear at the other side. But it was noticed that, when Jupiter is at its greatest distance from us, the reappearance of the moon from behind it is 16 minutes and 36 seconds later than when the planet is nearest to us. Plainly this was because light took so long to cover the additional distance. The distance was then imperfectly known, and the speed of light was underrated We now know the distance, and we easily get the velocity of light.

No doubt it seems far more wonderful to discover this within the walls of a laboratory, but it was done as long ago as 1850. A cogged wheel is so mounted that a ray of light passes between two of the teeth and is reflected back from a mirror. Now, slight as is the fraction of a second which light takes to travel that distance, it is possible to give such speed to the wheel that the next tooth catches the ray of light on its return and cuts it off. The speed is increased still further until the ray of light returns to the eye of the observer through the notch *next* to the one by which it had passed to the mirror! The speed of the wheel was known, and it was thus possible again to gather the velocity of light. If the shortest waves are $\frac{1}{67,000}$ of an inch in length, and light travels at 186,000 miles a second, any person can work out that about 800 trillion waves enter the eye in a second when we see "violet."

Sorting out Light-waves

The waves sent out on every side by the energetic electrons become faintly visible to us when they reach about $\frac{1}{35,000}$ of an inch. As they become shorter and more rapid, as the electrons increase their speed, we get, in succession, the colours red, orange, yellow, green, blue, indigo, and violet. Each distinct sensation of colour means a wave of different length. When they are all mingled together, as in the light of the sun, we get white light. When this white light passes through glass, the speed of the waves is lessened; and, if the ray of light falls obliquely on a triangular piece of glass, the waves of different lengths part company as they travel through it, and the light is spread out in a band of rainbow-colour. The waves are sorted out according to their lengths in the "obstacle race" through the glass. Anyone may see this for himself by holding up a wedge-shaped piece of crystal between the sunlight and the eye; the prism separates the

Photo: H. J. Shepstone.

LIGHTNING

In a thunderstorm we have the most spectacular display in lightning of a violent and explosive rush of electrons (electricity) from one body to another, from cloud to cloud, or to the earth. In this wonderful photograph of an electrical storm note the long branched and undulating flashes of lightning. Each flash lasts no longer than the one hundred-thousandth part of a second of time.

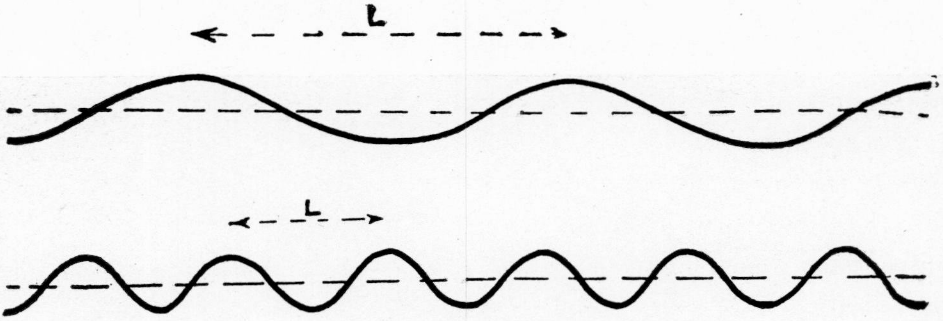

LIGHT WAVES

Light consists of waves transmitted through the ether. Waves of light differ in length. The colour of the light depends on the wave-length. Deep-red waves (the longest) are $\frac{7}{250000}$ inch and deep-violet waves $\frac{1}{67000}$ inch. The diagram shows two wave-motions of different wave-lengths. From crest to crest, or from trough to trough, is the length of the wave.

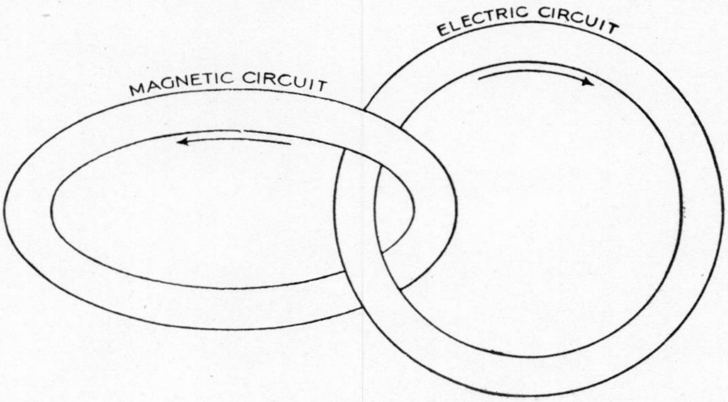

THE MAGNETIC CIRCUIT OF AN ELECTRIC CURRENT

The electric current passing in the direction of the arrow round the electric circuit generates in the surrounding space circular magnetic circuits as shown in the diagram. It is this property which lies at the base of the electro-magnet and of the electric dynamo.

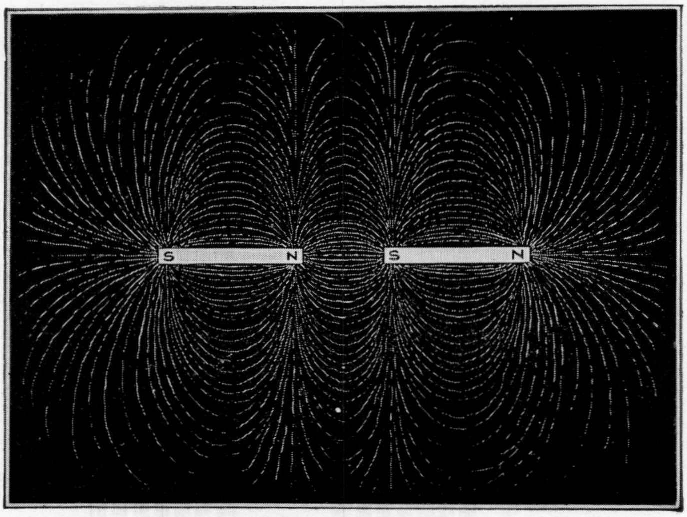

THE MAGNET

The illustration shows the lines of force between two magnets. The lines of force proceed from the north pole of one magnet to the south pole of the other. They also proceed from the north to the south poles of the same magnet. These facts are shown clearly in the diagram. The north pole of a magnet is that end of it which turns to the north when the magnet is freely suspended.

sunlight into its constituent colours, and these various colours will be seen quite readily. Or the thing may be realised in another way. If the seven colours are painted on a wheel as shown opposite page 280 (in the proportion shown), and the wheel rapidly revolved on a pivot, the wheel will appear a dull white, the several colours will not be seen. But *omit* one of the colours, then the wheel, when revolved, will not appear white, but will give the impression of one colour, corresponding to what the union of six colours gives. Another experiment will show that some bodies held up between the eye and a white light will not permit all the rays to pass through, but will intercept some; a body that intercepts all the seven rays except red will give the impression of red, or if all the rays except violet, then violet will be the colour seen.

The Fate of the World

Professor Soddy has given an interesting picture of what might happen when the sun's light and heat is no longer what it is. The human eye "has adapted itself through the ages to the peculiarities of the sun's light, so as to make the most of that wave-length of which there is most. . . . Let us indulge for a moment in these gloomy prognostications, as to the consequences to this earth of the cooling of the sun with the lapse of ages, which used to be in vogue, but which radioactivity has so rudely shaken. Picture the fate of the world when the sun has become a dull red-hot ball, or even when it has cooled so far that it would no longer emit light to us. That does not all mean that the world would be in inky darkness, and that the sun would not emit light to the people then inhabiting this world, if any had survived and could keep themselves from freezing. To such, if the eye continued to adapt itself to the changing conditions, our blues and violets would be ultra-violet and invisible, but our dark heat would be light and hot bodies would be luminous to them which would be dark to us."

§ 12

What the Blue "Sky" means

We saw in a previous chapter how the spectroscope splits up light-waves into their colours. But nature is constantly splitting the light into its different-lengthed waves, its colours. The rainbow, where dense moisture in the air acts as a spectroscope, is the most familiar example. A piece of mother-of-pearl, or even a film of oil on the street or on water, has the same effect, owing to the fine inequalities in its surface. The atmosphere all day long is sorting out the waves. The blue "sky" overhead means that the fine particles in the upper atmosphere catch the shorter waves, the blue waves, and scatter them. We can make a tubeful of blue sky in the laboratory at any time. The beautiful pink-flush on the Alps at sunrise, the red glory that lingers in the west at sunset, mean that, as the sun's rays must struggle through denser masses of air when it is low on the horizon, the long red waves are sifted out from the other shafts.

Then there is the varied face of nature which, by absorbing some waves and reflecting others, weaves its own beautiful robe of colour. Here and there is a black patch, which *absorbs* all the light. White surfaces *reflect* the whole of it. What is reflected depends on the period of vibration of the electrons in the particular kind of matter. Generally, as the electrons receive the flood of trillions of waves, they absorb either the long or the medium or the short, and they give us the wonderful colour-scheme of nature. In some cases the electrons continue to radiate long after the sunlight has ceased to fall upon them. We get from them "black" or invisible light, and we can take photographs by it. Other bodies, like glass, vibrate in unison with the period of the light-waves and let them stream through.

Light without Heat

There are substances—"phosphorescent" things we call them —which give out a mysterious cold light of their own. It is one

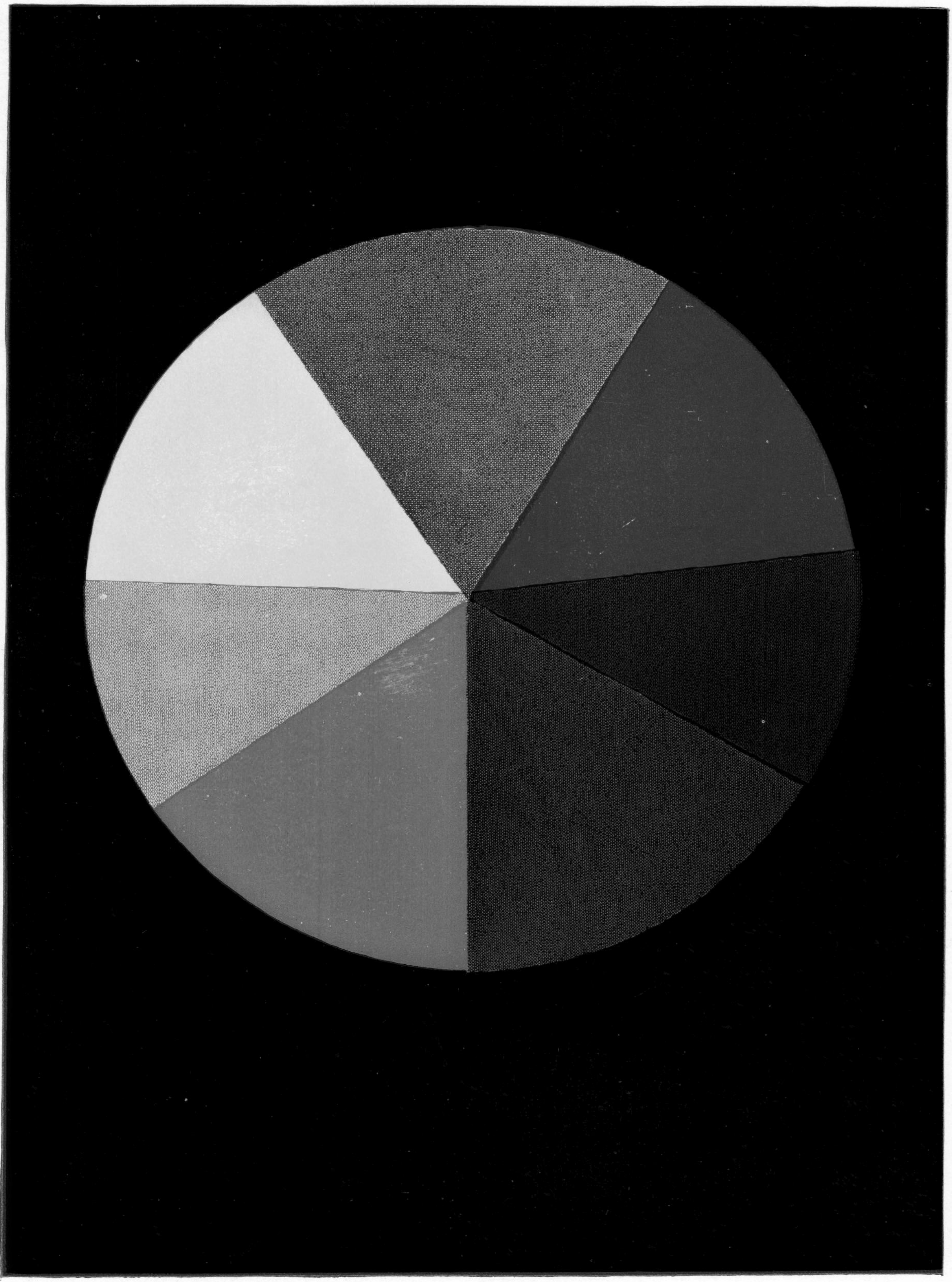

ROTATING DISC OF SIR ISAAC NEWTON FOR MIXING COLOURS

The Spectroscope sorts out the above seven colours from sunlight (which is compounded of these seven colours). If painted in proper proportions on a wheel, as shown in the coloured illustration, and the wheel be turned rapidly on a pivot through its centre, only a dull white will be perceived. If one colour be omitted, the result will be one colour—the result of the union of the remaining six.

of the problems of science, and one of profound practical interest. If we could produce light without heat our "gas bill" would shrink amazingly. So much energy is wasted in the production of heat-waves and ultra-violet waves which we do not want, that 90 per cent. or more of the power used in illumination is wasted. Would that the glow-worm, or even the dead herring, would yield us its secret! Phosphorus is the one thing we know as yet that suits the purpose, and—it smells! Indeed, our artificial light is not only extravagant in cost, but often poor in colour. The unwary person often buys a garment by artificial light, and is disgusted next morning to find in it a colour which is not wanted. The colour disclosed by the sun was not in the waves of the artificial light.

Beyond the waves of violet light are the still shorter and more rapid waves—the "ultra-violet" waves—which are precious to the photographer. As every amateur knows, his plate may safely be exposed to light that comes through a red or an orange screen. Such a screen means "no thoroughfare" for the blue and "beyond-blue" waves, and it is these which arrange the little grains of silver on the plate. It is the same waves which supply the energy to the little green grains of matter (chlorophyll) in the plant, preparing our food and timber for us, as will be seen later. The tree struggles upward and spreads out its leaves fanwise to the blue sky to receive them. In our coal-measures, the mighty dead forests of long ago, are vast stores of sunlight which we are prodigally using up.

The X-rays are the extreme end, the highest octave, of the series of waves. Their power of penetration implies that they are excessively minute, but even these have not held their secret from the modern physicist. From a series of beautiful experiments, in which they were made to pass amongst the atoms of a crystal, we learned their length. It is about the ten-millionth of a millimetre, and a millimetre is about the $\frac{1}{25}$ of an inch!

One of the most recent discoveries, made during a recent

eclipse of the sun, is that light is subject to gravitation. A ray of light from a star is bent out of its straight path when it passes near the mass of the sun. Professor Eddington tells us that we have as much right to speak of a pound of light as of a pound of sugar. Professor Eddington even calculates that the earth receives 160 tons of light from the sun every year!

ENERGY: HOW ALL LIFE DEPENDS ON IT

As we have seen in an earlier chapter, one of the fundamental entities of the universe is matter. A second, not less important, is called energy. Energy is indispensable if the world is to continue to exist, since all phenomena, including life, depend on it. Just as it is humanly impossible to create or to destroy a particle of matter, so is it impossible to create or to destroy energy. This statement will be more readily understood when we have considered what energy is.

Energy, like matter, is indestructible, and just as matter exists in various forms so does energy. And we may add, just as we are ignorant of what the negative and positive particles of electricity which constitute matter really are, so we are ignorant of the true nature of energy. At the same time, energy is not so completely mysterious as it once was. It is another of nature's mysteries which the advance of modern science has in some measure unveiled. It was only during the nineteenth century that energy came to be known as something as distinct and permanent as matter itself.

Forms of Energy

The existence of various forms of energy had been known, of course, for ages; there was the energy of a falling stone, the energy produced by burning wood or coal or any other substance, but the essential *identity* of all these forms of energy had not been suspected. The conception of energy as something which, like

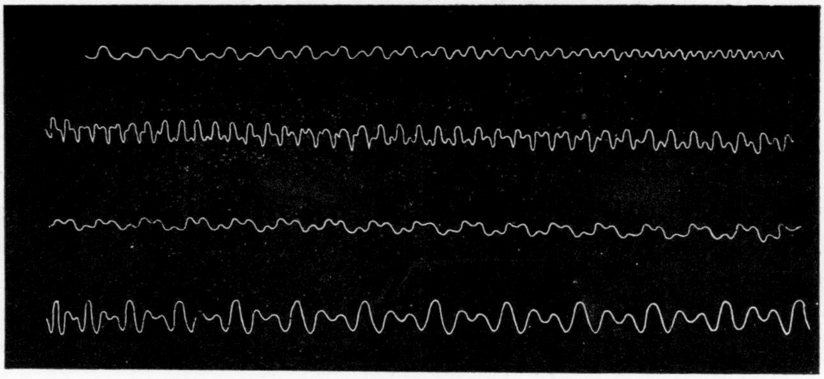

WAVE SHAPES

Wave-motions are often complex. The above illustration shows some fairly complicated wave shapes. All such wave-motions can be produced by superposing a number of simple wave forms.

THE POWER OF A MAGNET

The illustration is that of a "Phœnix" electric magnet lifting scrap from railway trucks. The magnet is 52 inches in diameter and lifts a weight of 26 tons. The same type of magnet, 62 inches in diameter, lifts a weight of 40 tons.

Photo: The Locomotive Publishing Co., Ltd.

THE SPEED OF LIGHT

A train travelling at the rate of sixty miles per hour would take rather more than seventeen and a quarter days to go round the earth at the equator, i.e. a distance of 25,000 miles. Light, which travels at the rate of 186,000 miles per second, would take between one-seventh and one-eighth of a second to go the same distance.

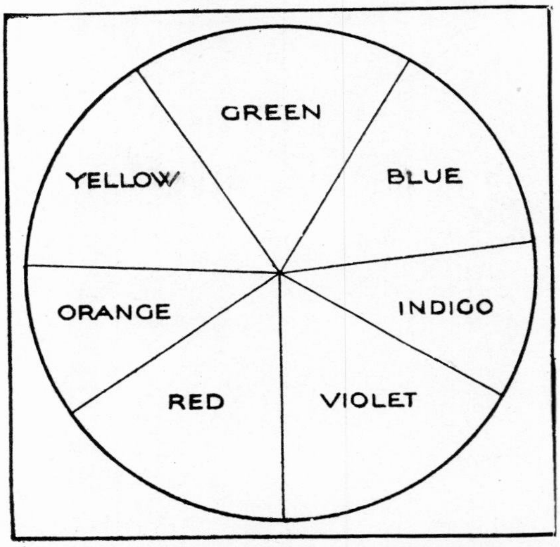

ROTATING DISC OF SIR ISAAC NEWTON FOR MIXING COLOURS

The Spectroscope sorts out the above seven colours from sunlight (which is compounded of these seven colours). If painted in proper proportions on a wheel, as shown in the coloured illustration, and the wheel turned rapidly on a pivot through its centre, only a dull white will be perceived. If one colour be omitted, the result will be one colour—the result of the union of the remaining six.

matter, was constant in amount, which could not be created nor destroyed, was one of the great scientific acquisitions of the past century.

It is not possible to enter deeply into this subject here. It is sufficient if we briefly outline its salient aspects. Energy is recognised in two forms, kinetic and potential. The form of energy which is most apparent to us is the *energy of motion;* for example, a rolling stone, running water, a falling body, and so on. We call the energy of motion *kinetic energy.* Potential energy is the energy a body has in virtue of its position—it is its capacity, in other words, to acquire kinetic energy, as in the case of a stone resting on the edge of a cliff.

Energy may assume different forms; one kind of energy may be converted directly or indirectly into some other form. The energy of burning coal, for example, is converted into heat, and from heat energy we have mechanical energy, such as that manifested by the steam-engine. In this way we can transfer energy from one body to another. There is the energy of the great waterfalls of Niagara, for instance, which are used to supply the energy of huge electric power stations.

What Heat is

An important fact about energy is, that all energy *tends to take the form of heat energy.* The impact of a falling stone generates heat; a waterfall is hotter at the bottom than at the top —the falling particles of water, on striking the ground, generate heat; and most chemical changes are attended by heat changes. Energy may remain latent indefinitely in a lump of wood, but in combustion it is liberated, and we have heat as a result. The atom of radium or of any other radio-active substance, as it disintegrates, generates heat. "Every hour radium generates sufficient heat to raise the temperature of its own weight of water, from the freezing point to the boiling point." And what is heat? *Heat is molecular motion.* The molecules of every substance, as we have seen on a previous page, are in a state of continual motion, and the more vigorous the motion the hotter the body. As wood or coal burns, the invisible molecules of these substances are violently agitated, and give rise to ether waves which our senses interpret as light and heat. In this constant movement of the molecules, then, we have a manifestation of the energy of motion and of heat.

That energy which disappears in one form reappears in another has been found to be universally true. It was Joule who, by churning water, first showed that a measurable quantity of mechanical energy could be transformed into a measurable quantity of heat energy. By causing an apparatus to stir water vigorously, that apparatus being driven by falling weights or a rotating flywheel or by any other mechanical means, the water became heated. A certain amount of mechanical energy had been used up and a certain amount of heat had appeared. The relation between these two things was found to be invariable. Every physical change in nature involves a transformation of energy, but the total quantity of energy in the universe remains unaltered. This is the great doctrine of the Conservation of Energy.

§ 13

Substitutes for Coal

Consider the source of nearly all the energy which is used in modern civilisation—coal. The great forests of the Carboniferous epoch now exists as beds of coal. By the burning of coal—a chemical transformation—the heat energy is produced on which at present our whole civilisation depends. Whence is the energy locked up in the coal derived? From the sun. For millions of years the energy of the sun's rays had gone to form the vast vegetation of the Carboniferous era and had been transformed, by various subtle processes, into the potential energy that slumbers in those immense fossilized forests.

The exhaustion of our coal deposits would mean, so far as our knowledge extends at present, the end of the world's civilisation. There are other known sources of energy, it is true. There is the energy of falling water; the great falls of Niagara are used to supply the energy of huge electric power stations. Perhaps, also, something could be done to utilise the energy of the tides—another instance of the energy of moving water. And attempts have been made to utilise directly the energy of the sun's rays. But all these sources of energy are small compared with the energy of coal. A suggestion was made at a recent British Association meeting that deep borings might be sunk in order to utilise the internal heat of the earth, but this is not, perhaps, a very practical proposal. By far the most effective substitutes for coal would be found in the interior energy of the atom, a source of energy which, as we have seen, is practically illimitable. If the immense electrical energy in the interior of the atom can ever be liberated and controlled, then our steadily decreasing coal supply will no longer be the bugbear it now is to all thoughtful men.

The stored-up energy of the great coal-fields can be used up, but we cannot replace it or create fresh supplies. As we have seen, energy cannot be destroyed, but it can become *unavailable*. Let us consider what this important fact means.

§ 14

Dissipation of Energy

Energy may become dissipated. Where does it go? since if it is indestructible it must still exist. It is easier to ask the question than to give a final answer, and it is not possible in this OUTLINE, where an advanced knowledge of physics is not assumed on the part of the reader, to go fully into the somewhat difficult theories put forward by physicists and chemists. We may raise the temperature, say, of iron, until it is white-hot. If we stop the process the temperature of the iron will gradually settle down to the temperature of surrounding bodies. As it does so, where does its previous energy go? In some measure it may pass to other bodies in contact with the piece of iron, but ultimately the heat becomes radiated away in space where we cannot follow it. It has been added to the vast reservoir of *unavailable* heat energy of uniform temperature. It is sufficient here to say that if all bodies had a uniform temperature we should experience no such thing as heat, because heat only travels from one body to another, having the effect of cooling the one and warming the other. In time the two bodies acquire the same temperature. The sum-total of the heat in any body is measured in terms of the kinetic energy of its moving molecules.

There must come a time, so far as we can see at present, when, even if all the heat energy of the universe is not radiated away into empty infinite space, yet a uniform temperature will prevail. If one body is hotter than another it radiates heat to that body until both are at the same temperature. Each body may still possess a considerable quantity of heat energy, which it has absorbed, but that energy, so far as reactions between those two bodies are concerned, *is now unavailable*. The same principle applies whatever number of bodies we consider. Before heat energy can be utilised we must have bodies with different temperature. If the whole universe were at some uniform temperature, then, although it might possess an enormous amount of heat energy, this energy would be unavailable.

What a Uniform Temperature would mean

And what does this imply? It implies a great deal: for if all the energy in the world became unavailable, the universe, as it now is, would cease to be. It is possible that, by the constant interchange of heat radiations, the whole universe is tending to some uniform temperature, in which case, although all molecular motion would not have ceased, it would have become unavailable. In this sense it may be said that the universe is running down.

NIAGARA FALLS

The energy of this falling water is prodigious. It is used to generate thousands of horse-power in great electrical installations. The power is used to drive electric trams in cities 150 to 250 miles away.

Photo: Stephen Cribb.

TRANSFORMATION OF ENERGY

An illustration of Energy. The chemical energy brought into existence by firing the explosive manifesting itself as mechanical energy, sufficient to impart violent motion to tons of water.

Photo: Underwood & Underwood.

"BOILING" A KETTLE ON ICE

When a kettle containing liquid air is placed on ice it "boils" because the ice is intensely hot *when compared with the very low temperature of the liquid air.*

If all the molecules of a substance were brought to a standstill, that substance would be at the absolute zero of temperature. There could be nothing colder. The temperature at which all molecular motions would cease is known: it is –273° C. No body could possibly attain a lower temperature than this: a lower temperature could not exist. Unless there exists in nature some process, of which we know nothing at present, whereby energy is renewed, our solar system must one day sink to this absolute zero of temperature. The sun, the earth, and every other body in the universe is steadily radiating heat, and this radiation cannot go on for ever, because heat continually tends to diffuse and to equalise temperatures.

But we can see, theoretically, that there is a way of evading this law. If the chaotic molecular motions which constitute heat could be *regulated,* then the heat energy of a body could be utilised directly. Some authorities think that some of the processes which go on in the living body do not involve any waste energy, that the chemical energy of food is transformed directly into work without any of it being dissipated as useless heat energy. It may be, therefore, that man will finally discover some way of escape from the natural law that, while energy cannot be destroyed, it has a tendency to become unavailable.

The primary reservoir of energy is the atom; it is the energy of the atom, the atom of elements in the sun, the stars, the earth, from which nature draws for all her supply of energy. Shall we ever discover how we can replenish the dwindling resources of energy, or find out how we can call into being the at present unavailable energy which is stored up in uniform temperature?

It looks as if our successors would witness an interesting race, between the progress of science on the one hand and the depletion of natural resources upon the other. The natural rate of flow of energy from its primary atomic reservoirs to the sea of waste heat energy of uniform temperature, allows life to proceed at a complete pace sternly regulated by the inexorable laws of supply and demand, which the biologists have recognised in their field as the struggle for existence.[1]

It is certain that energy is an actual entity just as much as matter, and that it cannot be created or destroyed. Matter and ether are receptacles or vehicles of energy. As we have said, what these entities really are in themselves we do not know. It may be that all forms of energy are in some fundamental way aspects of the same primary entity which constitutes matter: how all matter is constituted of particles of electricity we have already seen. The question to which we await an answer is: What is electricity?

§ 15

MATTER, ETHER, AND EINSTEIN

The supreme synthesis, the crown of all this progressive conquest of nature, would be to discover that the particles of positive and negative electricity, which make up the atoms of matter, are points or centres of disturbances of some kind in a universal ether, and that all our "energies" (light, magnetism, gravitation, etc.) are waves or strains of some kind set up in the ether by these clusters of electrons.

It is a fascinating, tantalising dream. Larmor suggested in 1900 that the electron is a tiny whirlpool, or "vortex," in ether; and, as such a vortex may turn in either of two opposite ways, we seem to see a possibility of explaining positive and negative electricity. But the difficulties have proved very serious, and the nature of the electron is unknown. A recent view is that it is "a ring of negative electricity rotating about its axis at a high speed," though that does not carry us very far. The unit of positive electricity is even less known. We must be content to know

[1] *Matter and Energy,* by Professor Soddy.

the general lines on which thought is moving toward the final unification.

We say "unification," but it would be a grave error to think that ether is the only possible basis for such unity, or to make it an essential part of one's philosophy of the universe. Ether was never more than an imagined entity to which we ascribed the most extraordinary properties, and which seemed then to promise considerable aid. It was conceived as an elastic solid of very great density, stretching from end to end of the universe, transmitting waves from star to star at the rate of 186,000 miles a second; yet it was believed that the most solid matter passed through it as if it did not exist.

Some years ago a delicate experiment was tried for the purpose of detecting the ether. Since the earth, in travelling round the sun, must move through the ether if the ether exists, there ought to be a stream of ether flowing through every laboratory; just as the motion of a ship through a still atmosphere will make "a wind." In 1887 Michelson and Morley tried to detect this. Theoretically, a ray of light in the direction of the stream ought to travel at a different rate from a ray of light against the stream or across it. They found no difference, and scores of other experiments have failed. This does not prove that there is no ether, as there is reason to suppose that our instruments would appear to shrink in precisely the same proportion as the alteration of the light; but the fact remains that we have no proof of the existence of ether. J. H. Jeans says that "nature acts as if no such thing existed." Even the phenomena of light and magnetism, he says, do not imply ether; and he thinks that the hypothesis may be abandoned. The primary reason, of course, for giving up the notion of the ether is that, as Einstein has shown, there is no way of detecting its existence. If there is an ether, then, since the earth is moving through it, there should be some way of detecting this motion. The experiment has been tried, as we have said, but, although the method used was very sensitive, no motion was discovered. It is Einstein who, by revolutionising our conceptions of space and time, showed that no such motion ever could be discovered, whatever means were employed, and that the usual notion of the ether must be abandoned. We shall explain this theory more fully in a later section.

INFLUENCE OF THE TIDES: ORIGIN OF THE MOON: THE EARTH SLOWING DOWN

§ 16

Until comparatively recent times, until, in fact, the full dawn of modern science, the tides ranked amongst the greatest of nature's mysteries. And, indeed, what agency could be invoked to explain this mysteriously regular flux and reflux of the waters of the ocean? It is not surprising that that steady, rhythmical rise and fall suggested to some imaginative minds the breathing of a mighty animal. And even when man first became aware of the fact that this regular movement was somehow associated with the moon, was he much nearer an explanation? What bond could exist between the movements of that distant world and the diurnal variation of the waters of the earth? It is reported that an ancient astronomer, despairing of ever resolving the mystery, drowned himself in the sea.

The Earth Pulled by the Moon

But it was part of the merit of Newton's mighty theory of gravitation that it furnished an explanation even of this age-old mystery. We can see, in broad outlines at any rate, that the theory of universal attraction can be applied to this case. For the moon, Newton taught us, pulls every particle of matter throughout the earth. If we imagine that part of the earth's surface which comprises the Pacific Ocean, for instance, to be turned towards the moon, we see that the moon's pull, *acting on the loose and mobile water,* would tend to heap it up into a sort

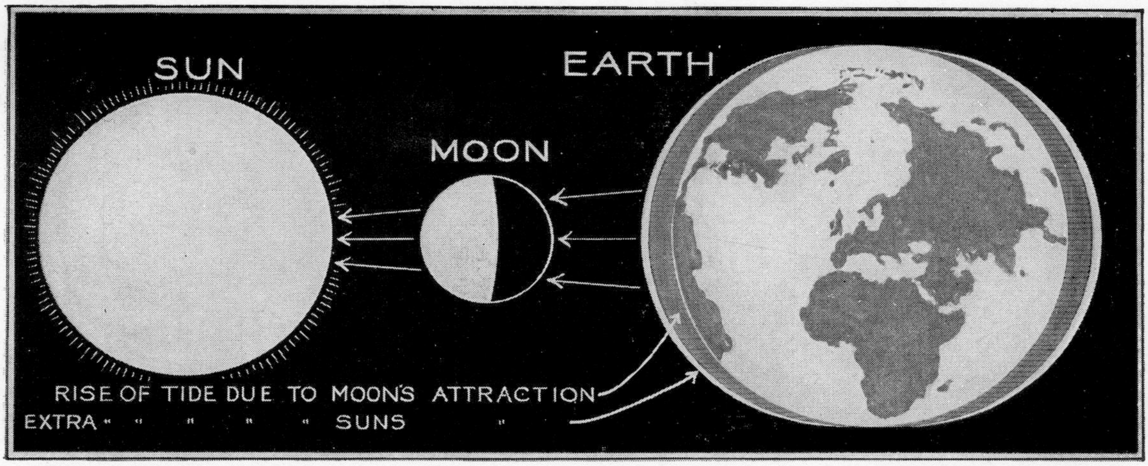

THE CAUSE OF TIDES

The tides of the sea are due to the pull of the moon, and, in lesser degree, of the sun. The whole earth is pulled by the moon, but the loose and mobile water is more free to obey this pull than is the solid earth, although small tides are also caused in the earth's solid crust The effect which the tides have on slowing down the rotation of the earth is explained in the text.

Photo: G. Brocklehurst.

THE AEGIR ON THE TRENT

An exceptionally smooth formation due to perfect weather conditions. The wall-like formation of these tidal waves (see next page also) will be noticed. The reason for this is that the downward current in the river heads the sea-water back, and thus helps to exaggerate the advancing slope of the wave. The exceptional spring tides are caused by the combined operation of the moon and the sun, as is explained in the text.

Photo: G. Brocklehurst.

A BIG SPRING TIDE, THE AEGIR ON THE TRENT

of mound. The whole earth is pulled by the moon, but the water is more free to obey this pull than is the solid earth, although small tides are also caused in the earth's solid crust. It can be shown also that a corresponding hump would tend to be produced on the other side of the earth, owing, in this case, to the tendency of the water, being more loosely connected, to lag behind the solid earth. If the earth's surface were entirely fluid the rotation of the earth would give the impression that these two humps were continually travelling round the world, once every day. At any given part of the earth's surface, therefore, there would be two humps daily, i.e. two periods of high water. Such is the simplest possible outline of the gravitational theory of the tides.

The actually observed phenomena are vastly more complicated, and the complete theory bears very little resemblance to the simple form we have just outlined. Everyone who lives in the neighbourhood of a port knows, for instance, that high water seldom coincides with the time when the moon crosses the meridian. It may be several hours early or late. High water at London Bridge, for instance, occurs about one and a half hours after the moon has passed the meridian, while at Dublin high water occurs about one and a half hours before the moon crosses the meridian. The actually observed phenomena, then, are far from simple; they have, nevertheless, been very completely worked out, and the times of high water for every port in the world can now be prophesied for a considerable time ahead.

The Action of Sun and Moon

It would be beyond our scope to attempt to explain the complete theory, but we may mention one obvious factor which must be taken into account. Since the moon, by its gravitational attraction, produces tides, we should expect that the sun, whose gravitational attraction is so much stronger, should also produce tides and, we would suppose at first sight, more powerful tides than the moon. But while it is true that the sun produces tides, it is not true that they are more powerful than those produced by the moon. The sun's tide-producing power is, as a matter of fact, less than half that of the moon. The reason of this is that *distance* plays an enormous role in the production of tides. The mass of the sun is 26,000,000 times that of the moon; on the other hand it is 386 times as far off as the moon. This greater distance more than counterbalances its greater mass, and the result, as we have said, is that the moon is more than twice as powerful. Sometimes the sun and moon act together, and we have what are called spring tides; sometimes they act against one another, and we have neap tides. These effects are further complicated by a number of other factors, and the tides, at various places, vary enormously. Thus at St. Helena the sea rises and falls about three feet, whereas in the Bay of Fundy it rises and falls more than fifty feet. But here, again, the reasons are complicated.

§ 17

Origin of the Moon

But there is another aspect of the tides which is of vastly greater interest and importance than the theory we have just been discussing. In the hands of Sir George H. Darwin, the son of Charles Darwin, the tides had been made to throw light on the evolution of our solar system. In particular, they have illustrated the origin and development of the system formed by our earth and moon. It is quite certain that, long ages ago, the earth was rotating immensely faster than it is now, and that the moon was so near as to be actually in contact with the earth. In that remote age the moon was just on the point of separating from the earth, of being thrown off by the earth. Earth and moon were once one body, but the high rate of rotation caused this body to split up into two pieces; one piece became the earth we now know, and the other became the moon. Such is the conclusion to which we are led by an examination of the tides. In the first place let us consider the energy produced by the tides. We see evidences of this energy all round the word's coastlines. Estuaries are scooped out, great rocks are gradually reduced to rubble, innumerable tons of matter are continually being set in movement. Whence is this energy derived? Energy, like matter, cannot be created from nothing; what, then, is the source which makes this colossal expenditure possible.

The Earth Slowing down

The answer is simple, but startling. *The source of tidal energy is the rotation of the earth.* The massive bulk of the earth, turning every twenty-four hours on its axis, is like a gigantic flywheel. In virtue of its rotation it possesses an enormous store of energy. But even the heaviest and swiftest flywheel, if it is doing work, or even if it is only working against the friction of its bearings, cannot dispense energy for ever. It must, gradually, slow down. There is no escape from this reasoning. It is the rotation of the earth which supplies the energy of the tides, and, as a consequence, the tides must be slowing down the earth. The tides act as a kind of brake on the earth's rotation. These masses of water, *held back by the moon,* exert a kind of dragging effect on the rotating earth. Doubtless this effect, measured by our ordinary standards, is very small; it is, however, continuous, and in the course of the millions of years dealt with in astronomy, this small but constant effect may produce very considerable results.

But there is another effect which can be shown to be a necessary mathematical consequence of tidal action. It is the moon's action on the earth which produces the tides, but they also react on the moon. The tides are slowing down the earth, and they are also driving the moon farther and farther away. This result, strange as it may seem, does not permit of doubt, for it is the result of an indubitable dynamical principle, which cannot be made clear without a mathematical discussion. Some interesting consequences follow.

Since the earth is slowing down, it follows that it was once rotating faster. There was a period, a long time ago, when the day comprised only twenty hours. Going farther back still we come to a day of ten hours, until, inconceivable ages ago, the earth must have been rotating on its axis in a period of from three to four hours.

At this point let us stop and inquire what was happening to the moon. We have seen that at present the moon is getting farther and farther away. It follows, therefore, that when the day was shorter the moon was nearer. As we go farther back in time we find the moon nearer and nearer to an earth rotating faster and faster. When we reach the period we have already mentioned, the period when the earth completed a revolution in three or four hours, we find that the moon was so near as to be almost grazing the earth. This fact is very remarkable. Everybody knows that there is a *critical velocity* for a rotating flywheel, a velocity beyond which the flywheel would fly into pieces because the centrifugal force developed is so great as to overcome the cohesion of the molecules of the flywheel. We have already likened our earth to a flywheel, and we have traced its history back to the point where it was rotating with immense velocity. We have also seen that, at that moment, the moon was barely separated from the earth. The conclusion is irresistible. In an age more remote the earth *did* fly in pieces, and one of those pieces is the moon. Such, in brief outline, is the tidal theory of the origin of the earth-moon system.

The Day Becoming Longer

At the beginning, when the moon split off from the earth, it obviously must have shared the earth's rotation. It flew round the earth in the same time that the earth rotated, that is to say, the month and the day were of equal length. As the moon began to get farther from the earth, the month, because the moon took longer to rotate round the earth, began to get correspondingly longer. The day also became longer, because the earth was slowing down, taking longer to rotate on its axis, but the month increased at a greater rate than the day. Presently the month became equal to two days, then to three, and so on. It has been calculated that this process went on until there were twenty-nine days in the month. After that the number of days in the month began to decrease until it reached its present value or magnitude, and will continue to decrease until once more the month and the day are equal. In that age the earth will be rotating very slowly. The braking action of the tides will cause the earth always to keep the same face to the moon; it will rotate on its axis in the same time that the moon turns round the earth. If nothing but the earth and moon were involved this state of affairs would be final. But there is also the effect of the solar tides to be considered. The moon makes the day equal to the month, but the sun has a tendency, by still further slowing down the earth's rotation on its axis, to make the day equal to the year. It would do this, of course, by making the earth take as long to turn on its axis as to go round the sun. It cannot succeed in this, owing to the action of the moon, but it can succeed in making the day rather longer than the month.

Surprising as it may seem, we already have an illustration of this possibility in the satellites of Mars. The Martian day is about one half-hour longer than ours, but when the two minute satellites of Mars were discovered it was noticed that the inner one of the two revolved round Mars in about seven hours forty minutes. In one Martian day, therefore, one of the moons of Mars makes more than three complete revolutions round that planet, so that, to an inhabitant of Mars, there would be more than three months in a day.

BIBLIOGRAPHY

ARRHENIUS, SVANTE, *Worlds in the Making.*
CLERK-MAXWELL, JAMES, *Matter and Motion.*
DANIELL, ALFRED, *A Text-Book of the Principles of Physics.*

DARWIN, SIR G. H., *The Tides*
HOLMAN, *Matter, Energy, Force and Work.*
KAPP, GISBERT, *Electricity.*
KELVIN, LORD, *Popular Lectures and Addresses.* Vol. i. *Constitution of Matter.*
LOCKYER, SIR NORMAN, *Inorganic Evolution.*
LODGE, SIR OLIVER, *Electrons* and *The Ether of Space.*
PERRIN, JEAN, *Brownian Movement and Molecular Reality.*
SODDY, FREDERICK, *Matter and Energy* and *The Interpretation of Radium.*
THOMPSON, SILVANUS P., *Light, Visible and Invisible.*
THOMSON, SIR J. J., *The Corpuscular Theory of Matter.*